essential **electronics**

essential electronics

owen bishop

JOHN MURRAY

© Owen Bishop 2004

First published in 2004
by John Murray (Publishers) Ltd, a division of the Hodder Headline Group
338 Euston Road
London NW1 3BH

Artwork by Oxford Designers and Illustrators Ltd
Cover design by John Townson/Creation

Typeset in 11/13pt Concorde Roman by Tech-Set Ltd, Gateshead, Tyne and Wear
Printed and bound in Spain

A catalogue entry for this title is available from the British Library

ISBN 0 7195 8056 0

Contents

▮ **Preface**   vi

▮ **Section 1**   Analysing networks   1

▮ **Section 2**   Logic circuits   18

▮ **Section 3**   Components   28

▮ **Section 4**   Analogue networks and circuits   42

▮ **Section 5**   Digital circuits   61

▮ **Section 6**   Operational amplifiers   83

▮ **Section 7**   Signal processing   93

▮ **Section 8**   Power supply systems   102

▮ **Section 9**   Power switching systems   107

▮ **Section 10** Analogue control systems   112

▮ **Section 11** Digital control systems   117

▮ **Section 12** Audio systems   129

▮ **Section 13** Communications systems   136

▮ **Answers**   152

▮ **Index**   181

Preface

Essential Electronics is intended primarily as a revision text for students working for AS and A2 examinations in Electronics. It is aimed at those who have already studied the subject for several terms and carried out a course of practical work. It covers the core material (and more) of examinations set by the AQA, the Oxford, Cambridge and RSA Examinations Boards and the Welsh Joint Education Committee. It is also suitable for other Level 3 specifications, such as Edexcel Advanced VCE Engineering, Unit 14, Electronics, and the BTEC National Diploma and Certificate courses in Electrical/Electronic Engineering, Unit 7, Electronics.

The book is divided into 13 sections, the first two sections dealing with the analysis of simple analogue and digital networks. After a third section describing a range of electronic components and their properties, the following four sections show how these are built into a wide range of circuits, both analogue and digital. Finally, six sections are devoted to the major types of electronic system.

The text is concise and concentrates on the key aspects of each topic. The diagrams are simply drawn and labelled, so that they can easily be reproduced by the student, and recalled for use in answers to examination questions.

A revision text needs to give the student plenty of practice at answering questions. Consequently, there is a comprehensive collection of questions at the end of each section. These begin with 'Ten quick questions' covering the contents of the section. These require only short – often only one word – answers, and give the student a broad idea of whether or not their revision has been thorough. These short questions are followed by questions needing longer written answers, often illustrated with simple diagrams. At the back of the book worked answers, including details of calculations, are given to all these questions, except those that require no more than simple recall of the text.

Revising electronics

Revising a subject should not be a last-minute, haphazard venture. These tips may help you:

1 At least two months before the exam, plan your revision timetable on paper. Make a realistic plan and keep to it.

2 Allow yourself a definite period of time each day (say half an hour) for revision, perhaps up to an hour at weekends.

3 Work at it. Do not just sit and gaze at the textbook! Make a written summary of the main points in each section or subsection. Try to summarise a whole topic on a single A4 sheet. Use your own style of 'shorthand' and abbreviations. Sketch the drawings to show their main features.

4 Try to make your summary shorter still.

5 Try to write it out again – from memory.

1 Analysing networks

In brief...

- From Ohm's law, we deduce that resistance = pd/current (p. 1).
- The effective resistance of resistors in series is the sum of their resistances (p. 2).
- The reciprocal of the effective resistance of resistors in parallel is the sum of the reciprocals of their resistances (p. 2).
- The sum of the currents entering or leaving a point is zero (Kirchhoff's current law, p. 2).
- The current division rule applies for resistors in parallel (p. 2).
- The sum of pds across branches of a loop is zero (Kirchhoff's voltage law, p. 3).
- The potential division rule applies for resistors in series (p. 3).
- The effect of two or more voltage or current sources are superposed (superposition theorem, p. 4).
- One or more voltage or current sources and one or more impedances may be represented by a single voltage source in series with an impedance (Thévenin's theorem, p. 4).
- Power = current × pd (p. 5).
- The ratio between two powers, pds or currents is expressed in decibels (p. 6).
- The root mean square of the voltage or current of an ac signal is 0.707 times the peak value (p. 6).
- Reactance (X) and impedance (Z) are equivalent in effect to resistance, but are dependent on frequency in circuits that include capacitors or inductors (p. 7).
- The rate of charging or discharging a capacitor from a constant voltage source is exponential. The time constant is RC. Various stages in charging and discharging occur at fixed multiples of the time constant (pp 8–9).
- When a capacitor is charged and discharged by a sinusoidal input, the pd across the capacitor lags behind the pd of the source by up to 90°, depending on frequency. The current flow leads the pd of the source by up to 90°, depending on frequency (pp 9–10).
- A capacitor and an inductor in parallel form a resonant network. The resonant frequency is that at which the impedances of the capacitor and inductor are equal (pp 10–11).
- Q is a measure of the sharpness of the peak response of a resonant network (p. 11). It is reduced by including a resistor in the resonant network (pp 11–12).

Questions on analysing networks begin on p. 13, with answers from p. 152.

1·1 Current and voltage laws

▮ Ohm's law equations

If the potential difference (pd) across a branch of a circuit is V volts and the current flowing through it is I amperes, the resistance of the branch is R ohms, where $R = V/I$. Equivalent equations are $I = V/R$ and $V = IR$.

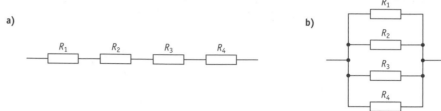

Resistances in series and in parallel

Figure 1.1 Resistors connected **a)** in series; **b)** in parallel

a)

b)

When two or more resistances are connected in series, their effective resistance R is the sum of their individual resistances. In Fig. 1.1a:

$$R = R_1 + R_2 + R_3 + R_4$$

When two or more resistances are connected in parallel, the reciprocal of their effective resistance R is the sum of the reciprocals of their individual resistances. In Fig 1.1b:

$$\frac{1}{R} = \frac{1}{R_1} + \frac{1}{R_2} + \frac{1}{R_3} + \frac{1}{R_4}$$

If there are only two resistances in parallel, a simpler equivalent of the equation above is:

$$R = \frac{R_1 \times R_2}{R_1 + R_2}$$

Kirchhoff's current law (KCL)

At any instant, the sum of currents arriving at and leaving a point in a network is zero. In Fig. 1.2:

$$I_1 + I_2 + I_3 + I_4 = 0$$

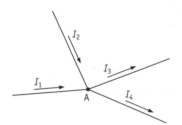

Figure 1.2 Using Kirchhoff's current law

Currents arriving at A are considered to be positive and currents leaving A are considered to be negative.

worked example

problem In Fig. 1.2, if $I_1 = 34\,\text{mA}$, $I_2 = 59\,\text{mA}$ and $I_4 = -25\,\text{mA}$, calculate I_3.

working Applying KCL (in mA):

$$34 + 59 + I_3 - 25 = 0$$
$$\Rightarrow \qquad I_3 = -34 - 59 + 25 = -68$$

solution I_3 is 68 mA, flowing away from A.

Current division rule

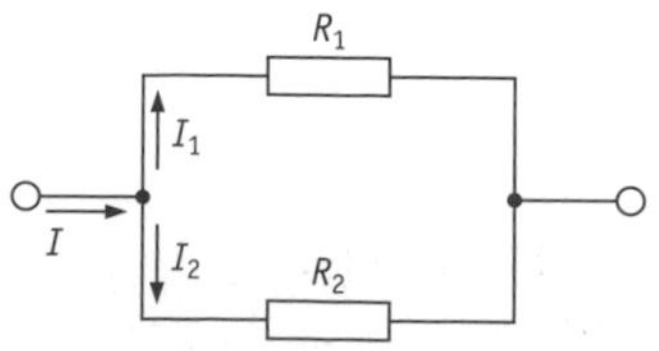

Given two or more resistors in parallel, the current flowing through each is inversely proportional to the resistance: $I_1 R_1 = I_2 R_2 = \ldots$. In the case of two resistors in parallel (Fig. 1.3):

$$I_1 = I \times \frac{R_2}{R_1 + R_2}$$

Figure 1.3 Current division

and

$$I_2 = I \times \frac{R_1}{R_1 + R_2}$$

▌ Kirchhoff's voltage law (KVL)

Figure 1.4 Using Kirchhoff's voltage law

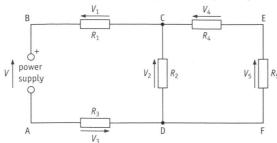

At any instant, the sum of the pds across the branches of a loop in a network is zero. A loop is any closed path through the network. There are three loops in Fig. 1.4: ABCDA, DCEFD and ABCEFDA. The coloured arrows indicate the pds across the resistors and the power supply. The head of the arrow points to what is assumed to be the more positive end. Each loop is summed by working round the loop in a clockwise direction. A pd is positive if we pass from the tail of the arrow to the head. The sums for the loops are:

ABCDA: $\quad V - V_1 - V_2 - V_3 = 0$

DCEFD: $\quad V_2 - V_4 - V_5 = 0$

ABCEFDA: $\quad V - V_1 - V_4 - V_5 - V_3 = 0$

If the *actual* pd across an element is opposite to the direction shown by the arrow, the subsequent calculations will give a negative voltage.

worked example

problem   In Fig. 1.4, if $V = 6$ V, $V_1 = 2$ V, $V_3 = 3$ V and $V_5 = 5$ V, find V_2 and V_4.

working   Applying KVL and using the equations written out above (in V):

$$6 - 2 - V_2 - 3 = 0 \quad \Rightarrow \quad V_2 = 6 - 2 - 3 = 1$$

Use the value of V_2 in solving the next equation:

$$1 - V_4 - 5 = 0 \quad \Rightarrow \quad V_4 = 1 - 5 = -4$$

The pd across R_4 is opposite to that shown by the arrow.
Check results by working the third equation:

$$6 - 2 - (-4) - 5 - 3 = 0$$

solution $V_2 = 1$ V; $V_4 = 4$ V, with E positive of C.

▌ Potential division rule

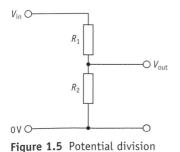

Figure 1.5 Potential division

Given two or more resistors in series, the pd across each is directly proportional to the resistance. In the case of two resistors in series (Fig. 1.5):

$$V_{\text{out}} = V_{\text{in}} \times \frac{R_2}{R_1 + R_2}$$

This circuit is also known as a **voltage divider** and is a frequently used network for providing a voltage that is lower than the supply voltage.

When a load is connected to this network, it is in parallel with R_2. Part of the current that would normally flow through R_2 now flows through the load. By Ohm's law, the pd across R_2 is reduced, which means that V_{out} is less than its calculated value. As a rule-of-thumb, the current drawn by the load must be less than a tenth of that flowing through the divider chain.

▌Superposition theorem

If there are two or more voltage or current sources in a network, the effect of each source is superposed on that of the other sources. This means that we can analyse such a network by considering the sources one at a time, replacing other current sources by open circuits and other voltage sources by short circuits. Having done this for all sources, we sum the currents and voltages for each resistor.

Figure 1.6 Diagrams **b)** and **c)** are stages in the superposition analysis of the circuit in **a)**

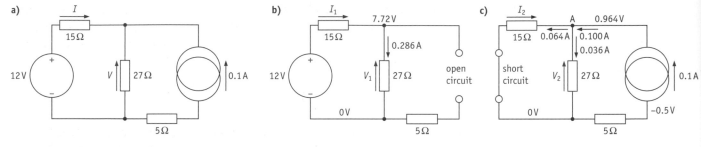

worked example

problem Find the values of V and I in Fig. 1.6a.

working 1 Replace the current source with an open circuit (Fig. 1.6b). Current flows from the voltage source, around the loop containing the 15 Ω and 27 Ω resistors. Total resistance in loop = 42 Ω (assuming none in voltage source). $I_1 = 12/42 = 0.286$ A, in the direction of the arrow. $V_1 = 0.286 \times 27 = 7.72$ V.

2 Replace the voltage source with a short circuit (Fig. 1.6c). Current flows through 15 Ω and 27 Ω in parallel. Effective resistance = $(15 \times 27)/(15 + 27) = 9.64$ Ω. Voltage across 15 Ω and 27 Ω is $V_2 = 0.100 \times 9.64 = 0.964$ V. At point A, current from source splits (KCL) to flow through 15 Ω and 27 Ω. Current through 15 Ω is $I_2 = -0.964/15 = -0.064$ A. Direction is opposite to I, so I_2 is negative.

solution Sum the voltages and currents produced by the two sources:

$$V = V_1 + V_2 = 7.72 + 0.964 = 8.68 \text{ V}$$

$$I = I_1 + I_2 = 0.286 + (-0.064) = 0.222 \text{ A}$$

▌Thévenin's theorem

Any two-terminal network consisting of one or more voltage or current sources and one or more impedances may be represented by a single voltage source in series with a single impedance. This is called the **Thévenin equivalent** of the network, and its behaviour is identical to that of the original network. The Thévenin equivalent is found by using the superposition method.

Figure 1.7 Diagrams **b)** and **c)** are stages in the superposition analysis of the circuit in **a)** to find the Thévenin voltage V_{Th}

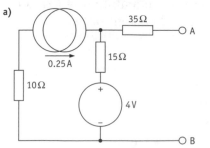

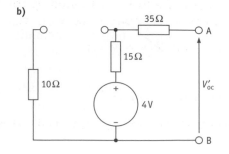

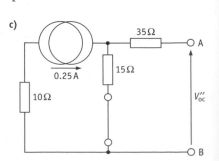

worked example

problem Find the Thévenin equivalent of the 2-terminal network in Fig. 1.7a.

working

1 Leave the output terminals AB as an open circuit. Find the open-circuit output voltage when the current source is replaced by an open circuit (Fig. 1.7b). No current flows through the resistors, so there is no voltage drop across them. The voltage at AB is $V'_{oc} = 4$ V.

2 Find the open-circuit voltage when the voltage source is replaced by a short circuit (Fig. 1.7c). The voltage at AB is the voltage drop across the 15 Ω resistor. There is no drop across the 35 Ω resistor as no current is flowing through it. The voltage at AB is $V''_{oc} = 0.25 \times 15 = 3.75$ V.

3 The Thévenin voltage V_{Th} is the total of V'_{oc} and V''_{oc}.
$V_{Th} = 4 + 3.75 = 7.75$ V.

4 Now short-circuit the output terminals. Find the short-circuit output current when the current source is replaced by an open circuit (Fig. 1.8a). The current between A and B is $I'_{sc} = 4/(15 + 35) = 0.08$ A.

Figure 1.8 Stages in the superposition analysis of the circuit of Fig. 1.7a to find the short-circuit output current

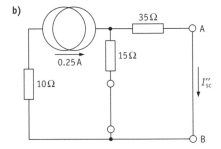

Figure 1.9 Thévenin equivalent of the circuit of Fig. 1.7a

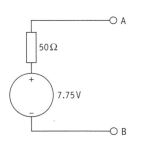

5 Find the short-circuit output current when the voltage source is replaced by a short circuit (Fig. 1.8b). By the current division rule,
$I''_{sc} = 0.25 \times 15/(15 + 35) = 0.075$ A.

6 Sum the currents: $I_{sc} = 0.08 + 0.075 = 0.155$ A. The Thévenin resistance is $R_{Th} = V_{Th}/I_{sc} = 7.75/0.155 = 50$ Ω.

solution The Thévenin equivalent of Fig. 1.7a is shown in Fig. 1.9.

1•2 Power

The power P dissipated in a device depends on the amount of current I flowing through it and the potential difference V across it:

$$P = IV$$

If I is in amps and V in volts, P is in watts.
For a resistor, I and V are related by the Ohm's law equation $R = V/I$, so we can also express power in terms of resistance and current or pd:

$$P = IV = (V/R)V = V^2/R$$

and

$$P = IV = I(IR) = I^2R$$

This power is dissipated as heat in the resistor.

Power is also mainly dissipated as heat in other devices but, depending on the device, some of the total power IV may be dissipated as other forms of energy such as light or motion.

■ Decibels

The ratio between two quantities can be expressed in decibels. Both quantities must be expressed in the same unit, and their ratio in decibels has no unit. In electronics, decibels are normally used for expressing the ratio between two powers. Given two powers P_1 and P_2, their ratio n in decibels (dB) is given by:

$$n = 10 \times \log_{10} (P_2/P_1)$$

worked example

problem   A 150 mW signal is amplified to 3.5 W. Express this amplification in decibels.

working $P_1 = 0.15$ W, $P_2 = 3.5$ W
$n = 10 \times \log_{10} (3.5/0.15) = 13.7$

solution   The amplification is 13.7 dB.

When comparing two voltages or two currents, recall that power is proportional to the square of the voltage or current. Thus $(P_2/P_1) = (V_2^2/V_1^2)$. Because squaring a quantity is equivalent to doubling its logarithm, the decibel equation becomes:

$$n = 20 \times \log_{10} (V_2/V_1)$$

Similarly:

$$n = 20 \times \log_{10} (I_2/I_1)$$

worked example

problem   A signal of amplitude 340 mV is fed into a lowpass filter. The amplitude of the output signal is 245 mV. Express this loss of amplitude in decibels.

working $V_1 = 340$ mV, $V_2 = 245$ mV
$n = 20 \times \log_{10} (245/340) = -2.85$

solution   The signal loss is -2.85 dB.

1●3 Root mean square (rms) values

A sinusoidal voltage or current is continually and regularly changing in value. The *average* value is zero. To make it possible to calculate the effects of alternating current, we define an average current called the the root mean square, or rms, current. This is the value of the steady dc that has the same heating effect as the ac. It can be shown that:

rms current = peak current/$\sqrt{2}$ = 0.707 × peak current

The rms voltage is defined in the equivalent way.

1•4 Reactance and impedance

When an alternating voltage is applied across a capacitor, the pd across the capacitor and the current flowing into (or out of) the capacitor are out of phase. This is because the pd across the capacitor depends on the current that has been flowing into (or out of) it during previous instants. This makes it impossible to apply Ohm's law to the pd and current *at any given instant*. To avoid this problem we consider the average pds and currents over a complete cycle by working with rms pds and currents.

If an rms voltage V_{rms} is applied across a capacitor, the rms current I_{rms} is given by:

$$I_{rms} = \frac{V_{rms}}{X_C}$$

X_C is the **capacitative reactance** of the capacitor C, and opposes the flow of current. It is analogous to resistance and has the same unit, the ohm.

It can be shown that:

$$X_C = \frac{1}{2\pi fC}$$

Similarly, with an inductor:

$$I_{rms} = \frac{V_{rms}}{X_L}$$

X_L is the **inductive reactance** of the inductor L, and opposes the flow of current. It is analogous to resistance and has the same unit, the ohm.

It can be shown that:

$$X_L = 2\pi fL$$

Impedance (symbol Z) is a general term covering resistance and both kinds of reactance. Its unit is the ohm.

Summing up:

Type of impedance	Equation	Effect of ac frequency	Effect on electrical energy
resistance	$R = V/I$	not affected by f	dissipates (as heat)
capacitative reactance	$X_c = 1/2\pi fC$	inversely proportional to f	stored as electric field between capacitor plates
inductive reactance	$X_L = 2\pi fL$	proportional to f	stored as magnetic field in inductor

▮ Impedances in series

Applying an ac signal to two or more impedances in series results in pds and currents that are out of phase with each other. The impedances cannot simply be added together, as can resistances in series. It can be shown that the total effective impedance Z of impedances R, X_C and X_L in series is given by:

$$Z = \sqrt{R^2 + (X_L - X_C)^2}$$

We calculate X_L and X_C at a *given frequency*, using the equations in the table above. Having obtained Z, we can use the relationship:

$$I_{rms} = \frac{V_{rms}}{Z}$$

worked example

problem   A 120 Ω resistor, a 2.2 μF capacitor and a 25 mH inductor are wired in series. What is their effective impedance at 600 Hz? What is the rms current if a sinusoidal signal of 2 V rms amplitude is applied to the circuit?

working $X_L = 2\pi \times 600 \times 25 \times 10^{-3} = 94.25\ \Omega$
$X_C = 1/(2\pi \times 600 \times 2.2 \times 10^{-6}) = 120.6\ \Omega$
$Z = \sqrt{(120^2 + (94.25 - 120.6)^2)} = 122.9\ \Omega$
$I_{rms} = 2/122.9 = 0.0163\ A$

solution   At 600 Hz, the impedance is 122.9 Ω and the rms current is 16.3 mA.

1•5 *RC* networks

■ Charging and discharging a capacitor

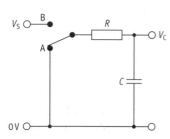

Figure 1.10 Circuit for charging and discharging a capacitor through a resistor

In the resistor–capacitor network of Fig. 1.10, the switch is in position A, both sides of the capacitor C are connected and so V_C, the pd across C, is 0 V. Then the switch is put in position B to connect the network to a constant voltage source V_S. Current flows through the resistor R and charges C. At the beginning the full voltage V_S is across R, so the current through it is $I = V_S/R$. As C becomes charged, the increasing pd across it results in a decreasing pd $(V_S - V_C)$ across R. In this way, the current through R is gradually reduced. Eventually, V_C equals V_S, no current flows and C is fully charged. The rate of rise of V_C is exponential, as shown in the graph of Fig. 1.11.

Figure 1.11 Voltage across a capacitor as it charges exponentially

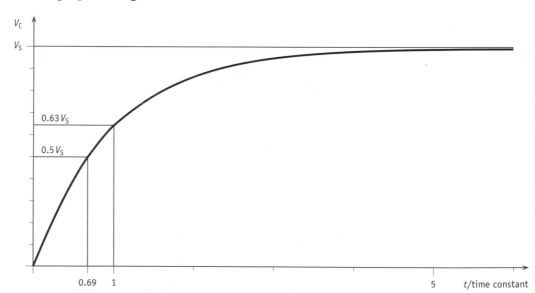

The equation relating V_C to time t is:

$$V_C = V_S (1 - e^{-t/RC})$$

From this we obtain the three relationships shown in Fig. 1.11. Given that the time constant is RC (seconds):

$V_C = 0.5V_S$ after time $0.69RC$
$V_C = 0.63V_S$ after time RC
$V_C \approx V_S$ after time $5RC$

If the capacitor is fully charged, and then the switch is put to position A, *C* discharges through *R*. It discharges exponentially, rapidly at first and then more slowly. The equation is:

$$V_C = V_S\, e^{-t/RC}$$

The three relationships obtained from this are:

$$V_C = 0.5V_S \text{ after time } 0.69RC \text{ (as before)}$$
$$V_C = 0.37V_S \text{ after time } RC$$
$$V_C \approx 0 \text{ after time } 5RC$$

▮ Phase in an *RC* network

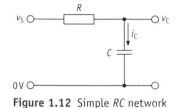

Figure 1.12 Simple *RC* network

A sinusoidal signal v_S is applied to the *RC* network illustrated in Fig. 1.12. The varying pds and the current in the network are plotted in Fig. 1.13. The current is plotted on a larger scale. During the positive half-cycles of v_S, current flows through *R* and charges *C*. The current at any instant is i_C. A pd builds up across *C*, and we measure this as v_C. However, the waveforms of v_C and i_C are not in phase with v_S. After v_S has reached its maximum (in the positive direction) and is decreasing to zero, current is still flowing into the capacitor and v_C is still increasing. Therefore, v_C reaches its maximum *after* v_S. Thus, v_C **lags** behind v_S.

Conversely, i_C is greatest when the capacitor carries only a small charge and has only a small pd across it. This occurs when v_S is increasing from zero and is beginning to charge the capacitor. Therefore i_C reaches its maximum before v_S. Later, the charge accumulating on *C* causes i_C to be reduced. Thus, i_C **leads** v_S.

Figure 1.13 Voltage and current waveforms for the network of Fig. 1.12

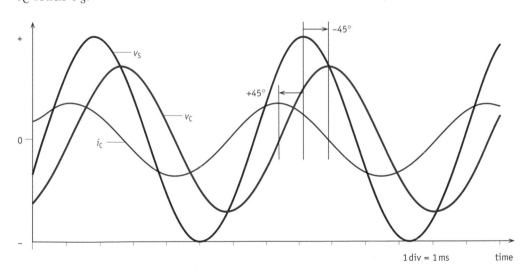

The waveforms are plotted in Fig. 1.13 for a signal of frequency 159 Hz. This frequency is that at which the impedance of *C* equals the resistance of *R* (see p. 5). The curves clearly demonstrate that v_C lags behind v_S, and that i_C leads v_S. The amount by which the signals are out of phase depends on the frequency of the signal. The period of one cycle here is approximately 6.3 ms, and the signals lag and lead by one eighth of a cycle. Usually, we express phase differences in degrees of angle, taking one complete cycle of the waveform to be 360°. Then v_C lags v_S by 45°, so the phase difference is −45°. Also, i_C leads v_S by 45°, so the phase difference is +45°.

Fig. 1.14 is a plot of the **frequency response** of this network as frequency is swept from 10 Hz to 10 kHz. The curve for amplitude is plotted on a decibel scale (p. 6). It shows that amplitude is greatest at low frequencies, and falls off for higher frequencies. A vertical line is marked at 159 Hz, which is labelled f_c. As explained on p. 49, this is the cut-off frequency of the network when considered as a lowpass filter. The amplitude of v_C at this frequency is -3 dB compared with the amplitude at very low frequencies.

Figure 1.14 Frequency response of the *RC* network of Fig. 1.12

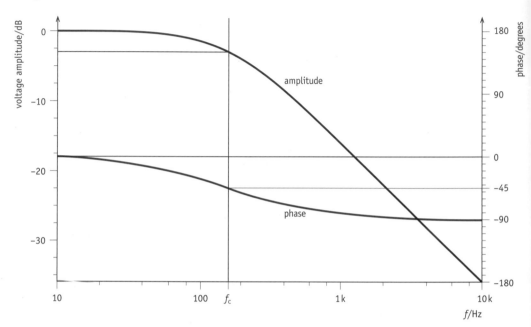

The graph also plots, in colour, the phase of v_C compared with v_S. This can be seen to be 0° at very low frequencies. At these frequencies, there is time for current to flow, to charge or discharge the capacitor in phase with v_S. The plot shows that there is a phase lag of 45° when the frequency is f_c, confirming the result shown in Fig. 1.13. The lag increases as frequency increases, eventually settling at 90° for signals of very high frequencies.

1•6 *LC* networks

▌ Resonance

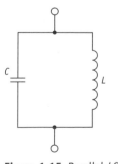

Figure 1.15 Parallel *LC* network

If a capacitor and inductor are connected in parallel (Fig. 1.15), and a sinusoidal signal of suitable frequency f is applied across them, the network **resonates**. The resonant frequency is that at which the impedance of the capacitor equals that of the inductor.

The impedance of the capacitor is:

$$X_C = 1/2\pi fC$$

The impedance of the inductor is:

$$X_L = 2\pi fL$$

At resonance:

$$X_C = X_L$$

$$1/2\pi fC = 2\pi fL$$

$$f^2 = \frac{1}{4\pi^2 LC}$$

and so the resonant frequency f_R is:

$$f_R = \frac{1}{2\pi\sqrt{LC}}$$

At resonance, the energy of the network oscillates: energy stored as the electric field of the capacitor is converted to energy stored as the magnetic field of the inductor, and back again repeatedly. Very little energy is lost from the network as the energy alternates between electrical and magnetic forms. For this reason, very little energy is required to maintain the oscillations, which die out only slowly if the signal source is removed. Conversely, if a small amount of energy is continuously supplied from an outside source at the resonant frequency, the amplitude of the oscillations may gradually build up to high values. This can be seen in a resonant filter circuit (see Fig. 1.16 below), in which a voltage source of 1 V amplitude can maintain oscillations in the network of amplitude 84 V at the resonant frequency.

▮ Quality factor

The frequency response of an *LC* network, such as that in Fig. 1.15, shows a peak at the resonant frequency. The sharpness of the peak is described by Q, the **quality factor**, which is defined by:

$$Q = \frac{f_R}{\text{bandwidth}}$$

In this equation, f_R is the centre frequency of the resonance peak, and the bandwidth is measured between the two -3 dB points. If a tuned network in a radio receiver has a very narrow peak, it is able to tune individually to stations that differ only slightly in frequency. It has a high Q and we say that the receiver is highly **selective**.

A similar equation is used to define the Q of any other circuit that produces an output that rises to a peak at or near the centre of the range. In this general case, $Q = f_0/\text{bandwidth}$, where f_0 is the general term for the centre frequency. A bandpass filter is an example of this.

Fig. 1.16 shows an *LC* filter network that includes a resistor R. As Fig. 1.17 overleaf demonstrates, the shape of the frequency response curve of this filter for a given pair of values of L and C depends on the value of R. A small value of R gives a sharp peak between the passband and the transition region. This is due to the filter resonating strongly. As R is increased, the peak becomes broader. With higher values of R, the peak disappears altogether because the resistor strongly damps out oscillations.

Figure 1.16 *RLC* filter network

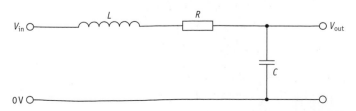

Figure 1.17 Frequency response of the *RLC* network of Fig. 1.16, for different values of *R*

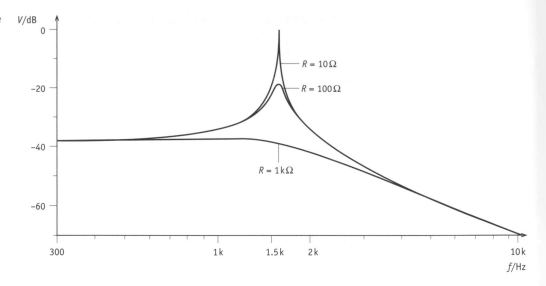

Fig 1.18 examines the effect of the resistor in more detail. The uppermost plot is for an *LC* network as in Fig. 1.16, with $L = 100$ mH, $C = 100$ nF and $R = 100\ \Omega$. The curve peaks sharply at $f_0 = 1.585$ kHz. This is close to the resonant frequency of the *LC* network without a resistor which, using the equation on p. 11, is $f_R = 1.592$ kHz. The line AB intersects with the response curve at the lower and upper cut-off points. These are 1.506 kHz and 1.664 kHz respectively. The bandwidth is thus 158 Hz and, from the equation $Q = f_0/\text{bandwidth}$, we calculate: $Q = 1585/158 = 10.0$. Summing up, when $R = 100\ \Omega$, the circuit behaves as a **bandpass filter** with $f_0 = 1.585$ kHz and $Q = 10.0$.

Figure 1.18 Network of Fig. 1.16 behaving as a bandpass filter and as a lowpass filter

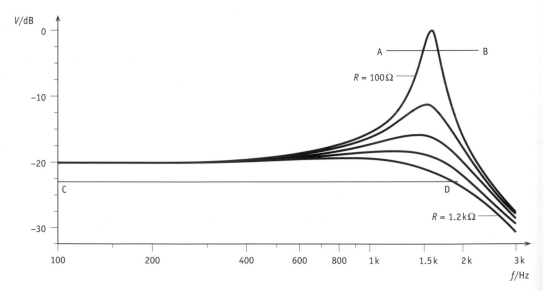

The other curves in Fig. 1.18 show the effect of increasing *R* in steps of about 300 Ω. The peak becomes broader and the centre frequency is gradually reduced. The lowest curve (when $R = 1200\ \Omega$) rises slightly at about $f_0 = 840$ kHz, then falls away with increasing frequency. The circuit is behaving as a **lowpass filter**. The line CD is drawn 3 dB below the peak, to locate the single cut-off point at $f_c = 1.750$ kHz. The effect of the filter network is to sharpen the 'knee' of the response curve (compare with Fig. 1.14). The best value for *R* is that which gives the sharpest knee to separate the passband from the transition region (see p. 49).

The value of Q for the filter is calculated from:

$$Q = \frac{\sqrt{L/C}}{R}$$

Note that when $R = 100\ \Omega$ this equation gives $Q = 10$, confirming the result obtained from Fig. 1.18.

worked example

problem In the network of Fig. 1.16, $L = 100$ mH and $C = 100$ nF. Calculate Q when $R = 10\ \Omega$, $100\ \Omega$, or $1\ k\Omega$.

solution For the three values of R, we calculate from $Q = \sqrt{(L/C)}/R$ that $Q = 100$, 10 and 1 respectively. As expected, the larger the value of R the smaller the value of Q.

▌ Ten quick questions

These questions all have short answers, sometimes only one word. Try them before you attempt the longer questions that follow.

1 What is meant by 'pd'?
2 What is the essential condition for expressing the ratio of two quantities in decibels?
3 What theorem is used for analysing circuits with two or more power sources?
4 How do we calculate the effective resistance of two or more resistances in series?
5 What is the longer name for Q?
6 Under what conditions does a parallel *LC* network oscillate most strongly?
7 What is the phase difference at the cut-off frequency, between a signal before and after it has passed through a lowpass filter?
8 What does Kirchhoff's voltage law say about the sum of the pds across the branches of a loop in a network?
9 A two-terminal network consisting of several voltage and current sources and one or more resistances may be represented by a single voltage source in series with a resistor. What is the name for this simpler network?
10 If a device has a current of 3.5 A flowing through it and there is pd 5.6 V across it, how much power is dissipated in the device?

▌ Questions on analysing networks

Work numerical questions to give an answer correct to three significant figures.

1 to **10** In each of the networks in Fig 1.19, the terminal on the left is 12 V positive of the terminal on the right. Find
   a) the effective resistance of the networks;
   b) the pd indicated by the coloured arrow;
   c) the current indicated by the black arrow.
At each stage in the calculations name the law or rule that is being applied.

Figure 1.19 Resistor networks for questions 1 to 10. Resistor values are in ohms

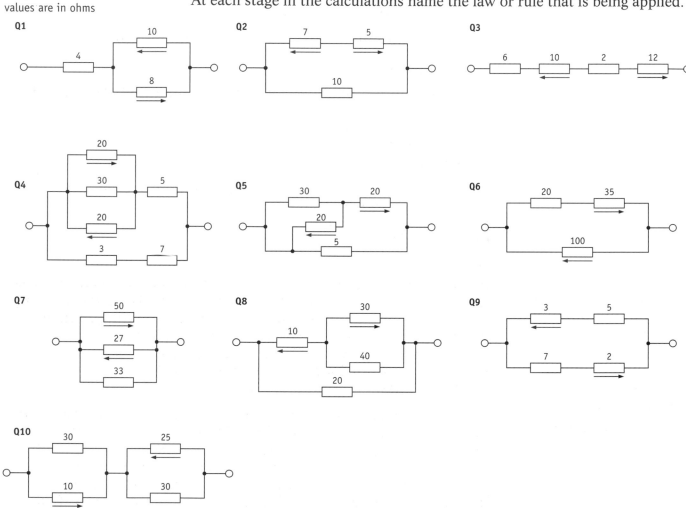

11 to **13** Analyse each of the networks in Fig. 1.20 to find the pds across all resistors and the currents through them.

Figure 1.20 Networks for questions 11 to 13

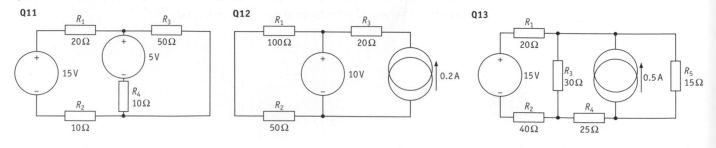

Figure 1.21 Networks for questions 14 to 16

Q14

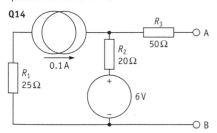

14 to **16** Determine the Thévenin equivalents of each of the networks in Fig. 1.21.

Q15

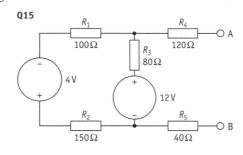

Q16

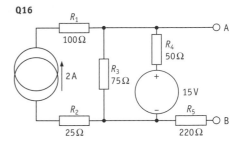

17 Prove the current division rule for two resistors in parallel.

18 Prove the potential division rule.

19 Calculate the power dissipated by these resistances, with the given pd across them:
a) $R = 470\,\Omega$, $V = 15\,V$;
b) $R = 2.2\,\Omega$, $V = 25\,V$;
c) $R = 5.6\,k\Omega$, $V = 3.5\,V$.

20 Calculate the power dissipated by these resistances, with the given current flowing through them:
a) $R = 2.2\,k\Omega$, $I = 0.5\,A$;
b) $R = 33\,\Omega$, $I = 15\,mA$;
c) $R = 1.2\,\Omega$, $I = 5.5\,A$.

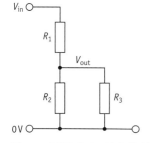

Figure 1.22 Potential divider network

21 A potential divider network consists of two resistors, R_1 and R_2 in series (Fig. 1.22). The load is represented by a resistor, R_3. Given the following values, calculate V_{out} with and without the load attached, the current through the load, and the power dissipated in the load.
a) $R_1 = 220\,\Omega$, $R_2 = 390\,\Omega$, $R_3 = 3.3\,k\Omega$, $V_{in} = 6\,V$;
b) $R_1 = 1\,k\Omega$, $R_2 = 2.2\,k\Omega$, $R_3 = 560\,\Omega$, $V_{in} = 24\,V$;
c) $R_1 = 1.2\,M\Omega$, $R_2 = 33\,k\Omega$, $R_3 = 3.3\,M\Omega$, $V_{in} = 15\,V$.

22 Design a potential divider network as in Fig. 1.22, built from resistors of the E12 series according to these specifications:
a) $V_{in} = 12\,V$, $V_{out} = 4.8\,V$ with no load, load resistance $(R_3) = 4.7\,k\Omega$;
b) $V_{in} = 5\,V$, $V_{out} = 0.9\,V$ with no load, load resistance $= 910\,\Omega$;
c) $V_{in} = 18\,V$, $V_{out} = 10.6\,V$ with no load, load resistance $= 22\,\Omega$.
In all cases, V_{out} when the load is attached must be within 10% of the unloaded value.

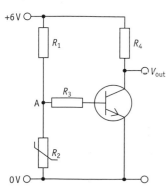

Figure 1.23 Thermistor switch network

23 Fig. 1.23 shows a thermistor switch network. If the resistance of the thermistor (R_2) is $19.8\,k\Omega$ at 35 °C, what should be the value of R_1 so that V_{out} goes high when the temperature just exceeds 35 °C?

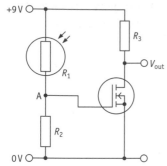

+9V

R_3

V_{out}

R_1

A

R_2

0V

Figure 1.24 LDR switch network

24 Fig. 1.24 shows a MOSFET switch (see section 4) with input from an LDR. The threshold voltage of the MOSFET is 3.5 V. Given that the resistance of R_2 is 12 kΩ, what is the resistance R_1 of the LDR when the MOSFET begins to switch on?

25 In Fig. 1.24 the MOSFET has an 'on' resistance of 0.5 Ω. Given that the resistance of R_3 is 100 Ω, what is the voltage V_{out} when the MOSFET is fully on? How much power is dissipated in R_3 and in the MOSFET, when the MOSFET is
a) off; **b)** on?

26 Calculate the gain of each of these circuits and express the power gain in decibels:
a) input = 5 mW, output = 120 mW;
b) input = 150 mW, output = 4.2 W;
c) input = 2 W, output = 750 mW;
d) input voltage amplitude = 135 mV, output voltage amplitude = 3.75 V;
e) input current amplitude = 5.6 A, output current amplitude = 3.2 A.

27 What is the maximum safe current through
a) a 100 Ω resistor rated at 3 W;
b) a 4.7 Ω resistor rated at 25 W?
In each case calculate the pd across the resistor that produces the maximum safe current.

28 A sinusoidal voltage signal has an amplitude of 11.5 V. What is its rms voltage?

29 A transformer produces a sinusoidal current output of amplitude 420 mA. What is the rms current?

30 A lamp shines with the same brightness when powered either by a 15 V dc supply or an ac supply. What is the rms voltage of the ac supply? What is the peak voltage of the ac supply?

31 Find the reactance of each of these capacitors:
a) 100 nF at 25 kHz;
b) 220 μF at 50 Hz;
c) 12 pF at 30 MHz;
d) 47 nF at 500 Hz;
e) 2.2 μF at 8 MHz.

32 Find the reactance of each of these inductors:
a) 10 H at 50 Hz;
b) 250 μH at 200 Hz;
c) 50 μH at 2 MHz;
d) 1 μH at 6.7 MHz;
e) 2.5 H at 15.6 Hz.

33 Describe what is meant by *resistance*, *reactance* and *impedance*, explaining how they are similar and how they differ.

34 A sinusoidal voltage signal of amplitude 2.5 V and frequency 75 Hz is applied across a 100 nF capacitor. What is the rms current 'through' the capacitor?

35 A sinusoidal current signal of amplitude 120 mA and frequency 3 kHz is applied across a 220 μF capacitor. What is the rms voltage across the capacitor?

36 A sinusoidal voltage supply of amplitude 325 V and frequency 50 Hz is applied across a 2.2 H inductor. What is the rms current through the inductor, ignoring the small resistance of the coil?

37 What must be the minimum working voltage of a capacitor used on a 230 V supply?

38 When ac of 6 V rms is applied to a 15 mH choke, the rms current is 0.4 A. What is the frequency of the ac?

39 A circuit includes components with a resistance of 500 Ω, a capacitance of 450 nF and an inductance of 1.5 mH, in series. What is the total impedance of the circuit at 27 kHz? If ac of rms voltage 4 V with a frequency of 27 kHz is applied to the circuit, what is the rms current?

40 A circuit includes components with a resistance of 110 Ω, a capacitance of 250 pF and an inductance of 33 mH, in series. What is the total impedance of the circuit at 27 kHz? If a current of 2.5 A rms with a frequency of 27 kHz flows in the circuit, what is the applied rms voltage?

41 A 47 nF capacitor is charged to 6 V. How much charge is it holding? It is then discharged by connecting a 120 Ω resistor across it. What current flows as discharge begins? What is the pd across the resistor after 5.64 μs? How much longer does the capacitor take to become discharged?

42 a) In Fig. 1.25, the capacitor is fully discharged, then the switch is turned to position A. How long does it take to charge the capacitor to 6 V?
 b) The capacitor is allowed to charge to 12 V, then the switch is turned to position B. If it takes 70.2 ms to discharge to 4.44 V, what is the value of R_2?

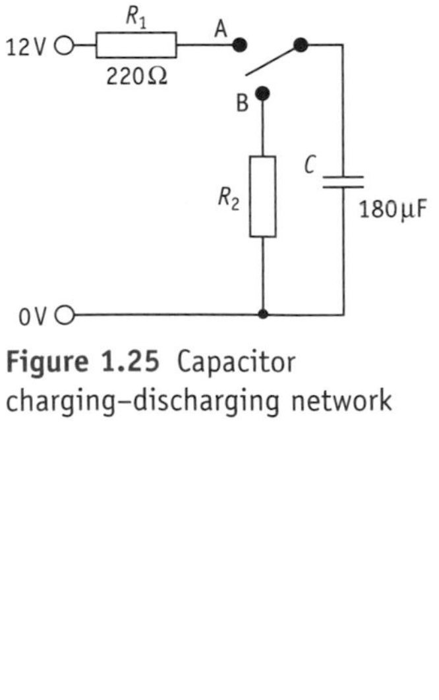

Figure 1.25 Capacitor charging–discharging network

43 Draw a sketch to show the relationship between the pd V_C and time as a capacitor is charged from 0 V to the supply voltage V_S. Mark the position on this graph at which the V_C is half the supply voltage. Prove that it takes 0.69 time constants to charge a capacitor to half the supply voltage.

44 Draw a sketch to show the relationships between the sinusoidal pd (v_S) applied across an RC network (Fig. 1.12), the pd across the capacitor (v_C) and the current flowing into or out of the capacitor (i_C). Briefly explain the phase differences between these curves.

45 What is the resonant frequency of a parallel LC network in which $C = 470$ μF and $L = 200$ mH? What can be said about the impedances of the capacitor and inductor at this frequency?

46 A parallel LC network has a 2.2 mH inductor and its resonant frequency is 2 kHz. What is the value of the capacitor?

47 Describe what is meant by Q. In a resonant LC network, with resonant frequency 800 kHz, the bandwidth extends from 750 kHz to 853 kHz. What is the Q of this network?

48 a) Explain how a resistor is used to control the Q of an LC lowpass filter.
 b) Design a lowpass filter with a cut-off point of approximately 32 kHz and a Q of 1.5. Assume that the resistor is of low value so that the cut-off frequency f_c is approximately equal to the resonant frequency f_R of the LC network.

2 Logic circuits

In brief...
- Logical operations are performed electronically by logic gates. There are six commonly used types of gate: NOT, AND, OR, NAND, NOR and exclusive-OR (pp 18–19). They are represented in circuit diagrams by logic gate symbols.
- The logical operators are summarised by truth tables (p. 19).
- Logical operations are described and manipulated by Boolean algebra. This is used to describe logic circuits in terms of logical equations (pp 19–20). There are special symbols to represent the logical operations.
- Logical identities are used in Boolean algebra for simplifying logical equations to aid in the design of logic circuits (pp 21–22). These include the two identities that express de Morgan's theorem.
- Logical equations may also be simplified by drawing Karnaugh maps (p. 23).
- All logical operations can be performed by NAND gates or by NOR gates, which is often a convenience when building a circuit (p. 24).

Questions on logic circuits begin on p. 25, with answers from p. 156.

2•1 Logic gates

Gates are electronic circuits with one or more inputs and one output. The logic states are represented by the voltages at the inputs and output. In positive logic, 'true' is represented by '1', or by a high voltage (usually the supply voltage or close to it). 'False' is represented by '0', or by a low voltage (usually 0 V or close to it).

The six commonly used logic gates are described below. Their circuit symbols are shown in Fig. 2.1.

Figure 2.1 Logic gates: note AND, OR, NAND and NOR may have more than two inputs

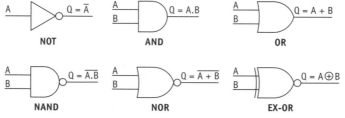

NOT (or INVERT) This has one input (often called A) and one output (often called Q). Q is always the INVERT of A. That is, if A = 1 then Q = 0, and if A = 0 then Q = 1.

AND This has two or more inputs, A, B, … The output is 1 (high) only if all inputs are 1. That is, if A = 1 AND B = 1 AND …, then Q = 1. Otherwise, Q = 0 (low).

OR This has two or more inputs. The output is 1 if any one or more of the inputs is 1. That is, if A = 1 OR B = 1 OR …, then Q = 1. If all inputs are low then Q = 0.

NAND This is the equivalent of an AND gate followed by a NOT gate. Its output is the INVERT of an AND gate.

NOR   This is the equivalent of an OR gate followed by a NOT gate. Its output is the INVERT of an OR gate.

Exclusive-OR (or EX-OR)   This has only two inputs. The output is 1 if any one but not both of the inputs is 1.

Fig. 2.1 also shows the symbols used in Boolean algebra for representing the logical operators. The operator AND may be represented by a dot, as shown, or the dot may be omitted.

2•2 Truth tables

Truth tables summarise the action of logic gates. They show the output for all possible combinations of inputs. The truth tables of NOT and EX-OR gates, and of the 2-input versions of AND, OR, NAND and NOR gates, are set out in the table below:

Inputs		Output, Q					
		NOT	AND	OR	NAND	NOR	EX-OR
B	A	$\overline{A}$	A•B	A + B	$\overline{A•B}$	$\overline{A + B}$	A ⊕ B
0	0	1	0	0	1	1	0
0	1	0	0	1	1	0	1
1	0	1	0	1	1	0	1
1	1	0	1	1	0	0	0

(Remember $A \oplus B = A\overline{B} + \overline{A}B$.)

2•3 Boolean algebra

A typical Boolean statement or equation is:

$$A + B = Q$$

The '+' symbol represents OR, so an equivalent statement is:

A OR B = Q

Expanding this to reveal its meaning, we obtain:

If A is true OR B is true, THEN Q is true.

This is beginning to look like an ordinary sentence written in English, and we now need to define what we mean by 'Q', 'A', and 'B'. One possible set of meanings could relate this statement to the circuit in Fig. 2.2. This is a simple

Figure 2.2 A circuit that performs a logical operation

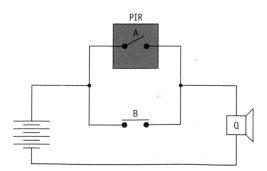

security system. A passive infrared detector (PIR) closes switch A when it is triggered by a moving warm object, such as a human body. B is a push-button for sounding the alarm manually. Q is a siren. The siren sounds if the PIR detects a person, or if someone presses the button. Putting this into more logical form:

> IF the PIR is triggered OR the button is pressed THEN the siren sounds.

To turn the statement above into a Boolean equation, we define that:

A = 1 means that the PIR is triggered; A = 0 means the inverse, that the PIR is NOT triggered.

B = 1 means that the button is pressed; B = 0 means that it is NOT pressed.

Q = 1 means that the siren is sounding; Q = 0 means that it is NOT sounding.

Now we can write out the statement more logically:

> IF A = 1 OR B = 1, THEN Q = 1

Normally we omit the '= 1's and write simply:

> IF A OR B, THEN Q

In its Boolean form this becomes:

> A + B = Q

Given this statement and knowing whether A and B are true, we can use the truth table to find the state of Q. For example: knowing that the PIR is not triggered (A = 0) and that the button is pressed (B = 1), the third row of the OR truth table (p. 19) tells us that Q is true (= 1). The siren is sounding.

In the questions (p. 25) there are several more examples of turning statements into Boolean equations.

The circuit in Fig. 2.3 is the same as that in Fig. 2.2 but includes a power switch C, so that we can turn off the security system when it is not needed. If C = 1 means that the power switch is closed, then the logic of the system becomes:

> (A + B).C = Q

Figure 2.3 A circuit that combines two logical operations

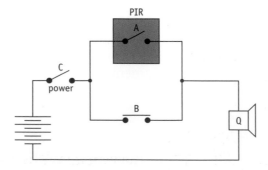

Including the AND operator (represented by the dot in the logic statement) ensures that the siren sounds only when C is closed AND the PIR is triggered OR the button is pressed. The brackets mean that the OR operation is resolved before the AND operation.

▌ Logic circuits

The circuits in Figs. 2.2 and 2.3 are examples of **wired logic**. More often, we perform logical operations with logic gates. Figs. 2.4 and 2.5 have the same logic as Figs. 2.2 and 2.3. They do not show the power connections to the gates, nor the interfaces at the inputs and output of the gates.

Figure 2.4 (left) Equivalent of Fig. 2.2, using a logic gate

Figure 2.5 (right) Equivalent of Fig. 2.3, using two logic gates

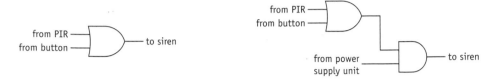

Gates are generally preferred to wired logic because they are more reliable and are available for all the logical operators.

▌ Identities

Identities are equations uscd for simplifying logical statements in Boolean algebra. Think of the identities as defining how a given logic gate operates – its inputs on the left of the equation and its output on the right. 'A' and 'B' represent inputs or outputs that may be 0 or 1. '0' and '1' in the identities represent inputs that are always 0 or always 1. There are five main groups of identities:

1 Simple OR identities:

$$A + 0 = A \qquad\qquad A + A = A$$

$$A + 1 = 1 \qquad\qquad A + \overline{A} = 1$$

The first identity, for example, describes the action of a 2-input OR gate in which one input is A (0 or 1) and the other input is permanently connected to 0 V. The truth table shows that in this case the output is always the same as the A input.

2 Simple AND identities:

$$A.0 = 0 \qquad\qquad A.A = A$$

$$A.1 = A \qquad\qquad A.\overline{A} = 0$$

3 Double inversion:

$$\overline{\overline{A}} = A$$

4 De Morgan's theorem:

$$\overline{A + B} = \overline{A}.\overline{B}$$

$$\overline{A.B} = \overline{A} + \overline{B}$$

5 Miscellaneous identities:

$$A(B + C) = AB + AC \qquad \text{(Remember 'AB' is a shorter way of writing 'A.B')}$$

$$A + BC = (A + B)(A + C)$$

$$A + AB = A \qquad \text{(Redundancy theorem)}$$

$$A(A + B) = A$$

$$A + \overline{A}B = A + B$$

$$CA + \overline{C}B + AB = CA + \overline{C}B \qquad \text{(Race hazard theorem)}$$

The identities may be proved by drawing up a truth table, using the six operations listed in the truth table on p. 19.

worked example

problem   Prove that:

$$A + BC = (A + B)(A + C)$$

working

1	2	3	4	5	6	7	8
C	B	A	BC	A + BC	A + B	A + C	(A + B)(A + C)
0	0	0	0	0	0	0	0
0	0	1	0	1	1	1	1
0	1	0	0	0	1	0	0
0	1	1	0	1	1	1	1
1	0	0	0	0	0	1	0
1	0	1	0	1	1	1	1
1	1	0	1	1	1	1	1
1	1	1	1	1	1	1	1

Columns 1 to 3 list all possible combinations of the variables A, B, and C. Column 4 contains the corresponding values of B AND C, taken from the AND truth table. Column 5 is the OR of the values in Columns 3 and 4. This is the left-hand side of the identity.

Column 6 is A OR B, and column 7 is A OR C, both taken from the OR truth table. Column 8 is the AND of the values in columns 6 or 7. This is the right-hand side of the identity.

solution   Comparison reveals that columns 5 and 8 have identical entries, so proving the identity.

Identities are used to simplify logic designs. As an example, take Fig. 2.6. The output of each gate except the last has been written beside the symbol. The output of the 3-input gate is the NOR of these:

$$Q = \overline{\overline{AB} + \overline{BC} + CD}$$

Figure 2.6 Logic circuit with four inputs

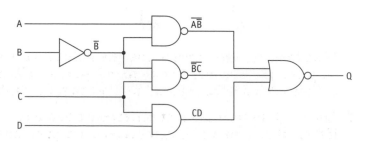

The equation is simplified in stages, using the identities, as listed below:

Use de Morgan and double inversion to convert NOR to AND:	$Q = A\overline{B}.\overline{B}C.\overline{CD}$
Use de Morgan to convert the $\overline{CD}$ term:	$Q = A\overline{B}.\overline{B}C.(\overline{C} + \overline{D})$
Use $A.A = A$ to simplify first two terms:	$Q = A\overline{B}C.(\overline{C} + \overline{D})$
Use $A(B + C) = AB + AC$:	$Q = A\overline{B}C\overline{C} + A\overline{B}C\overline{D}$
Use $A.\overline{A} = 0$:	$Q = A\overline{B}.0 + A\overline{B}C\overline{D}$
Use $A.0 = 0$:	$Q = 0 + A\overline{B}C\overline{D}$
Use $A + 0 = A$:	$Q = A\overline{B}C\overline{D}$

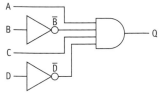

Figure 2.7 Simpler logic circuit that has the same action as Fig. 2.6

The equation is reduced to a single term. This represents the array of logic gates shown in Fig. 2.7. The number of gates used is reduced from five to three.

This simplification can also be made by writing out the 16-line truth table. The final column, Q, has 0 in every line except one. This is the line for which $A = 1$, $B = 0$, $C = 1$ and $D = 0$.

2•4 Karnaugh maps

Karnaugh maps are used for simplifying logical expressions. They are related to truth tables but are set out in a way that makes it easier to analyse them. They may be used with expressions containing two or more variables. First we will take a typical expression with five terms, each with three variables:

$$Q = \overline{A}\,\overline{B}\,\overline{C} + \overline{A}\,B\,\overline{C} + \overline{A}\,\overline{B}\,C + \overline{A}\,B\,C + A\,\overline{B}\,C$$

Each of the three variables may be true or false, and the expression shows that Q is true when any one of five particular combinations of states of A, B and C occur. The aim is to reduce this expression to its simplest equivalent.

1 Draw the map. With three variables the Karnaugh map has eight (2^3) cells:

Figure 2.8 Karnaugh map

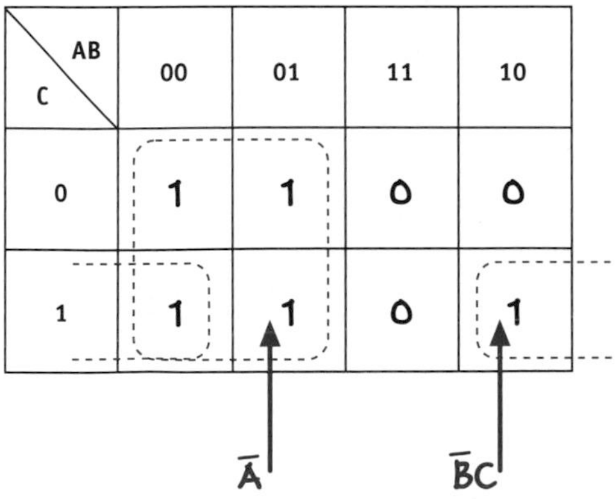

AB / C	00	01	11	10
0	1	1	0	0
1	1	1	0	1

$\overline{A}$ $\overline{B}C$

Note that only one variable changes state as we pass from one cell to an adjacent cell. The map 'wraps round' so that cells in the left-hand column are considered to be adjacent to those in the right-hand column.

2 Enter a '1' in each cell that corresponds to a term in the expression, or a '0' if there is no term in the expression corresponding to the cell. In this case the map has five 1s, and the remaining cells hold 0. The completed map of the expression above is shown in Fig. 2.8.

3 Look for rectangular groups of 2, 4, or 8 cells containing a '1': either couples (groups of 2 cells), 2×2 groups of 4 cells, 4×1 groups of 4 cells, or possibly a group of 8 cells. This map has a group of 4 and a wrapped-round group of 2.

4 Find the variable state that is common to all cells in each group. In this example, the 4 cells on the left all share the inverse of the variable A. This means that all the terms that contain $\overline{A}$, when 'ORed' together, are equal to $\overline{A}$:

$$\overline{A}\,\overline{B}\,\overline{C} + \overline{A}\,B\,\overline{C} + \overline{A}\,\overline{B}\,C + \overline{A}\,B\,C = \overline{A}$$

Four of the five terms in the original expression thus simplify to $\overline{A}$. The group of 2 cells share B and C, so:

$$\overline{A}\,\overline{B}\,C + A\,\overline{B}\,C = \overline{B}\,C$$

Combining these two results:

$$Q = \overline{A} + \overline{B}\,C$$

2•5 NAND or NOR logic

All logical operations may be performed by using only NAND gates or only NOR gates. This simplifies the layout and construction of circuit boards using ICs. The circuit design using only one type of gate may sometimes increase the number of gates, and hence ICs, required. However, using a single type of gate reduces delays in circuit action that can occur when using gates of different types, thus avoiding the risk of incorrect action in high-speed applications.

Fig. 2.9 shows how different functions may be built using only NAND gates. Use the truth table on p. 19 to confirm the action of these combinations of gates.

Figure 2.9 Using NAND gates to perform other operations

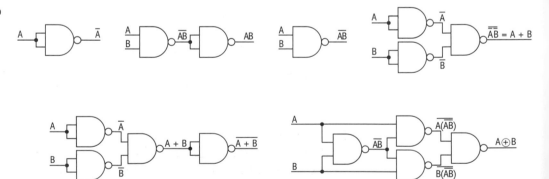

▌Ten quick questions

1 What 2-input logic gate gives a high output only if both its inputs are high?

2 What is the other name for a NOT gate?

3 Which logical operation does this symbol represent: $\oplus$?

4 What logical statement is identical to $A + A$?

5 How many cells has a Karnaugh map with four variables?

6 What is the rule about variable changes as we pass from one cell of a Karnaugh map to an adjacent cell?

7 An exclusive-OR gate has a high output. What can we say about its inputs?

8 Write an equation to illustrate the redundancy theorem.

9 What two types of gate can be used exclusively for performing any logical operation?

10 What is the name of the theorem illustrated by the following identity?

$$\overline{A \cdot B} = \overline{A} + \overline{B}$$

▌Questions on logic circuits

1 Describe what is meant by a logic gate.

2 **a)** Describe the action of the following gates by writing their truth tables: NOR; INVERT; exclusive-OR.

 b) Explain how we can use a NOR gate to operate as an INVERT gate.

3 Describe the action of a NAND gate. Write the truth table for a 3-input NAND gate. Draw the gate symbol and mark its inputs and outputs with Boolean symbols.

4 A passenger plane flies to an offshore island only on Thursdays and Sundays. Given these statements:

 A = it is Thursday
 B = it is Sunday
 Q = the plane has taken off for the island

 link the statements as a logical statement including the operator OR. Write the truth table. Use the truth table to find the value of Q when it is Friday.

5 The interior lamp of a microwave oven comes on when the door is open. It also comes on during cooking. Express these facts as a logical statement and write out the truth table. Which line in the truth table never occurs in a correctly operating oven?

6 A security system is designed to switch on a floodlight if it detects a person moving, but to do this only at night. It has a built-in clock that gives a high output for 30 s after the system has been triggered.

 a) Describe the operation of this system as a logical statement, as a truth table, and draw the logic circuit diagram.

 b) What sensors are used to detect a moving person, and whether it is day or night?

 c) What IC would you use for the timing operation and in what type of circuit?

7 In some circuit designs it might be more convenient to use an OR gate instead of an AND gate. Use de Morgan's theorem to find the alternative logic circuit for the system in question 6.

8 Write a truth table to describe the operation of the circuit in Fig. 2.10. What is the Boolean expression for this action?

9 Design a logic circuit to decode the output of 3-bit binary counter. The output of the decoder is to go high when the input number is 6. Write the truth table and the Boolean expression and describe the circuit.

10 Design a logic circuit to decode the output of 3-bit binary counter. The output of the decoder is to go high when the input number is 3 or 5. Write the Boolean expression and draw the circuit diagram.

11 The output of a 2-to-1 line multiplexer follows input A when the S (select) input is 0, and follows input B when S is 1. Write the truth table of this circuit and its Boolean expression. Draw the circuit.

12 Simplify:

a) $Q = \overline{A}\,\overline{B}\,\overline{C} + A\,\overline{B}\,\overline{C}$;

b) $Q = \overline{AB}(\overline{A} + B)$.

13 Write the truth table of the circuit in Fig. 2.11. What logical operation does it perform?

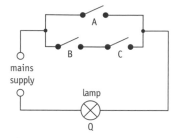

Figure 2.10

Figure 2.11

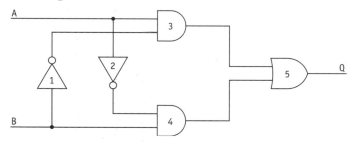

14 By using truth tables, prove the identities:

a) $A + AB = A$;

b) $A(A + B) = A$;

c) $\overline{A + B} = \overline{A}\,\overline{B}$;

d) $\overline{AB} = \overline{A} + \overline{B}$.

Note: identity **a)** is the redundancy theorem; identities **c)** and **d)** are the two de Morgan identities.

15 Use a truth table to prove that gate 4 in Fig. 2.12 produces A EX-OR B.

Figure 2.12

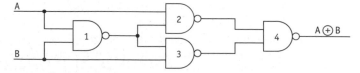

16 Use Boolean identities to simplify the expression for the output of gate 4 of Fig. 2.12, which is:

$$Q = \overline{A(\overline{AB})} \cdot \overline{B(\overline{AB})}$$

17 Draw circuit diagrams to show how 2-input NOR gates may be used to build **a)** INVERT; **b)** 2-input OR; **c)** 2-input AND.

18 Simplify

    a) $AB + A\overline{B} + \overline{A}B$;

    b) $AB(A + \overline{B}) + (A + B)(\overline{A} + B)$;

    c) $\overline{AB}(\overline{A} + B)$.

19 State de Morgan's theorem in words.

20 Write a Boolean expression to describe the action of the circuit in Fig. 2.13, listing the output of each gate. Simplify the circuit, if possible, using Boolean logic and draw the simplified version.

Figure 2.13

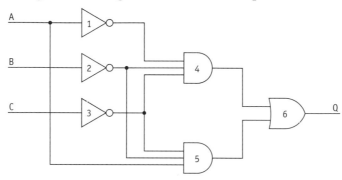

21 Design a 2-bit encoder circuit. This has two inputs, A and B, and four outputs, '0', '1', '2', '3'. When a binary number 00 to 11 is applied to A and B, the corresponding one of the four outputs goes high.

22 Fig. 2.14 is the circuit of a 2-bit parity generator. Write its truth table and explain what it does.

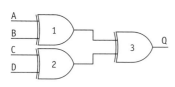

Figure 2.14 Parity generator

23 Use the Karnaugh map technique to simplify:

    a) $A\,B + A\,\overline{B} + \overline{A}\,\overline{B}$;

    b) $\overline{A}\,\overline{B}\,\overline{C} + A\,\overline{B}\,\overline{C}$;

    c) $A\,\overline{B}\,\overline{C} + A\,\overline{B}\,C + A\,B\,\overline{C} + A\,B\,C$;

    d) $\overline{A}\,\overline{B}\,\overline{C} + \overline{A}\,B\,\overline{C} + \overline{A}\,B\,C + \overline{A}\,B\,C + A\,\overline{B}\,C$.

24 Use the Karnaugh map technique to simplify:

    a) $\overline{A}\,B\,\overline{C}\,D + \overline{A}\,B\,C\,D + \overline{A}\,\overline{B}\,C\,D$;

    b) $\overline{A}\,\overline{B}\,\overline{C}\,D + \overline{A}\,\overline{B}\,C\,D + \overline{A}\,B\,\overline{C}\,D + \overline{A}\,B\,C\,D + A\,B\,C\,D$;

    c) $\overline{A}\,\overline{B}\,\overline{C}\,\overline{D} + A\,\overline{B}\,\overline{C}\,\overline{D} + \overline{A}\,B\,\overline{C}\,D + A\,B\,\overline{C}\,D + A\,\overline{B}\,\overline{C}\,D + A\,B\,C\,D + A\,\overline{B}\,C\,D + \overline{A}\,\overline{B}\,C\,D$.

25 An industrial process has eight stages, numbered 0 to 7. During stages 2, 3, 5 and 6 the workpiece has to be sprayed with water to keep it cool. The water supply to the spray is controlled by a solenoid valve, which is opened and closed by a logic circuit (Fig. 2.15). Write a logical expression for the value of Q and use a Karnaugh map to find a simpler expression.

26 Convert the circuit of the security system in question 6 (see Fig. A2.2, p. 157) to a version that uses only NAND gates.

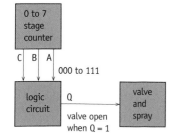

Figure 2.15

27 A traffic light is driven by a 2-bit counter. The output of the counter cycles through 00 (red), 01 (amber), 10 (green) and 11 (green). Design the logic needed to drive the lamps, using only NOR gates.

28 Design a circuit that is equivalent to Fig. A2.5 (p. 158), but using only NAND gates.

3 Components

In brief...

- Passive components are unable to produce a gain in power. They include resistors, capacitors, inductors and diodes (pp 28–30).
- Active components are able to produce a gain in power, the power usually coming from the circuit power supply. They include bipolar junction transistors, field effect transistors, thyristors and triacs (pp 30–33).
- Sensors provide an input to a circuit, dependent upon external conditions. Some are passive and some are active. Sensors include light-dependent resistors, photodiodes, phototransistors, microphones, thermistors and potentiometers (pp 33–35).
- Actuators provide a output from a circuit, by means of which it is able to have an effect on external conditions. Actuators include lamps, light-emitting diodes, solenoids, relays, motors, speakers and audible warning devices (pp 35–38).

Questions on components begin on p. 39, with answers from p. 161.

3·1 Passive components

The properties of resistors, capacitors and inductors, and of networks built from them, are described in section 1. Here wc discuss diodes.

A **diode** consists of a block of semiconductor in which a region of n-type semiconductor (the cathode) is in contact with a region of p-type semiconductor (the anode). The semiconductor may be silicon or (less often) germanium. The diode may be connected into a circuit in two ways: it may be **forward biased** or **reverse biased**.

Figure 3.1 Forward bias characteristic of a silicon diode

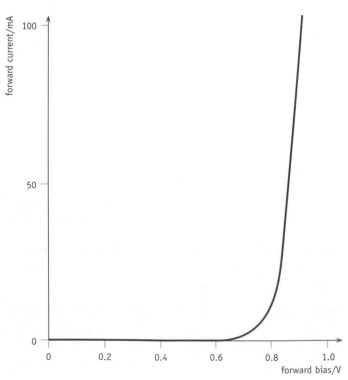

Forward bias The anode is positive of the cathode. Current flows through the diode from anode to cathode. Fig. 3.1 shows the forward bias characteristic, obtained by varying the pd across the diode and measuring the current through it. No current flows if the pd is less than about 0.6 V (for a silicon diode) or 0.2 V (for a germanium diode). Above these voltages the current increases steeply with pd. When a diode is conducting in this way there is a pd across it, known as the **forward voltage drop**. This is approximately 0.7 V for a silicon diode, but varies between 0.5 V and 0.9 V, depending on the current flowing and the type of diode. However, the voltage/current ratio is not constant (as it is with a resistor) so conduction is described as **non-ohmic**.

Reverse bias The cathode is positive of the anode. Only a very small reverse current flows, even when the reverse bias pd is 100 V or more (Fig. 3.2). This **leakage current** is measured in microamps, whereas the forward bias current is usually measured in milliamps.

Figure 3.2 Reverse bias characteristic of a silicon diode. Contrast with Fig. 3.1 and note the differing scales

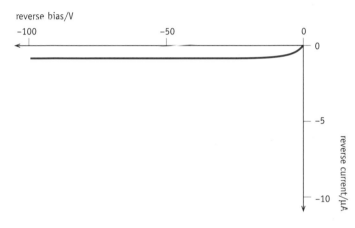

▌ Types of diode

Fig. 3.3 illustrates several types of diode and their symbols. Note that the use of the circles around the symbols is optional.

Figure 3.3 Diodes: symbols (circles optional) and packages

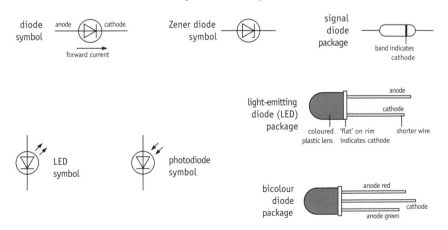

Small signal diode This is a low-current general-purpose diode, such as the 1N4148 which has a maximum forward current of 100 mA and is able to withstand a reverse pd of 75 V.

Power diode This is a heavy-duty diode suitable for use in rectifier circuits (see p. 55). Depending on the type, they are rated at 1 W, 5 W, 10 W or more. They are able to withstand reverse pds of several hundred volts. The high-power types are housed in a metal stud mounting for attaching to a heat sink.

Figure 3.4 Reverse bias characteristic of a Zener diode. Contrast with Fig. 3.2

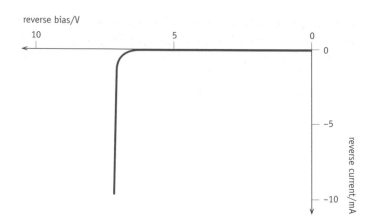

Zener diode This is a diode whose reverse bias characteristic (Fig. 3.4) shows a sharp 'knee' at the **Zener voltage**. When the reverse pd exceeds this voltage, the diode conducts readily without being destroyed. Zener diodes are made with specified Zener voltages such as 3.3 V, 3.6 V, ..., up to 200 V. They are used in voltage stabilising networks (see p. 43).

Light emitting diode (LED) See p. 35.

Photodiode See p. 33.

3·2 Active components

■ Bipolar junction transistor (BJT)

There are two types of BJT. The **npn** transistors have a thin layer of p-type silicon sandwiched between two layers of n-type. The pnp transistors have n-type between two layers of p-type. The action of pnp transistors is complementary to that of npn; the discussion below is confined to npn transistors.

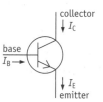

Figure 3.5 Symbol for an npn BJT (circle optional), showing the flow of currents

The three layers of a BJT are called the **collector**, the **base** and the **emitter** (Fig. 3.5). In use, the collector is made a few volts positive of the emitter. If a current I_B flows into the base, a much larger current I_C flows into the collector. A current I_E flows out of the emitter, and:

$$I_E = I_B + I_C$$

Because I_C is very much greater than I_B, we may often take $I_C \approx I_E$.

The BJT is a current amplifying device. We express its gain in two ways:

■ **large signal current gain**: symbol h_{FE} and equal to I_C/I_B;
■ **small signal current gain**: symbol h_{fe} and equal to i_c/i_b, where i_c is the amount of *change* in I_C resulting from a *change* i_b in I_B.

The gains are *ratios* and therefore have no units. In practice, these gains are more or less equal and the difference between them can be ignored.

The relationship between I_B and I_C is the **forward transfer characteristic** (Fig. 3.6). It can be seen that the curve is almost a straight line, with gradient almost exactly h_{FE} or h_{fe} for all values of I_B. As shown in the figure, $h_{fe} = 1.4/15[\text{mA}/\mu\text{A}] = 93$. The gain of a BJT is typically around 100, but may range from 10 up to 800. Power BJTs generally have the lowest gain.

The junction between the base and the emitter is the equivalent of a forward-biased diode. This means that no base current flows if the pd between base and emitter is less than about 0.7 V. When base current is flowing, there is a **forward voltage drop** V_{BE} of about 0.7 V between base and emitter. This may range between 0.5 V and 0.9 V, depending on the transistor and on the size of the base current.

BJTs are used as switches (p. 44) and as amplifiers (p. 50).

Figure 3.6 Forward transfer characteristic of an npn BJT

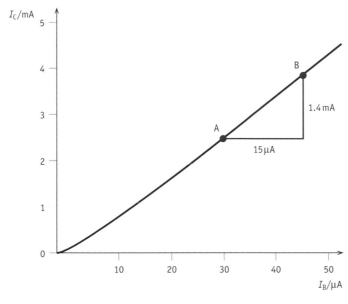

■ Field effect transistor (FET)

There are two main types of FET: metal oxide silicon FETs (MOSFETs) and junction FETs (JFETs). Here we consider only the most commonly used type, the **n-channel enhancement MOSFET**.

The three terminals of a MOSFET are called the **drain**, the **gate** and the **source** (Fig. 3.7a). In use, the drain is made a few volts positive of the source. If the voltage at the drain is sufficiently more positive than that at the source, a drain current I_D flows in at the drain and out at the source (Fig. 3.7b). The gate is insulated from the main body of the transistor, so no current flows in or out by this terminal. The resistance of the insulating layer is of the order of $10^{10} \, \Omega$. We say that FETs have high input impedance, which is one of their most important advantages.

In a FET, the drain *current* I_D is related to the gate–source *voltage* V_{GS}. The gain is expressed as:

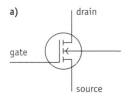

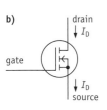

Figure 3.7 a) Symbol for n-channel enhancement MOSFET (circle optional); **b)** usual connection and flow of current when in use

$$g_m = \frac{i_d}{v_{gs}}$$

In words, the gain is the *change* in drain current per unit *change* in gate–source pd. Because this quantity is obtained by dividing a current by a pd, it is a *conductance*. Because i_d is an input and v_{gs} is an output, we call g_m the **transconductance** of the FET. It has the same unit as conductance, the seimens (symbol S).

The relationship between I_D and V_{GS} is the **forward transfer characteristic** (Fig. 3.8). The figure shows that there is no conduction through the MOSFET if the gate–source pd is below the **threshold voltage**. This is usually in the region of 2 to 5 V. Above that voltage, transconductance is not constant, but increases with increasing drain current. This results in distortion of signals of large amplitude. The transconductance of a MOSFET may range from 0.1 S to 20 S.

Figure 3.8 Forward transfer characteristic of an n-channel enhancement MOSFET

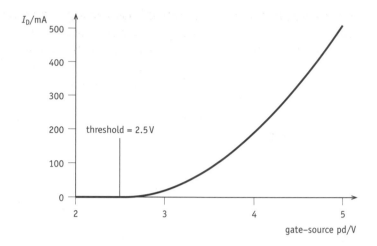

A MOSFET may be used as a voltage-controlled resistor. As the gate–source voltage is increased, the drain–source resistance decreases, leading to an increase in drain current, as shown in Fig. 3.8. The drain–source resistance is very low in certain types of MOSFET. In general-purpose MOSFETs it is usually about 5 Ω, but it is as low as 0.5 Ω in types designed for power switching.

MOSFETs are used as switches (p. 45) and as amplifiers (p. 52). One disadvantage of a MOSFET is that the gate insulation is fairly easily destroyed or penetrated by electrostatic charge. Precautions must be taken to avoid such charges when handling MOSFETs and other devices with MOSFET inputs. These precautions include wearing clothes made of natural fibres (cotton or wool), wearing an earthed strap around one wrist to earth the body, earthing the working surface, and not working on carpet made of nylon or other synthetic fibres. Components should be stored either wrapped in metal foil or with their terminal wires embedded in conductive plastic foam.

▌ Thyristor

A thyristor is a four-layer (pnpn) device that is equivalent to a pnp transistor and an npn transistor connected as in Fig. 3.9a. No current flows through the device when the gate–cathode pd is less than 0.7 V. No current flows if the cathode is positive of the anode. Thyristors are made to withstand reverse voltages of several hundred volts.

If the device is forward biased and a positive pulse is applied to the gate, it briefly turns Q1 slightly on. This pulls down the voltage at the base of Q2, turning it slightly on. Current begins to flow to the base of Q1, turning it further on, even though the pulse at the gate may have ended. This is **positive feedback**. Turning Q1 further on turns Q2 further on, and the process very rapidly results in both transistors being fully on. Current flows in through the anode terminal (emitter of Q2) and out through the cathode (emitter of Q1).

Once current has begun to flow, it continues to flow indefinitely. It ceases only when:

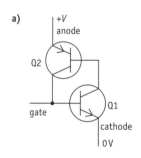

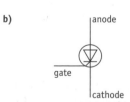

Figure 3.9 a) BJT equivalent of a thyristor; **b)** symbol (circle optional)

- ▌ the supply is turned off; or
- ▌ the supply is reversed; or
- ▌ the current falls below a given minimum known as the **holding current**.

Once current has ceased to flow, it does not flow again until the power supply (if cut off or reversed) is restored and a positive pulse is applied to the gate. Typically, only a low-voltage low-current pulse is required to switch a large current. For example, a thyristor may require a 2 V pulse at a gate current of only 1 mA to trigger a current of 5 A through the device. The holding current through the device is usually only a few milliamps.

The one-way conduction of the thyristor makes it similar to a diode. The names of its main terminals further suggest its diode-like property. The symbol for the thyristor (Fig. 3.9b) is similar to that of a diode, but with the gate terminal added.

Thyristors are used as switching devices in power control circuits, both dc and ac (see p. 107).

■ Triac

A triac is the equivalent of two thyristors connected anode to cathode, so it conducts in either direction (Fig. 3.10). Like the thyristor, it does not conduct until it is triggered by a pulse applied to its gate terminal, but the pulse may be either positive or negative. After triggering, the triac conducts until the power supply is turned off, or the current falls below the holding current.

Triacs are used in ac power control circuits (see p. 109).

Figure 3.10 Symbol for a triac (circle optional); MT = main terminal

3•3 Sensors

A sensor receives information from its surroundings and produces a corresponding electrical signal.

■ Light-dependent resistor

A light-dependent resistor (LDR) consists of a block or disc of cadmium sulphide or similar material, with a pattern of two electrodes coated on to its upper surface (Fig. 3.11a). When light shines on the disc, it causes an increase in the number of free electrons in the material. This reduces the electrical resistance between the electrodes. Typically, the resistance of an LDR ranges from 80 Ω in bright daylight to 10 MΩ in darkness.

Figure 3.11 a) Construction of a light-dependent resistor (LDR); **b)** symbol (circle optional)

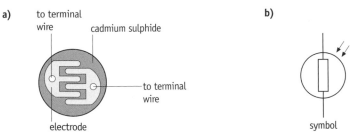

An LDR has the advantage of high sensitivity (a large change of resistance for a given change in light intensity) and can be used with ac. Its response time (200 ms) is slow compared with other light sensors. Its symbol is shown in Fig. 3.11b.

■ Photodiode

Light shining on a diode causes additional charge carriers to be set free. If the diode is reverse biased, these increase the leakage current in proportion to the light intensity. Normally, diodes are enclosed in a light-proof case so that this effect does not occur. Photodiodes, however, have a case of moulded transparent plastic, or a metal case with a clear lens at one end. Infrared photodiodes have a case of a plastic that is transparent to infrared but not to visible light.

Typical leakage current, with a reverse bias of 10 V, is 30 nA in the dark and 60 µA in daylight.

Photodiodes have high sensitivity and a linear response. They have a fast response time, typically 250 ns but some types have even faster times, down to 0.5 ns.

■ Phototransistor

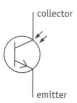

Figure 3.12 Symbol for a phototransistor that has no base connection (circle optional)

If an npn transistor is housed in a transparent case, light falls on the transistor, setting free additional electrons in the base region. This is equivalent to supplying the transistor with additional base current, so the collector current increases in proportion. The gain of the transistor results in increased sensitivity. It is therefore more sensitive to low light levels than is a photodiode. However, its response time is slower, usually in the range 2 μs to 15 μs.

Some phototransistors have a base terminal wire, so that the base can be biased almost into conduction. It then requires very little light to affect the transistor. It is not essential to make a connection to this terminal, however; other types have no such base connection (Fig. 3.12).

■ Microphone

There are a number of different kinds of microphone, operating on different principles. A commonly used type is the **electret microphone**, a variation of the capacitor microphone. The microphone comprises two metal plates. One of these is fixed and the other vibrates when sound waves strike it. The capacitance between the plates varies as the distance between them varies. This description applies also the capacitor microphone but the electret microphone has a special layer of dielectric between the plates. During manufacture, the dielectric is first heated and then cooled while it is in a strong electric field. When it is cool it retains the electric field permanently. For this reason the electret microphone does not require a power supply. There may be a voltage amplifier circuit built in to the microphone case, however, and this needs a supply of a few volts.

Electret microphones are sensitive to sounds in the range 50 Hz to 18 kHz (almost the whole range of the human ear). They have good linearity, which means that sound reproduction has high fidelity.

■ Thermistor

A thermistor is a resistor made from a semiconductor with a high temperature coefficient. The resistivity of semiconductors decreases with increasing temperature, so these are **negative temperature coefficient** (ntc) devices. Thermistors are made in the form of beads, discs or rods, and may be encapsulated in glass for protection. They are available in a range of resistances, from 100 Ω to 470 kΩ.

An advantage of thermistors is that they can be made very small. The smallest beads are only 0.5 mm in diameter. They can be inserted into small cavities and can therefore be used to measure the temperature of very small spaces or objects. Their small size also means that they have low heat capacity and thus a rapid response to changes of temperature.

A disadvantage of thermistors is that their response is not linear. They are suited to circuits that are to be triggered at one particular temperature, but not to circuits that respond to temperature over a range of values. They respond with reasonable precision over a limited temperature range.

A further disadvantage is that measuring the resistance of a thermistor involves passing a current through it. This heats the thermistor and so introduces error into the measurement. The measuring circuit must be designed to use as small a current as possible.

■ Potentiometer

A potentiometer is a variable resistor, made in rotary or slide form. It is not primarily intended to be a sensor but can be used as such. If a pd is applied across the track of a slide potentiometer, the voltage at its wiper is related to the linear position of the wiper (Fig. 3.13). In this way, the potentiometer is used to sense linear position.

Similarly, a rotary potentiometer may be used to sense angular position. An example is a rotary potentiometer used to feed back angular position in a servomotor.

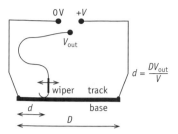

Figure 3.13 Principle of using a slide potentiometer to sense linear position

3•4 Actuators

An actuator converts an electrical signal into an action that affects its surroundings. All actuators are **transducers**; that is, they convert one form of energy (electrical energy) into another form of energy (for example light, heat or motion). Some sensors too are transducers, but not all.

■ Light sources

Actuators that are light sources include the following.

Filament lamp   When a current passes through the filament it becomes very hot and emits visible light.

Advantages: lamps of high light intensity (1 kW or more) are available; operate on dc and ac.
Disadvantages: significant amounts of power are wasted as heat; relatively short life (filament eventually burns out); fragile; resistance of filament is low when it is cold, so a current surge when switched on may cause the filament to fuse.
Uses: illumination; indicators.

Neon lamp   Current passing through the neon gas at low pressure excites the atoms, which glow red. Other rare gases (e.g. argon) are used for other colours.

Advantages: long life; efficient; tubes can be made in a variety of shapes for decorations and displays.
Disadvantage: needs relatively high operating voltage (minimum is about 70 V).
Uses: panel lamps; decoration; displays (especially for advertising).

Light-emitting diode (LED)   This emits light when passing current in the forward direction. The current required is typically in the range 5 mA to 30 mA. It requires a series resistor to limit the current (see overleaf). The forward voltage drop is about 2 V. LEDs are destroyed if subjected to a reverse pd of more than about 5 V. Colours available include red, orange, yellow, green, blue and white. They are also made as infrared emitters. Bicolour LEDs (see Fig. 3.3, p. 29) are usually red/green. The light intensity ranges from a few millicandela for panel indicator lamps to 5 candela or more for the high-intensity types used for illuminating small areas.

Advantages: compared with filament lamps they have better reliability; long life; greater efficiency (much less heat); high operating speed.
Disadvantage: much lower light intensity than filament lamps.
Uses: indicators; displays (including 7-segment and dot-matrix); signalling (fibre-optic systems).

An LED requires a series resistor to limit the current to a safe level. Allowing for a 2 V forward voltage drop, the resistor value is calculated from:

$$R = (V_S - 2)/I$$

where R is the series resistor, V_S is the supply voltage and I is the limited current.

worked example

problem   If the supply voltage is 12 V and the current is to be limited to 20 mA through an LED, what should be the value of the series resistor R?

working $R = (12 - 2)/0.02 = 500 \ \Omega$

solution   The nearest E24 value is 510 Ω.

▋ Solenoid

This consists of a coil with a soft-iron plunger that can slide easily in or out of the coil (Fig. 3.14). The plunger is coupled to a mechanism which is actuated when the plunger is drawn into the coil. The device is used with the plunger initially about half-way in the coil. When a current is passed through the coil, the plunger is pulled forcibly into the coil. The action is in one direction only, and a spring or other device is needed to pull the plunger out of the coil when the current is switched off. Some solenoids have a rotary action.

Figure 3.14 The action of a solenoid

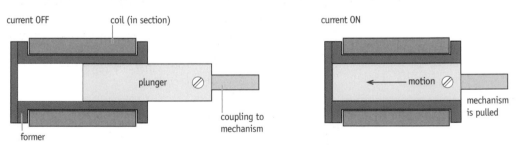

current OFF   coil (in section)   current ON

plunger

coupling to mechanism

former

motion

mechanism is pulled

Advantage: enables remote operation of mechanisms.
Disadvantage: requires relatively high current.
Uses: operating valves for control of fluids; door catches and similar mechanisms.

A solenoid is an inductive device, so a protective diode (see p. 42) is required if a transistor is used to switch the current.

▋ Relay

A relay is a current-controlled switch (Fig. 3.15). The coil has a soft-iron core. When a current is passed through the coil, the core becomes magnetised and attracts a spring-loaded armature. The armature moves towards the core, opening the normally-closed (n.c.) contacts and closing the normally-open (n.o.) contacts. Other types may have other arrangements of contacts.

Figure 3.15 Relay with changeover contacts (n.o. = normally open, n.c. = normally closed)

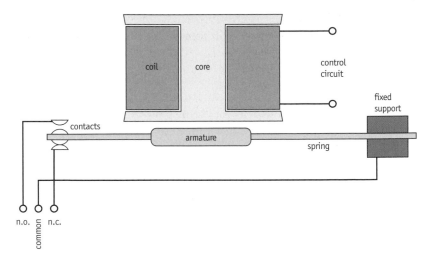

Relays are made in a range of sizes, from ultra-miniature types suitable for mounting on a circuit board with contacts rated for low voltages and currents, to heavy-duty relays capable of switching currents of 10 A or more at mains voltage.

Advantages: can switch large currents, either dc or ac; can switch two or more different circuits at the same time.
Disadvantages: can be bulky; slow-acting.

▌ Motor

There are many types of motor; three types often used in electronic systems are described here.

Low-voltage dc motor   This is run on voltages from 3 V to 12 V, taking a current of a few hundred milliamps.

Advantage: cheap.
Disadvantage: speed depends on mechanical load but a speed control circuit can compensate for this.
Uses: wide ranging, including cooling fans, toy vehicles, robots.

Stepper motor   This has four sets of coils that are energised in sequence, as listed in the following table:

Step number	Coil 1	Coil 2	Coil 3	Coil 4
0	on	off	on	off
1	off	on	on	off
2	off	on	off	on
3	on	off	off	on

As the coils are switched from one state to the next, the rotor turns by 15° clockwise. The rate of rotation is controlled exactly by the rate of switching the coils. The direction of rotation is controlled by running the sequence as above, or in the reverse direction. Switching may be done by using a special IC, or by a microcontroller circuit.

Advantages: speed of rotation depends on rate of switching, not on load; the rate of acceleration or deceleration of the motor is also under control.
Use: ideal for automatic control systems.

For more precise control of angle, a different switching sequence produces turns of 7.5° per step. Motors with 1.8° step angle are also available.

Servomotor The motor (usually a dc motor) has built-in reduction gearing to slowly turn a lever. The lever drives a mechanism such as a pointer, a robot arm, a remote TV camera mount or a turntable. There is a rotary potentiometer on the same spindle as the lever. The angular position of this is read as a voltage, produced as in Fig. 3.13, and is used to feed back the angular position of the lever to the control circuit. Current is supplied to the motor by the control circuit to turn the lever until it reaches the required position.

Advantage: precise control of angular position.
Use: in automatic control.

▌ Speaker

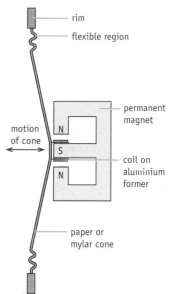

Figure 3.16 Section through a moving-coil speaker

This converts an analogue electrical signal at audio frequencies into sound waves in air. In a moving-coil speaker (the commonest type) the permanent magnet is made of a special steel that is strongly magnetised. The **voice coil** is wound on an aluminium former and suspended in the narrow gap between the poles of the magnet (Fig. 3.16). When an alternating audio signal is passed through the coil, the coil moves in and out as the current changes direction. This motion is transferred to the **cone** and from the cone to the air around it, producing sound. The speaker is mounted in a circular hole in a wooden or plastic wall known as a **baffle**. This prevents sound waves generated by the rear of the cone from coming round and partly cancelling the sound waves generated by the front of the cone.

The impedance of a speaker is the sum of the reactance and the resistance of the coil, the equation being $Z^2 = X^2 + R^2$. This is usually quoted at a frequency of 1 kHz. Typical impedances are 4 Ω and 8 Ω.

▌ Audible warning device

There are many different types of audible warning device (AWD), mainly buzzers and sirens, which all have a piezo-electric sound generator. The device normally includes a built-in oscillator circuit so that sound is produced when dc power is applied. A siren may emit a single tone, pulsed tones or a warbling sound, depending on the oscillator circuit.

AWDs operate on relatively low voltages, 3 V upwards to about 30 V, and require very little current (a few tens to a few hundreds of milliamps). The most powerful AWDs generate a sound level of 100 dB or more, which is sufficient for use in both domestic and industrial alarm systems.

▋ Ten quick questions

1 Which terminal of a MOSFET is made the most positive?
2 How many layers has a thyristor?
3 How do we describe a diode that has its anode positive of its cathode?
4 What is h_{FE}?
5 What happens to the resistance of a light-dependent resistor as light intensity increases?
6 Name the useful property of a thermistor.
7 What is a triac?
8 In what unit is transconductance measured?
9 What type of diode conducts substantial current in the reverse direction?
10 What type of microphone has a permanent pd across it?

▋ Questions on components

1 Name three types of *passive* component and state in a few words what each does.

2 What is meant by the terms forward bias, forward voltage drop, and leakage current, when applied to a silicon diode?

3 **a)** Name three types of diode. What are their distinguishing features?
 b) Describe an application for *one* type of diode, including a diagram of the circuit used.

4 The circuit in Fig. 3.17 remotely controls two fluid valves through a single pair of wires. Each valve is normally closed but opens when power is applied to it. Explain how the switch is set
 a) when the tank is filling;
 b) when the tank is held full of fluid;
 c) when the tank is emptying.
 d) At what stages does the indicator LED come on? What is the voltage amplitude of the ac passing through the coil of each valve when a single valve is switched on? How much current passes through the LED when it is on?

Figure 3.17

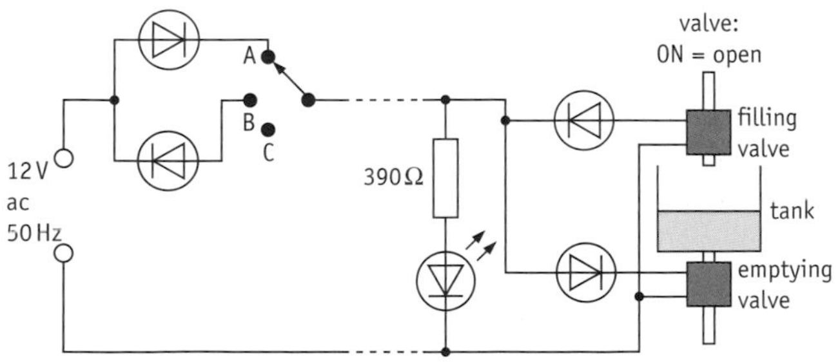

5 **a)** A Zener diode is rated at 400 mW and its Zener voltage is 6.8 V. What is the maximum reverse current that it can pass?
 b) A Zener diode is rated at 5 W and its Zener voltage is 12 V. What is the maximum reverse current that it can pass?

6 **a)** Name the three terminals of an npn bipolar junction transistor (BJT). Which of these is made the most negative when the transistor is connected into a circuit?

   b) When a BJT is used as an amplifier, what does it amplify? What is the difference in voltage at its base and emitter terminals?

7 **a)** Define the small signal current gain, h_{fe}, of a BJT.

   b) The collector of a BJT is 10 V positive of its emitter. If the current flowing into the base of a BJT increases by 1.2 mA, and its h_{fe} is 260, name and state the changes in size of the other currents flowing into or out of the transistor.

8 The base current to a BJT is 24 mA and the collector current is 8.16 A. What is the large signal current gain?

9 In Fig. 3.18, the large signal current gain of the BJT is 200, and the collector current is 2 mA. Calculate **a)** V_{out}; **b)** the base current; **c)** V_{in}.

10 Explain the meaning of these terms when applied to a MOSFET: **a)** drain; **b)** transconductance; **c)** threshold voltage; **d)** drain current.

11 A MOSFET has $g_m = 800$ mS. If the drain current decreases by 5.6 mA, what is the change in the gate–source voltage?

12 What is the essential difference between the action of a MOSFET and that of a BJT? What are the advantages and disadvantages of a MOSFET, when compared with a BJT?

13 Describe three precautions that should be taken to avoid damage to MOSFET devices from electrostatic charge.

14 List the properties of a thyristor. In what way does a triac differ from a thyristor?

15 Compare the features of a *light-dependent resistor*, a *photodiode* and a *phototransistor*. Which of these would you choose for use as a sensor in
   a) a fibre-optic receiver of fast pulsed signals;
   b) a broken light-beam intruder detector;
   c) an object-counter that operates at low light intensity?
   In each case state one reason for your choice.

16 Explain, with the use of a circuit diagram, how to interface a named type of light sensor to a logic circuit.

17 Describe how an electret microphone works. Draw the circuit of a pre-amplifier for the signal from the microphone.

18 What is a thermistor? Explain the advantages of using a thermistor as a heat sensor.

19 Describe the principle of operation of **a)** a filament lamp and **b)** a light-emitting diode. Why are LEDs usually preferred to filament lamps as indicators?

20 **a)** Calculate the value of the series resistor needed to limit the current through an LED to 20 mA on a 9 V dc supply. What is the nearest resistor to this in the E24 series?

   b) An LED operating on an 18 V supply has a 680 Ω series resistor. What is the current through the LED?

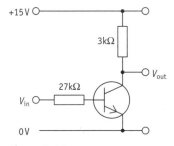

+15V

3kΩ

V_{out}

27kΩ

V_{in}

0V

Figure 3.18

21 Using symbols for the following components, draw a circuit for switching on an LED when the temperature exceeds a given level:

power input terminals, variable resistor, 2 fixed resistors, BJT, thermistor, LED.

22 Using symbols for the following components, draw a circuit for switching on a relay if the room is suddenly darkened:

power input terminals, variable resistor, LDR, MOSFET, relay.

Include in your diagram one other essential component and state why it is necessary. You are not required to draw the circuit switched by the relay.

23 The resistance of a thermistor is measured at several temperatures, with these results:

Temperature/°C	0	10	20	30	40	50
Resistance/kΩ	47	29	19	12	8	6

Plot a graph to show how the resistance varies with temperature. What does the graph tell us about the resistance–temperature relationship? From the graph, find **a)** the resistance at 37 °C; **b)** the temperature at which the resistance is 22 kΩ.

24 Using the same thermistor as in question 23, design a MOSFET circuit to switch on an LED as the temperature rises above 18 °C. The current through the LED is to be 20 mA. Assume that the supply voltage is 12 V, and that the threshold voltage of the MOSFET is 3 V and its 'on' resistance is 1 Ω.

25 Describe the operation of a stepper motor. What rate of switching is needed to make a 15° stepper motor turn at a rate of 5 rpm? What are the advantages of a stepper motor compared with an ordinary dc motor?

26 Name *three* actuator devices that operate by electromagnetism. Describe one use for each.

4 Analogue networks and circuits

In brief...

- Diode applications include use as a protective diode, a diode clamp, and a Zener voltage stabiliser (pp 42–44).
- Transistor switches can be based on BJTs or MOSFETs (pp 44–45). The Darlington pair has very high gain (pp 45–46).
- Monostables produce a single pulse, and astables an indefinite series of pulses. They are built from BJTs or from the 555 or 7555 timer IC (pp 46–49).
- Passive resistor–capacitor filters include lowpass and highpass versions (pp 49–50). Active filters are described in section 6, p. 86.
- Simple transistor amplifiers can be based on the common-emitter, common-collector, common-source and common-drain connections, each with distinctive properties (pp 50–53). Class AB and B amplifiers are more powerful, so heat sinks and their thermal resistance need to be considered (pp 53–55).
- Power supplies to produce low-voltage dc from ac mains need a transformer, and either a half-wave or a full-wave rectifier (pp 55–56).

Questions on analogue networks and circuits start on p. 57, with answers from p. 163.

4•1 Diode applications

■ Protective diode

A protective diode is required when a transistor is used to switch an inductive load (Fig. 4.1a). When the transistor is turned off the sudden collapse of the magnetic field in the inductor causes an emf to be generated in the coil. The emf is proportional to the rate of collapse of the field; this is rapid, so the emf is high. The emf generates a heavy current that flows in the same direction as the original current through the coil (see Fig. 4.1b), but is much larger than the original current. The diode conducts this current away, so protecting the transistor from being damaged.

Figure 4.1 Use of a protective diode

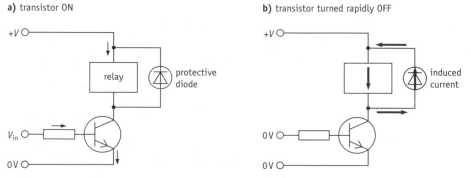

a) transistor ON

b) transistor turned rapidly OFF

■ Diode clamp

In Fig. 4.2a, V_{in} is a square-wave signal which passes through a coupling capacitor. Its amplitude is 6 V and it is offset so that it alternates between 0 V and +12 V. It is assumed that the RC combination has a long time constant (p. 8). V_{out} has the same frequency and amplitude as V_{in}, but is centred on 0 V.

This effect also occurs with other waveforms such as sine waves. It is a disadvantage if, for example, V_{out} is fed to a transistor, which comes on only when V_{out} reaches its most positive levels, and is therefore off for over half of each cycle.

Figure 4.2 Use of diode clamps

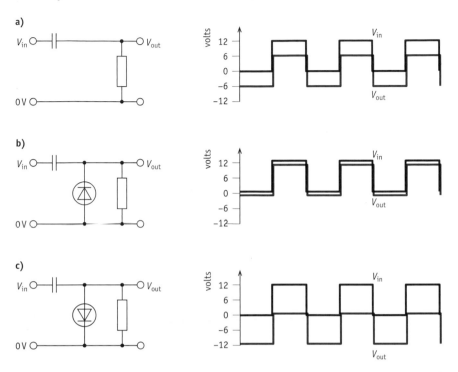

Fig. 4.2b shows a diode used to restore the dc level of the signal, by **clamping** the *lowest* value of V_{out} to the 0 V line. V_{out} cannot go negative as in Fig. 4.2a, because the diode discharges the capacitor. V_{out} is about 0.7 V below V_{in} because of the diode's forward voltage drop.

The diode is reversed in Fig. 4.2c, and this clamps the *highest* value of V_{out} to the 0 V line. Actually, it is clamped to 0 V plus 0.7 V for the voltage drop. V_{out} may be clamped to other voltages by connecting the anode of the diode to another fixed voltage instead of to 0 V.

▌ Zener voltage stabiliser

In Fig. 4.3, the output voltage is V_Z, the Zener voltage of the diode, provided that $V_S > V_Z$ and that a minimum current of about 5 mA is flowing through the diode. The voltage-dropping resistor R accounts for most of the difference between V_S and V_Z when the load is drawing its maximum current and 5 mA is flowing through the diode. To calculate R:

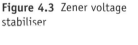

Figure 4.3 Zener voltage stabiliser

$$R = \frac{V_S - V_Z}{I_{load} + 0.005}$$

worked example

problem Find a value for R in a Zener stabiliser in which V_S is 9 V, V_Z is 4.7 V, and the maximum load current is 70 mA.

working $R = (9 - 4.7)/(0.07 + 0.005) = 57.3\ \Omega$

solution Take the next smaller E24 value, 56 Ω.

The Zener diode must be rated to the power dissipated in it when carrying maximum current, that is, when the load is drawing no current.

$$\text{power} = V_Z(I_{\text{load}} + 0.005)$$

worked example

problem What is the minimum power rating required for the Zener diode in the previous example?

working Power $= 4.7(0.07 + 0.005) = 0.353\,\text{W}$

solution A 400 mW Zener is safe to use.

The dropper resistor must be rated to the power dissipated in it.

$$\text{power} = (V_S - V_Z)(I_{\text{load}} + 0.005)$$

worked example

problem What is the minimum power rating for the dropper resistor in the example above?

working Power $= (9 - 4.7)(0.07 + 0.005) = 0.323\,\text{W}$

solution A 0.5 W resistor must be used.

4•2 Transistor switches

∎ Type of transistor switch

Transistor switches may be based on a BJT or a MOSFET. A BJT is usually operated in the common-emitter mode (p. 50), and a MOSFET in the common-source mode (p. 52). The transistor is saturated when switched on, so that the collector–emitter voltage or drain–source voltage is approximately zero. A negligible amount of power is dissipated in the transistor when it is on, and no power is dissipated when it is off. A heat sink is not required, provided that the transition from 'off' to 'on' is reasonably fast.

An example of a BJT switch is shown in Fig. A3.1 and a MOSFET switch in Fig. A3.2 (see p. 163). In each case, the sensor and series resistor form a potential divider network. The transistor is off when the output from the network is low, and on when it exceeds a given value. In Fig. A3.1 the sensor is positive of the resistor, so the output is high (transistor on) when the resistance of the sensor is small (higher temperature). In Fig. A3.2 the resistor is positive of the sensor, so the output is high when the resistance of the sensor is high (low light). The action of the circuits is inverted by exchanging the sensor and resistor.

The resistor in series with the sensor may be variable, to allow for variations in the resistance of the sensor (depending on type and manufacture) and for setting the level at which the circuit changes state. Once the correct setting of the variable resistor has been decided, it can be replaced by a fixed resistor. Or, as in Figs. 4.4a and b opposite, it may be replaced by a fixed resistor in series with a variable resistor, for fine adjustment of switching level.

A current-limiting resistor is needed in a BJT switch to limit the base current to a safe amount. In the MOSFET, the high input impedance of the gate makes this unnecessary. A protective diode is needed in either type of switch if the load is inductive (see p. 42).

Voltage divider networks similar to those in Figs A3.1 and A3.2 are used for other resistive sensors, such as a position-sensing potentiometer (see Fig. 3.13, p. 35). Photodiodes and phototransistors are non-resistive sensors. The networks for connecting these to a transistor switch are shown in Fig. 4.4. In Fig. 4.4a the photodiode is reverse biased. When it is sufficiently illuminated, a leakage current flows through the photodiode and through the resistors. The resistors have high values, so that a small leakage current generates a relatively large pd. As the light increases, the pd increases and turns on the BJT. Note the current-limiting resistor. In Fig. 4.4b the collector current of the phototransistor increases with increasing light. This increases the pd across the resistors and turns off the MOSFET. Note the protective diode across the motor, which is an inductive load.

Figure 4.4 Transistor switches:
a) photodiode and BJT;
b) phototransistor and MOSFET

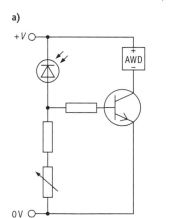
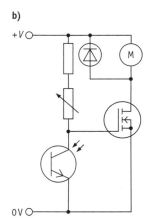

If the change in temperature or light level is slow, the transistor switches that we have discussed turn on or off slowly. In some applications this does not matter but, if a rapid 'snap' action is important, a **Schmitt trigger** circuit should be used. It is possible to build a trigger from transistors, but a simpler and more satisfactory trigger can be built from an operational amplifier, as described on p. 89.

Comparing BJTs and MOSFETs

Factors to consider in designing switching circuits are:

- MOSFETs have very high input impedance, so require virtually no current to drive them;
- power MOSFETs with an 'on' resistance as low as 0.5 Ω are available;
- MOSFETs are faster than BJTs, but BJTs are fast enough for most uses;
- BJTs require a current-limiting resistor at the base input, which slightly complicates circuit board layout and construction;
- for a given power rating, BJTs are cheaper than MOSFETs.

The Darlington pair

This consists of two BJTs (usually npn) connected as in Fig. 4.5. For Q1, $I'_C = I'_B \times h'_{FE}$. For Q2, $I''_C = I''_B \times h''_{FE}$. But $I''_B = I'_E \approx I'_C$, so:

$$I''_C = I'_B \times h'_{FE} \times h''_{FE}$$

In words, the gain of the pair is equal to the product of the individual gains.

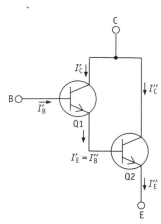

Figure 4.5 Darlington pair

Darlington pairs are usually in a 3-pin package, with the two transistors connected on the same chip. However, a pair may be built from two separate transistors. In this case, Q2 can be a power transistor.

4·3 Monostables and astables

▮ BJT monostable

A BJT **monostable** consists of two BJT switches, each connected so that its output becomes the input of the other (Fig. 4.6). One connection is resistive (R_3), the other is capacitive (C_1). Monostables are useful as pulse generators and in delay circuits.

R_1 and R_2 must have lower resistance than R_3 or R_4. Either or both of R_1 and R_2 can be low-resistance devices suited to switching by BJTs, such as filament lamps, LEDs or AWDs. The figure shows the output being taken at the collector of Q2, but an inverted output can be taken at the collector of Q1.

Figure 4.6 BJT monostable, or pulse generator

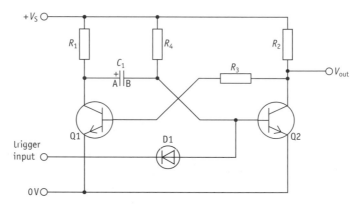

The circuit has one stable state: Q1 off and Q2 on, V_{out} low. Plate A of C_1 is at the supply voltage (V_S) and plate B is at 0.7 V, because of the base–emitter voltage drop. A low pulse to the trigger input briefly turns Q2 off. The voltage at its collector rises to V_S. Q1 is turned on. Q1 and Q2 have both changed state, and V_{out} is high ($= V_S$). The circuit is unstable in this state. The voltage at the collector of Q1 (and at plate A of C_1) falls from V_S to zero, that is by $-V_S$. This pulls down the voltage at plate B by the same amount, taking it negative to $(0.7 - V_S)$. Current flows through R_4, gradually raising the voltage on plate B. When this reaches $+0.7$ V, Q2 is switched on again, making V_{out} low ($= 0$ V). This turns off Q1, and the circuit is now back to its original stable state.

A summary of the action is illustrated in Fig. 4.7.

Figure 4.7 Summary of BJT monostable action

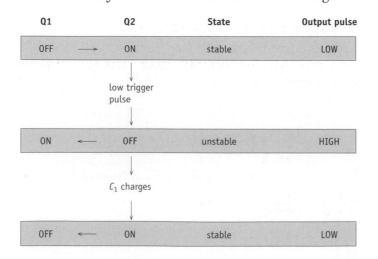

The length of the high output pulse is the time taken to charge C_1 from $(0.7 - V_S)$ to $+0.7$ V. It can be shown that this is approximately equal to $0.69R_4C_1$.

▌ BJT astable

Like a monostable, an **astable** can exist in two states, but it is not stable in either state. It automatically alternates between one state and the other. Also like a monostable, an astable consists of two cross-connected BJT switches (Fig. 4.8), but in the astable the connections are both capacitative. Astables are useful as system clocks and tone generators.

Figure 4.8 BJT astable, or oscillator

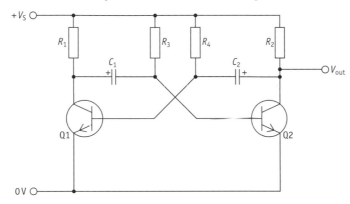

R_1 and R_2 must have lower resistance than R_3 or R_4. Either or both of R_1 and R_2 can be low-resistance devices suited to switching by BJTs, such as filament lamps, LEDs or AWDs. The figure shows the output being taken at the collector of Q2, but an inverted output can be taken at the collector of Q1.

At a certain stage in the operating cycle, Q2 is turned on, its collector voltage falls and V_{out} is low. Through C_2, this lowers the voltage at the base of Q1 from $+0.7$ V to $(0.7 - V_S)$, a negative value, turning Q1 off. The circuit stays in this state while current flows through R_4, gradually raising the base voltage of Q1. When this reaches 0.7 V, Q1 turns on, Q2 is turned off (through C_2) and V_{out} goes high. Now the circuit is in its alternate state, with the base of Q2 negative and C_1 being charged through R_3. As soon as the base of Q2 reaches 0.7 V, Q2 turns on again, V_{out} goes low again, and the cycle repeats.

A summary of the action is illustrated in Fig. 4.9.

The periods for each state are $0.69R_4C_2$ and $0.69R_3C_1$. If $R = R_3 = R_4$, and if $C = C_1 = C_2$, then the total oscillation period is $0.69(2RC) = 1.38RC$ and the mark–space ratio of the output waveform is 1. By choosing suitable values for the resistors it is possible to build an astable with other mark–space ratios.

Q1	Q2	Output pulse
OFF ← ON		LOW

C_2 charges

| ON → OFF | | HIGH |

C_1 charges

| OFF ← ON | | LOW |

action repeats

Figure 4.9 Summary of BJT astable action

▌ 555 timer IC monostable

The 555 timer IC and its low-current CMOS version, the 7555, are the basis for a precision monostable circuit with the minimum of additional components (Fig. 4.10).

Figure 4.10 Monostable based on 7555 IC

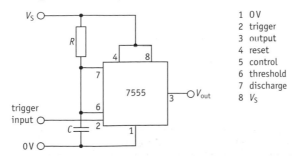

1 0V
2 trigger
3 output
4 reset
5 control
6 threshold
7 discharge
8 V_S

In its stable state, the trigger input is held at V_S. The output is 0 V. The capacitor has no charge. Current flowing through R is diverted into the IC through the threshold pin (pin 6) and on through the IC and pin 1 to the 0 V line.

The circuit is triggered by a brief negative-going pulse on the trigger input. This must fall to below $V_S/3$. On triggering, the output rises sharply to V_S. Current no longer flows into pin 6 but goes to the capacitor, gradually raising the pd across it. The pd is sensed by pin 6. When it reaches $2V_S/3$, the output falls to 0 V and C is rapidly discharged through pin 7. The IC is now ready to be triggered again.

The trigger pulse must be brief. If the trigger input is held below $V_S/3$ after C has charged, the output stays high until the trigger input is allowed to rise above $V_S/3$. The IC has a reset input (pin 4), which is often disabled by connecting it directly to the supply line, as in Fig. 4.10. If pin 4 is suitably connected, a low pulse resets the IC at any stage after it has been triggered. Its output falls immediately to 0 V.

Pin 5 is the control pin which is used to modify the action of the IC; details of this are not needed here. In the case of the 555, it is usual to connect a 10 nF capacitor between this pin and the 0 V line. In the 7555, this pin can be left unconnected. The 555 produces spikes on the supply lines when it switches states. These can be decoupled by wiring a 10 μF capacitor across the supply as close as possible to pins 1 and 8. This is not needed with the 7555.

The length of the high output pulse is the time taken to charge the capacitor from 0 V to $2V_S/3$. The formula is $t = 1.1RC$. Note that timing is independent of the supply voltage.

■ 555 timer IC astable

In the astable circuit built from the 555 timer IC, or the 7555, the trigger input of the IC is connected to the threshold pin so that the IC is triggered every time the charge on C falls below $V_S/3$. Thus, C continually charges to $2V_S/3$ and discharges to $V_S/3$. The IC produces an indefinite series of high output pulses. There is an additional resistor (R_2, Fig. 4.11) compared with the monostable circuit, so that the capacitor is charged through R_1 and R_2 in series, but is discharged through only R_2.

Figure 4.11 Astable based on 7555 IC

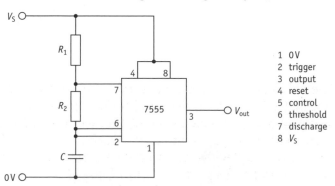

The charging time (t_1) with output high is:

$$t_1 = 0.69(R_1 + R_2)C$$

The discharging time (t_2) with output low is:

$$t_2 = 0.69R_2C$$

The total period (*t*) is the sum of these:

$$t = t_1 + t_2 = 0.69(R_1 + 2R_2)C$$

The frequency (*f*) of the pulsed signal is:

$$f = \frac{1}{t} = \frac{1.44}{(R_1 + 2R_2)C}$$

As for the monostable, timing is independent of the supply voltage. It can be seen from the formulae above that $t_1 > t_2$. The mark–space ratio is thus necessarily greater than 1. It is given by:

$$\text{mark–space ratio} = \frac{t_1}{t_2} = \frac{(R_1 + R_2)}{R_2}$$

4•4 Frequency-dependent *RC* networks

▌ Lowpass *RC* filter

A lowpass *RC* filter (Fig. 4.12a) can be thought of as a potential divider (Fig. 4.12b), but with impedances instead of simple resistances. The impedance of a resistor is independent of frequency, but the impedance of a capacitor falls as frequency increases (see p. 7). Consequently, at *low frequencies* the impedance of *C* is much greater than that of *R*, and almost all the signal voltage (v_{in}) is dropped across the capacitor. v_{out} is equal to or almost equal to v_{in}. The signal is passed through the filter at full or nearly full strength.

The effect is reversed at *high frequencies*. The impedance of *C* is much less then that of *R*. Most of the signal voltage is dropped across *R* and only a small signal appears at v_{out}.

In summary, the filter passes low frequencies and blocks high frequencies.

Figure 4.12 Lowpass *RC* passive filter: **a)** network; **b)** network redrawn as a potential divider; **c)** frequency response

a)

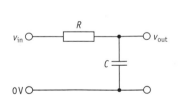

b)

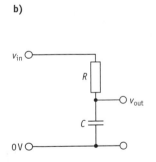

c)

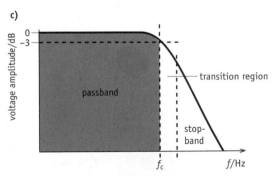

The effect is illustrated by a graph of the **frequency response** of the filter (Fig. 4.12c), in which the amplitude of v_{out} is plotted against frequency. So that it may plot a wide range of frequencies and a wide range of amplitudes, such a graph is best plotted on logarithmic scales. The amplitude of v_{out} is plotted on a decibel scale, relative to the constant amplitude of v_{in}. Zero on the scale indicates that $v_{out} = v_{in}$. The **−3 dB level** is that at which the *power* of v_{out} is half that of v_{in}. This is also known as the **half-power level**.

The **passband** of a lowpass filter extends from 0 Hz (dc) up to the frequency at which v_{out} is at the half-power level. This **cut-off frequency**, f_c, is given by:

$$f_c = \frac{1}{2\pi RC}$$

Note that this is also the frequency at which R and C have equal impedances. At this frequency, $Z_C = 1/2\pi f C = R$. Rearranging this equation gives the cut-off frequency equation.

Above f_c the response falls off gradually in the **transition region**, and eventually the curve falls as a straight line. The straight line region is called the **stopband**. The slope of the line is such that power is reduced by 6 dB for each doubling of frequency. A doubling of frequency is an **octave**, so the slope of the curve is expressed as $(-6\,\text{dB/octave})$. It can also be expressed as $(-10\,\text{dB/decade})$.

The phase of v_{out} lags behind that of v_{in} by an amount that depends on frequency (see p. 10). At low frequencies the phase lag is very small, but it increases to $-45°$ at f_c, and it is $-90°$ at the highest frequencies.

Lowpass passive filters can also be based on an LC network (see p. 11).

■ Highpass *RC* filter

If the resistor and the capacitor of the lowpass filter are interchanged, we obtain a highpass filter (Fig. 4.13). It can again be thought of as a potential divider, which now blocks low frequencies and passes high frequencies. The cut-off frequency again occurs when the impedances of R and C are equal, so the same formula applies for f_c.

Figure 4.13 Highpass *RC* passive filter: **a)** network; **b)** network redrawn as a potential divider; **c)** frequency response

a)

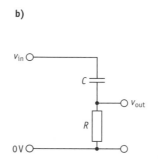

b)

c)

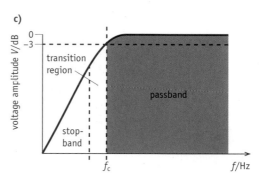

The stopband extends to a little below f_c, and the slope of the line here is $(+6\,\text{dB/octave})$, or $(+10\,\text{dB/decade})$. There is a small transition region in which the curve starts to level off. The passband extends from f_c up to the highest frequencies.

The phase of v_{out} leads that of v_{in} by an amount that depends on frequency. At low frequencies the phase lag is 90°, but it decreases to 45° at f_c, and is very small at the highest frequencies.

4·5 Simple BJT and MOSFET amplifiers

■ Common-emitter amplifier

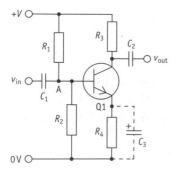

Figure 4.14 Common-emitter amplifier

The input and output of the common-emitter amplifier in Fig. 4.14 are coupled to other circuits, such as a microphone (through C_1) and a power amplifier (through C_2).

When the amplifier is quiescent (receiving no signal), the voltage at point A is fixed by the potential divider network, R_1 and R_2. A current flows from A into the base of Q1. A larger collector current (typically 1 mA) passes through R_3, the transistor and R_4. Values of R_3, R_4 and the collector current are such that the voltage at C_2 is about half of the supply, $V/2$.

A positive-going signal voltage, v_{in}, applied to C_1, causes the voltage at A to rise. This increases the base current, which leads to an increase in the collector current. The pd across R_3 increases, leading to a *fall* in the output voltage. This is an **inverting amplifier**.

This is also a **voltage amplifier**. Consider what happens if the capacitor C_3 is omitted from the circuit. Given that the input v_{in} *changes* by a small (positive or negative) amount Δv_{in}, the base voltage v_B changes by an equal amount, which we will call v_b. The base–emitter voltage drop is constant, and so the emitter voltage v_E changes by an equal amount, v_e. Thus:

$$\Delta v_{in} = v_b = v_e$$

Applying Ohm's law:

$$i_e = v_e/R_4$$

where i_e is the change in emitter current; and:

$$\Delta v_{out} = -i_c.R_3$$

where i_c is the change in collector current.

Combining these equations and assuming that $i_c \approx i_e$ (see p. 30):

$$\Delta v_{out} = -i_c.R_3 = -i_e.R_3 = -v_e.R_3/R_4 = -\Delta v_{in}.R_3/R_4$$

$$\Rightarrow \quad \text{voltage gain} = \frac{\Delta v_{out}}{\Delta v_{in}} = \frac{-R_3}{R_4}$$

The **voltage gain** is thus independent of the gain of the transistor (see p. 30) and also of variations in temperature. Note that it is negative. The gain is not as large as the gain that can be obtained by omitting R_4 and C_2, and connecting the emitter of Q1 directly to the 0 V line, but the circuit has the advantage of stability. This means that any transistor may be used in the circuit, either of the same or a diffcrent type.

Without the capacitor C_3, v_E varies because of the signal voltage, among other causes. There is negative feedback of these variations in v_E. The action is: increase of v_B (tending to *increase* v_{BE}) → increase of i_B → increase of i_C → increase of i_E → increase of v_E (tending to decrease v_{BE}). The signal is partly cancelled out, which accounts for the reduced gain. The effect of adding C_3 (typically 100 μF) is to **bypass** the signal at the emitter to the 0 V line. This prevents feedback of the signal (restoring the signal gain) while still allowing the feedback to compensate for other variations in v_E, due to differences in h_{FE}, temperature changes and other causes. The signal at the collector is unaffected by this action and passes through C_2 to become v_{out}.

In the quiescent state v_{out} is ideally $V/2$, so that v_{out} can swing as far as possible above and below this value without distorting the signal.

Input and output coupling: C_1, R_1 and R_2 form a highpass filter in which R_1 and R_2 are in parallel. The f_c of this filter must be set low enough to pass all the frequencies that the circuit is intended to amplify. Similarly, C_2 and R_3 form a highpass filter at the output.

Input impedance: this is mainly due to the parallel resistances of R_1 and R_2. Since these cannot have high values if they are to pass sufficient current to the base, the input impedance of a common-emitter amplifier is not high; it is generally of medium value.

Output impedance: this is mainly due to R_3, and is usually low.

Uses: amplifying audio and other analogue signals.

A summary of properties is given in the table on p. 53.

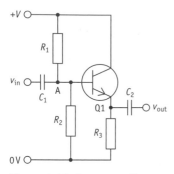

Figure 4.15 Common-collector amplifier

■ Common-collector amplifier

When the common-collector amplifier in Fig. 4.15 is quiescent (receiving no signal), the voltage at point A is fixed by the potential divider network, R_1/R_2. A current flows from A into the base of Q1. A larger collector current (typically 1 mA) passes through the transistor and R_3. Values of R_3 and the collector current are such that, as for the common-emitter amplifier, the voltage at C_2 is about half of the supply, $V/2$.

A positive-going signal voltage, v_{in}, applied to C_1, causes the voltage at A to rise. This increases the base voltage v_B. Because v_{BE} is constant (≈ 0.7 V), this leads to an equal increase in v_E and thus to v_{out}. The voltage gain of the amplifier is 1. This is often called **unity gain**. Because v_{out} is only slightly less than v_{in}, the amplifier is **non-inverting**. It is often called an **emitter follower**.

Input impedance: as for the common-emitter amplifier (see p. 51).
Output impedance: this is mainly due to the emitter resistance of the transistor, which is only a few tens of ohms.
Use: impedance matching (as a buffer between a high-impedance source and a low-impedance load).

A summary of properties is given in the table on p. 53.

■ Common-source amplifier

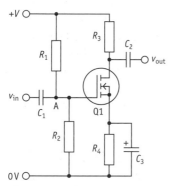

Figure 4.16 Common-source amplifier

The circuit for a common-source amplifier based on an n-channel enhancement MOSFET (Fig. 4.16) is identical to that of the common-emitter npn BJT amplifier (Fig. 4.14), except for the value of the biasing resistors. Because the gate of the MOSFET takes virtually no current, high-value resistors (in the megohm range) are used for biasing. This has the advantage that it makes the input impedance very high.

The stabilising function of the source resistor (R_4) and the bypass capacitor (C_3) is similar to that in the common-emitter amplifier.

In operation, the gate is biased to a little more than the threshold voltage. In most transistors this is between 2 V and 4 V; it varies quite widely between different transistors of the same type. The relationship between gate–source voltage and drain current is not linear, leading to distortion of large signals. Multi-stage amplifiers often have a MOSFET amplifier as the first stage, because of the high input impedance. The signal is small and less subject to distortion at this stage. Later stages are based on BJTs because of their good linearity.

It takes less time to change the charge on the gate than it does to change the current flowing through the base of a BJT. For this reason, MOSFETs are suited for high-frequency signals in, for example, radio-frequency amplifiers.

Uses: low-signal amplifiers and pre-amplifiers; radio-frequency amplifiers; amplifiers of signals from high-impedance sources.

A summary of properties is given in the table on p. 53.

■ Common-drain amplifier

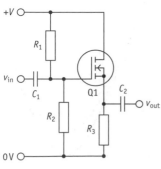

Figure 4.17 Common-drain amplifier

The circuit for a common-drain MOSFET amplifier (Fig. 4.17) is identical to that of the common-collector BJT amplifier (Fig. 4.15) except for the values of the biasing resistors. As in the common-source amplifier, these can be in the megohm range, giving high input impedance.

The voltage gain of the amplifier is a little less than 1, giving the circuit the alternative name, **source follower**.

▪ Properties of BJT and MOSFET amplifiers compared

Property	Common-emitter	Common-collector	Common-source	Common-drain
Function	voltage amplifier	voltage follower	voltage amplifier	voltage follower
Polarity	inverting	non-inverting	inverting	non-inverting
Voltage gain	medium	≈ 1	medium	≈ 1
Current gain	high	high	high	high
Power gain	high	high	high	high
Input impedance	medium	medium-high	very high	very high
Output impedance	low	very low	low	very low
Other features	good linearity, fixed voltage gain $(= R_3/R_4)$	power amplifier	moderate linearity, high frequency	power amplifier

▪ Class AB and B amplifiers

Amplifiers of the types described above are known as Class A amplifiers. The transistor is continuously conducting, even when there is no signal, so such amplifiers are inefficient. They waste 50% of the energy supplied to them.

Fig. 4.18 shows a Class B amplifier. This is a **complementary push–pull amplifier**. It consists of two emitter follower amplifiers, one based on an npn BJT, the other based on a pnp BJT. The transistors have similar characteristics (such as h_{FE}), but are of opposite polarity and are therefore termed 'complementary'. The speaker acts as the emitter resistor for both amplifiers. The amplifier runs on a split supply.

Neither transistor is conducting when there is no signal, so no current passes through the speaker. This is efficient and is characteristic of Class B amplifiers. The npn transistor conducts when the signal swings positive, and the pnp transistor conducts when the signal swings negative.

The main disadvantage of this type of amplifier is that neither transistor conducts when the signal voltage is between -0.7 V and $+0.7$ V. This means that a signal of amplitude less than 0.7 V does not appear across the speaker. Further, larger signals are seriously distorted as shown in Fig. 4.19. As

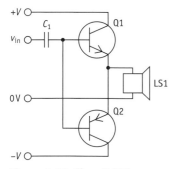

Figure 4.18 Class B BJT amplifier

Figure 4.19 Crossover distortion of a Class B BJT amplifier

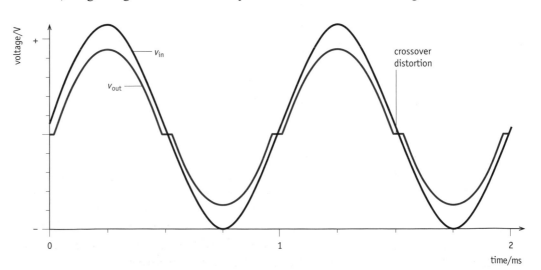

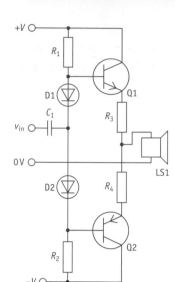

Figure 4.20 Class AB BJT amplifier

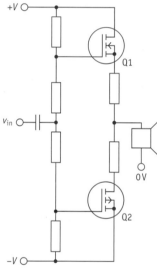

Figure 4.21 Class B MOSFET amplifier

the signal swings from positive to negative or from negative to positive, there is a short period when the signal is lost. This is called **crossover distortion**.

The solution to this problem is to bias the base of each transistor so that it is ready to conduct immediately the signal departs from 0 V in either direction. This is done by a pair of diodes, using their forward voltage drop of 0.7 V to bias the transistors. In Fig. 4.20, the diode D1 and the base–emitter junction of Q1 are both forward-biased pn junctions. As the base–emitter drop of Q1 varies with temperature, the drop across D1 varies equally. Changes in the bias provided by the diode compensate for changes of base–emitter drop. Similarly, D2 compensates for changes in the base–emitter drop of Q2. This almost completely eliminates crossover distortion. Amplifiers of this kind are called Class AB amplifiers.

Class B amplifiers are also built from a complementary pair of MOSFETs. In the basic push–pull circuit of Fig. 4.21, Q1 is an n-channel enhancement MOSFET and Q2 is its p-channel equivalent. The transistors are connected as common-drain (or source follower) amplifiers. The chain of four resistors biases the gates to the threshold voltages, so that Q1 amplifies the positive half cycles and Q2 amplifies the negative half-cycles. There is no crossover distortion as described for the BJT version, because the transistors begin to conduct as soon as v_{in} goes positive or negative. In practice, the threshold voltage varies from one MOSFET to another of the same type; a slightly more complicated biasing chain is needed.

Class B and AB amplifiers have a voltage gain of a little less than 1. They have a high current gain and therefore a high power gain. They are often used as the final stage in audio amplifiers. Early stages use common-emitter voltage amplifiers. The signal from these is then given power to drive a speaker by using a Class B or AB amplifier.

▌ Heat sinks

Power transistors carry heavy currents (often rated in amps) so they become very hot. They are destroyed if they become hotter than about 150 °C. Overheating may be prevented by clipping or bolting a heat sink to the transistor. This is made of metal (usually aluminium) and is shaped to have fins that bring it in contact with the air. The efficiency of the heat sink is maximised by:

▌ a layer of silicone grease between the transistor and the heat sink, which maximises conduction;
▌ the high thermal capacity of the aluminium (or copper) of which the sink is made;
▌ a painted matt black surface to maximise radiation;
▌ fins to maximise heat loss by convection;
▌ vents in the case to allow air to circulate freely, or a fan may be used for forced circulation in the most highly powered amplifiers;
▌ in larger heat sinks, many fins of large surface area; one or more transistors may be bolted to it.

Many types of transistor have a metal tag built in, to conduct heat directly from the active region of the device. Often this tag has an electrical connection to one of the layers of the transistor. A mica washer may be needed to electrically insulate such a tag from the heat sink.

▮ Thermal resistance

This is the resistance offered to the flow of heat between a hot region of an object and a cooler region. Consider the case in which the hot region is being heated to a temperature of t °C by a heat source operating at P watts, and the cooler region is losing heat to the surroundings which have an ambient temperature t_A °C. The thermal resistance, R_θ, in °C/W, is:

$$R_\theta = \frac{t - t_A}{P}$$

worked example

problem A power transistor is operating at 50 W, without a heat sink. The temperature of the active region of the transistor is 67.5 °C and the ambient temperature (at the tag) is 30 °C. What is the thermal resistance between active region and tag?

working Thermal resistance $R_\theta = (67.5 - 30)/50 = 37.5/50 = 0.75$ °C/W

In practice, the heat generated in a transistor has to pass through one or more thermal resistances:

▮ active region to tag: see data sheets (typically 1 °C/W);
▮ tag to sink: greased mica washer is about 0.1 °C/W;
▮ sink to air: ranges from 30 °C/W for small clip-on sinks down to 2 °C/W for large multi-finned types (see data sheets).

These resistances are in series and are summed to find the total resistance between the active region and the air around.

4•6 Power supplies

A typical power supply suitable for electronic circuits converts ac at mains voltage to dc at a much lower voltage.

▮ Transformer

A transformer consists of two or more coils wound on the same soft-iron former. Consider the case where there are two coils, the primary coil and the secondary coil. Assume that the transformer is ideal, having no loss of power. If n_p and n_s are the numbers of turns in the primary and secondary coils, and V_p and V_s are the rms voltages across the coils:

$$\frac{V_p}{V_s} = \frac{n_p}{n_s}$$

If I_p and I_s are the rms currents through the coils, the inverse relationship applies:

$$\frac{I_p}{I_s} = \frac{n_s}{n_p}$$

▮ Rectifiers

Diode rectifier circuits include the following.

Half-wave rectifier This simple diode circuit (Fig. 4.22a, overleaf) converts ac to pulsed dc (Fig. 4.22b). With an ac (sinusoidal) input, the diode conducts on the positive half-cycle. The result is a series of pulses at the same frequency as the ac. Because of the diode's forward voltage drop, the peak value is 0.7 V less than that of the ac from the transformer. This simple circuit is inefficient because the diode is conducting for only half the time.

Figure 4.22 Half-wave rectifier, its input and output

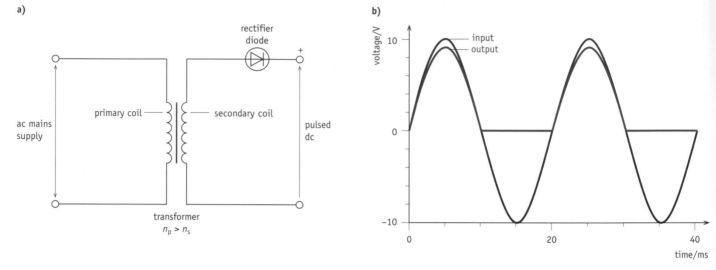

a)

b)

Full-wave rectifier This consists of a **bridge** of four diodes (Fig. 4.23a). The bridge may be built from four separate diodes or may be a ready-made unit. It converts ac to pulsed dc (Fig. 4.23b). With an ac input, D1 and D2 conduct on the positive half-cycle. D3 and D4 conduct on the negative half-cycle. The result is a series of pulses at *double* the frequency of the ac. Because the current flows through two diodes on each half-cycle, the peak value is 1.4 V less than that of the ac from the transformer. This circuit is efficient and widely used.

Figure 4.23 Full-wave rectifier, its input and output

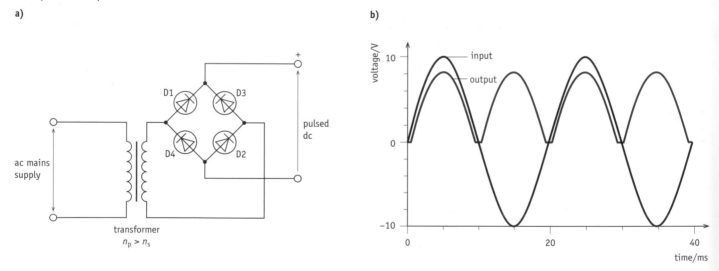

a)

b)

Power supplies are described in more detail in section 8.

■ Ten quick questions

1 What is the name of a circuit that exists in two states, but is stable in only one?
2 What is the current gain of a Darlington pair?
3 What is the voltage gain of a common-drain amplifier?
4 Name a single-transistor BJT amplifier that is non-inverting.
5 Which type of transistor is the faster, BJT or MOSFET?
6 What is the frequency of a 7555 astable, given the values of R_1, R_2 and C?
7 What is the rate of fall of power in the stopband of a lowpass RC filter?
8 What is the formula for the cut-off frequency of an RC lowpass filter?
9 Give an alternative name for the common-collector amplifier.
10 In what type of circuit does crossover distortion occur?

■ Questions on analogue networks and circuits

1 What is meant by a 'protective diode'? Give two examples of circuits in which a protective diode is important.

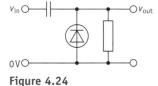

Figure 4.24

2 In Fig. 4.24 the input voltage v_{in} is a sine wave, amplitude 4.5 V, superimposed on a dc voltage of +4.5 V. Draw a graph of v_{out}, assuming that the frequency of v_{in} is 1 kHz.

3 Draw a diagram of a Zener voltage stabiliser network. Given that the supply voltage is 18 V, the stabilised voltage is to be 5.6 V, and the load draws a maximum of 275 mA, calculate the values and minimum power ratings of the components.

4 A Zener voltage stabiliser has a supply voltage of 24 V, a Zener voltage of 12 V and a load with resistance 27 Ω. Calculate the minimum power rating of the components.

5 Fig. 4.25 shows an intruder detection system. The filament lamp and R_2 are on opposite sides of a corridor. Explain how the system works.

Figure 4.25 Intruder detection system

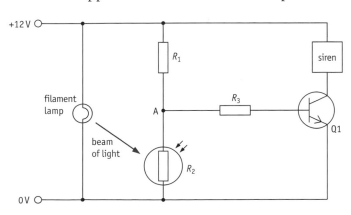

6 In a fire prevention system, a shower of cold water is turned on whenever the temperature exceeds a pre-set level. The shower is controlled by a solenoid-operated valve which turns on the water when the solenoid is on. Draw a diagram of a MOSFET switching circuit for this system.

7 Compare BJTs and MOSFETs as switching transistors.

8 A BJT switch turns on an LED when the ambient light level falls below a set intensity. What device can be used as a sensor? The current through the LED is to be 30 mA, and the h_{FE} of the transistor is 120. What base current is needed to switch the LED on?

9 Given a photodiode, a MOSFET, two mains-powered lamps and any other components that you need, design a warning system for a photographer's darkroom. The lamps illuminate two signs placed outside the darkroom door. One of the signs says 'Busy – keep out!' and is to be switched on when the darkroom light is off. The other says 'Enter now!' and is to be switched on when the darkroom light is on. Explain how your system operates.

10 Fig. 4.26 is a 'door alert' circuit to operate a solid-state buzzer by using a touch switch. The touch switch consists of two metal plates about 1 cm square, mounted on a plastic panel. The buzzer sounds when we press a finger on the plates to bridge the gap between them.
   a) What do we call two BJTs connected as in the figure? Explain the action of the two BJTs.
   b) If h_{FE} is 120 for each BJT, what is the h_{FE} of the two?
   c) The buzzer needs 10 mA to make it sound; what base current is needed to produce this?

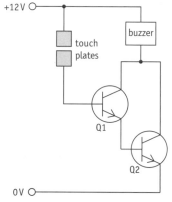

Figure 4.26

11 Design a circuit for a battery-powered thermostat which is to hold a small incubator at 37 °C. The heater element is rated at 12 V and 15 W.

12 Describe a monostable circuit based on two BJTs. Describe its action.

13 A BJT monostable is to switch on a 6 V, 60 mA lamp for approximately 5 s when it is triggered by pressing a button. Draw the circuit required.

14 On a model railway, a BJT astable is used to flash two red LEDs at a level-crossing gate. The LEDs flash alternately at a frequency of 1 Hz. Design the circuit.

15 Draw the circuit of a monostable based on a 7555 timer IC. What is the length of one pulse if the timing capacitor is 470 nF and the timing resistor is 560 kΩ?

16 Fig. 4.27 shows an astable circuit built from a 7555 timer IC.
   a) Write the formula for the frequency of the output. If $R_2 = 1$ kΩ, $C = 1$ μF, and the frequency of the tone from the speaker is 450 Hz, what is the resistance of R_1?
   b) What happens to the frequency of the tone if R_1 is shaded from the light?
   c) What happens to the frequency if the supply voltage is increased?

Figure 4.27

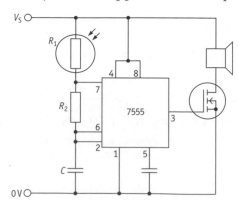

17 A lowpass passive filter is made with $R = 330\,\Omega$ and $C = 47\,nF$. What is the cut-off frequency? What is the phase change at this frequency? Draw a sketch of the frequency response of this filter.

18 What is the meaning of the term '$-3\,dB$ point'? What is the $-3\,dB$ point for a lowpass RC filter in which $R = 5.6\,k\Omega$ and $C = 2.2\,nF$?

19 Describe how the phase difference of a 100 kHz lowpass filter varies as frequency varies between 0 Hz and 1 MHz.

20 **a)** A passive RC highpass filter has $R = 10\,k\Omega$ and $C = 60\,pF$. What is its $-3\,dB$ point?
   b) Describe the transition region of the frequency response of a highpass filter.

21 Draw the circuit diagram of a common-emitter amplifier. In a stabilised common-emitter amplifier, the collector resistor is $3.3\,k\Omega$ and the emitter resistor is $820\,\Omega$. What is the voltage gain of the amplifier?

22 Explain how the feedback capacitor acts to restore the gain of a common-emitter amplifier.

23 The biasing resistors of a common-emitter amplifier are $4.7\,k\Omega$ and $22\,k\Omega$. The input capacitor is $4.7\,\mu F$. Describe the filtering action of these components at the input of the amplifier.

24 State the properties of a common-emitter amplifier and compare them with those of a common-collector amplifier.

25 What is the alternative name for the common-collector amplifier? Explain the reason for this name and give the main use of this type of amplifier.

26 Draw the circuit of a common-source amplifier. Describe the biasing of this amplifier.

27 List three important properties of the common-source amplifier.

28 Draw the circuit of a common-drain amplifier. What is the voltage gain of this amplifier? What is an alternative name for this amplifier?

29 A Class B amplifier is termed a 'complementary push–pull amplifier'. Explain the reasons for this name.

30 **a)** What is the disadvantage of a Class A amplifier?
   b) Draw the circuit of an amplifier that does not have this disadvantage and state why not.

31 Sketch the shape of a sine wave that has been subject to crossover distortion. In what type of amplifier does this occur? Explain the reason for this distortion.

32 What is a heat sink? Why is a heat sink sometimes essential in an amplifier?

33 Describe a heat sink that you have used. Explain how it operates.

34 What is the reason for putting a thin layer of silicone grease between a heat sink and the metal tag of a transistor?

35 The thermal resistances of a transistor and its heat sink are: active region to tag, 1.5 °C/W; silicone grease, 0.1 °C/W; heat sink, 17 °C/W. What is the total thermal resistance of the assembly? If the air temperature is 27 °C and the transistor is damaged by a temperature of 150 °C, what is the maximum power at which the transistor may be run?

36 In the MOSFET switch of Fig. 4.4b (p. 45), the motor takes a current of 1.2 A. The 'on' resistance of the MOSFET is 5 Ω. The transistor would be damaged by a temperature over 150 °C and the air temperature may rise as high as 30 °C. What is the thermal resistance of the heat sink needed for the transistor? (Ignore thermal resistances of the transistor and grease).

37 What does a transformer do? A transformer has 120 turns in its primary coil and 550 turns in its secondary coil. If a current of 400 mA rms flows in the primary coil and the rms pd across the coil is 6 V, what is the pd and current for the secondary coil?

38 A transformer produces 18 V rms from the 230 V rms mains supply. If the primary coil has 450 turns, how many turns has the secondary coil?

39 A 120 Hz sine wave is fed to the transformer in question 37. The output of the transformer is fed to a half-wave rectifier. Sketch the waveform of the input and output from the rectifier. Indicate upper and lower peak levels.

40 What are the advantages of a full-wave rectifier compared with a half-wave rectifier? What do we call the network of four diodes in a full-wave rectifier? Sketch the output waveform of the rectifier.

5 Digital circuits

In brief...

- One-bit input interfaces connect the outside world to a logic circuit (pp 61–62).
- One-bit output interfaces connect a logic circuit to the outside world (p. 62).
- The output of a combinational logic circuit depends on the present states of its inputs. Examples of this type of circuit are: half adder, full adder, priority encoder, decimal-to-binary converter, binary-to-decimal converter, data selector (multiplexer), arbitrary truth tables, data distributor (demultiplexer), data decoder and BCD-to-7-segment display driver (pp 62–67).
- The output of a sequential logic circuit depends on the present and previous states of its inputs. Examples of this type of circuit are: set-reset flip-flop, monostable, astable, D-type flip-flop, divide-by-2 circuit, 4-bit up ripple counter, 4-bit down ripple counter, 4-bit modulo-n counter, 4-bit BCD counter, synchronous counters, shift registers and modulo-n synchronous ring counters (pp 67–80).

Questions on digital circuits begin on p. 80, with answers from p. 165.

5•1 One-bit input interfaces

These are interfaces between the outside world and a logic circuit (the term 'logic circuit' includes a microcontroller or computer input terminal). They are binary inputs, with two states: high (1) or low (0).

■ Switches

Figs 5.1a and b show a switch and a resistor providing a 1-bit input interface to a logic gate. In Fig. 5.1a the input is **active-high**. It is normally low but goes high when the switch is closed. If the switch is a push button, the input goes high when the button is pressed. Conversely, the input in Fig. 5.1b is **active-low**.

Figure 5.1 One-bit switch interfaces

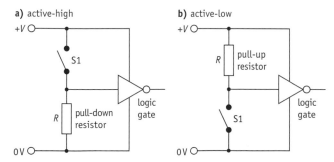

The switch network is usually connected to the same supply rails as the logic gate. The value of R depends on the input impedance of the logic gate. A $10\,\text{k}\Omega$ resistor is often suitable. The switch allows for manual input to the logic circuit, and may be a toggle switch, a push button or similar manually operated switch.

The switch may act as a sensor. Examples are a mercury tilt-switch, a pressure mat or a limit switch. A limit switch is often used on industrial machinery. Usually it is a microswitch positioned so that it closes when some part of the machine reaches a given position. This provides feedback to the control system, informing it of the present position of that part of the machine.

■ Pulse generators

Monostables (see Fig. 4.6, p. 46, and Fig. 4.10, p. 47) and astables (see Fig. 4.8, p. 47, and Fig. 4.11, p. 48) have logic-compatible outputs that are used for timing purposes. An example is the astable 'clock' that synchronises the logical operations in a computer.

■ Sensors

These are interfaced to a logic circuit by transistor switches (see Fig. 1.23, p. 15, and Fig. 1.24, p. 16). The output of the switch is logic high or logic low, depending on the response of the sensor to outside events.

5•2 One-bit output interfaces

An output of a logic circuit is either low or high. When a logic output is high, it is able to *source* a current of only a few milliamps, sometimes much less. This is sufficient to drive a transistor switch acting as a 1-bit interface. The transistor is connected as in Figs 4.4a and b (p. 45), with the logic circuit output replacing the sensor–resistor network.

Some logic circuits, such as microcontrollers, have output buffers that source as much as 25 mA. These can power LEDs and other low-current devices directly, without an interface. A series resistor is needed to limit current.

LEDs are particularly useful in logic circuits to indicate the state of various inputs and outputs. In Fig. 5.2 a logic output is shown as (a) a source and (b) a sink. In (a) the LED is on when the output is high; in (b) the LED is on when the output is low.

Figure 5.2 Logic outputs, driving an LED indicator

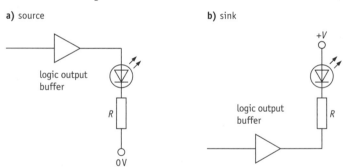

a) source

logic output buffer

R

0V

b) sink

+V

logic output buffer

R

5•3 Combinational logic circuits

The state of the output (or outputs) in **combinational logic** circuits depends on the present combination of states of the input or inputs.

■ Half adder

A half adder adds two 1-bit binary numbers represented by A and B, producing a 1-bit sum S, and the carry-out bit C_o. The truth table is:

Inputs		Outputs	
B	A	C_o	S
0	0	0	0
0	1	0	1
1	0	0	1
1	1	1	0

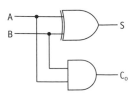

Figure 5.3 Half adder

Figure 5.4 Half adder built with NAND gates

The basic truth tables on p. 19 show that S is equal to $A \oplus B$, and that C is equal to $A \cdot B$. Fig 5.3 shows the circuit. The circuit has no provision for a carry-in digit, which is why it is called a half adder.

The circuit of Fig. 5.3 may be uneconomical if no other EX-OR or AND gates are being used in a system. Fig. 5.4 shows how to build a half adder from NAND gates. The exclusive-OR section is the same as in Fig. 2.12, p. 26. One of the gates of the EX-OR section provides $\overline{AB}$, which is inverted to give AB, which equals C_o.

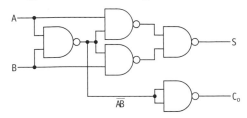

■ Full adder

A full adder adds two 1-bit binary numbers, A and B, and a carry-in digit, producing a 1-bit sum S, and the carry-out bit C_o. The truth table is shown below.

Inputs			Outputs	
C_i	B	A	C_o	S
0	0	0	0	0
0	0	1	0	1
0	1	0	0	1
0	1	1	1	0
1	0	0	0	1
1	0	1	1	0
1	1	0	1	0
1	1	1	1	1

When $C_i = 0$, the S output is $A \oplus B$, as in the half adder. When $C_i = 1$, the output is $\overline{A \oplus B}$. The two EX-OR gates in Fig. 5.5 provide this function: the first gate provides $A \oplus B$, and the second gate performs the true/invert action on its output.

Figure 5.5 Full adder

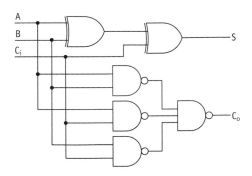

The carry-out shows **majority logic**. It takes the value of the majority of A, B and C_i. This is obtained by NANDing the three inputs in pairs, then NANDing the three NANDs. Question 7, p. 81, investigates this.

▌ Priority encoder

The inputs of the circuit are numbered from 1 upward. The larger the number, the higher its priority. If all inputs are low, the outputs are all low. If any one or more inputs is high, the outputs show the number of the active input with the highest priority. For a circuit with three inputs the truth table is shown below, and Fig. 5.6 shows the circuit.

Inputs			Outputs		Priority
3	2	1	Q1	Q0	
0	0	0	0	0	nil
0	0	1	0	1	1
0	1	0	1	0	2
0	1	1	1	0	2
1	0	0	1	1	3
1	0	1	1	1	3
1	1	0	1	1	3
1	1	1	1	1	3

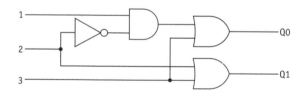

Figure 5.6 Priority encoder

▌ Decimal-to-binary converter

This may also be called a **decimal-to-binary-decoder**. The truth table below refers to a converter for numbers 1 to 3. The circuit has two outputs to indicate binary 01 to 11, and assumes that no more than one input is high at any time.

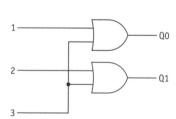

Figure 5.7 Decimal-to-binary converter

Inputs			Outputs	
3	2	1	Q1	Q0
0	0	0	0	0
0	0	1	0	1
0	1	0	1	0
1	0	0	1	1

Output Q0 is high for 1 OR 3, output Q1 is high for 2 OR 3, so the circuit uses two OR gates (Fig. 5.7). When all inputs are low the output is 00, indicating 'no input'.

▌ Binary-to-decimal converter

This is also know as a **binary-to-decimal decoder**. It has an input for each binary digit, and an output for each decimal value. The truth table at the top of p. 65 covers a converter with 2-bit input, and four outputs, 0 to 3. Fig. 5.8 shows the circuit.

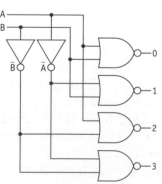

Figure 5.8 Binary-to-decimal converter

Truth table for binary-to-decimal converter, Fig. 5.8

Inputs		Outputs			
B	A	3	2	1	0
0	0	0	0	0	1
0	1	0	0	1	0
1	0	0	1	0	0
1	1	1	0	0	0

▌ Data selector

This is also known as a **multiplexer**. It has two or more data inputs and one data output. There are one of more 'select' inputs. Data is fed through to the output from the selected *one* of the data inputs. Which one is selected depends on the state of the 'select' inputs.

In the 2-to-1 line selector illustrated by thc truth table below and Fig. 5.9, there are two data inputs, one data output, and a single 'select' input. If 'select' is 0, data from input A reaches the output. If 'select' is 1, data from input B reaches the output. 'Select' is a 1-bit address selector, and there are only two addresses, 0 and 1, corresponding to inputs A and B.

Inputs			Output
B	A	Select	Q
X	0	0	0
X	1	0	1
0	X	1	0
1	X	1	1

'X' means '0 or 1'; the value does not matter because that input is not selected.

Figure 5.9 Data selector

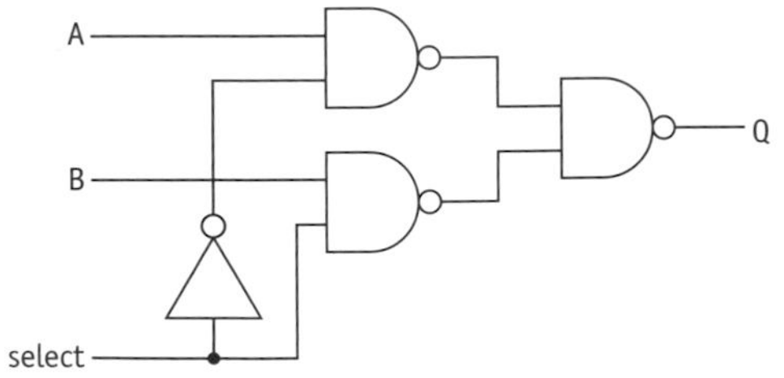

Data selectors with a greater number of inputs (often 4, 8, or 16) are made as ICs. They often have an additional input, called 'strobe', or 'enable'. Output is low when the 'strobe' input is made high, independently of the states of the other inputs.

A data selector provides a simple way to build a circuit with an **arbitrary truth table**. This is a truth table in which the outputs are not easily derived from the input by any of the standard logic functions. Each data input is permanently connected either to logic high (usually the supply line) or to logic low (usually the 0 V line). For each combination of select inputs the output is 0 or 1, depending on the wiring. An example is given in Fig. 5.10. If the select input is 011, for example, the output is 1, because input 3 is connected to the supply. If the select input is 110, the output is low, and so on.

A similar technique makes use of a ROM chip (see p. 119). The address inputs have the same action as the select inputs of the data selector. The difference is that each address is that of a word, consisting of 4, 8 or more bits.

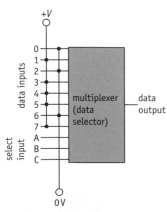

Figure 5.10 Producing an arbitrary truth table with a data selector

There is an output for each bit. The ROM is programmed by writing data into it, according to the truth table. When any given address is present at the address inputs, the corresponding data word appears at the outputs. As an example, a ROM could be programmed with the time zones of a number of cities and used in an electronic clock to generate the local time for any of these cities on request. To build a logical system to do this using logic gates would be complicated. A ROM is programmed quickly and cheaply.

■ Data distributor

This is also known as a **demultiplexer**. It has a single input and several outputs (Fig. 5.11). The data at the input is routed to one of the outputs according to the state of the 'select' inputs.

Figure 5.11 Features of a multiplexer and a demultiplexer

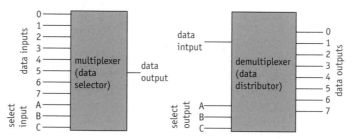

The truth table of a 2-line to 4-line data distributor is shown below. When the data input is 1, the *one* selected output is 1.

Inputs			Outputs			
Data	Select		Q3	Q2	Q1	Q0
	B	A				
0	X	X	0	0	0	0
1	0	0	0	0	0	1
1	0	1	0	0	1	0
1	1	0	0	1	0	0
1	1	1	1	0	0	0

■ Data decoder

A data decoder is similar to a data distributor, except that it has no data input. A basic decoder behaves as in the last four lines of the truth table above, as if there is a data input that is permanently high. At any time, *one* of the outputs is high, depending on the logic levels at the select inputs. The binary-to-decimal converter (p. 64) is an example of a data decoder.

Decoders are available as ICs for BCD to decimal. BCD, or **binary-coded decimal**, is a way of representing digital numbers by coding its digits separately. For instance, the decimal number 382 is represented in BCD as 0011 1000 0010. A separate IC is used for converting each digit. This has four binary inputs (equivalent to 'select') and ten decimal outputs. One of the outputs is high, depending on the binary input.

■ BCD-to-7-segment decoder

The action of a 7-segment decoder is another good example of an arbitrary truth table. It could be implemented by using a number of data selectors or a ROM, as described on p. 65. However, so many digital circuits have a numerical output that a wide range of specialised decoder ICs is manufactured. One of the best known is the 4511, which takes a BCD input and produces an output for driving one digit of a display.

The 4511 is a CMOS IC, with four select inputs and seven outputs. The outputs act as sources, so a common-cathode display is needed, as in Fig. 5.12. They are able to source up to 25 mA, which is enough to drive an LED; series resistors are required to limit current.

Figure 5.12 Seven-segment display driver (4511)

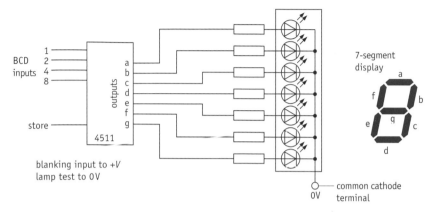

When a BCD value is placed on the inputs, and the 'store' input is low, some of the outputs go high to produce the corresponding decimal digit on the display. For example, to display the digit '4', the BCD input is 0100 and outputs b, c, f and g go high. No outputs go high if the BCD input is 1010 to 1111 (decimal 10 to 15).

If the 'store' input is low, the outputs change with changing input. If the 'store' input is made high, the BCD input is stored in latches in the IC. This 'freezes' the display, even if the inputs change, until 'store' is made low again. This feature makes it possible to read the display when the input is changing rapidly.

5●4 Sequential logic circuits

The state of the output (or outputs) in **sequential logic** circuits depends on *previous* states of the input or inputs, as well as their present states.

▌ Set-reset flip-flop

This is usually called an **S-R flip-flop**. It can be built from a pair of cross-connected NAND or NOR gates. The truth table for the circuit using NOR gates (Fig. 5.13) is:

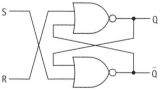

Figure 5.13 Set-reset flip-flop, using NOR gates

Inputs		Outputs	
S	R	Q	$\overline{Q}$
0	0	no change	
0	1	0	1
1	0	1	0
1	1	not allowed	

The circuit is a **bistable** circuit: it is stable in either of two states. Both inputs are normally held low. When the S (set) input is made high, the Q output goes high and the $\overline{Q}$ output goes low, if they are not already in these states.

This puts the circuit in the stable state, of being **set**. There is no further change when the S input is made low again.

The converse happens when R (reset) is made high; $\overline{Q}$ goes high and Q goes low. The circuit is in its other stable state, of being **reset**. There is no further change when the R input is made low again.

If both inputs are made high, both outputs become 0, but this is not a stable state. As soon as the inputs are made low again, the output changes to 01 or 10, depending on which input is the last to go low.

The S-R flip-flop has applications as a 1-bit memory circuit.

▌ Monostable

Fig. 5.14 shows a **monostable** circuit using NAND gates, which normally has a high output and generates a low pulse on a rising edge (when the input changes from low to high). The action is as follows.

1 Stable state: input A low, output of gate 1 high. *C* fully charged, output of gate 2 high.

Figure 5.14 Monostable, using NAND gates

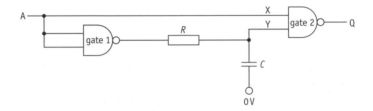

2 Triggering into unstable state: make A high, causing output of gate 2 to go low. At the same time, the output of gate 1 goes low, *C* begins to discharge through *R*, input Y of gate 2 begins to fall. When Y reaches logic low level, gate 2 goes high again, ending the pulse.

3 Recovery: input A returned to low, output of gate 2 stays high. Output of gate 1 goes high, charging *C* through *R*, raising input Y of gate 2. This causes no further change to output of gate 2. The circuit is stable.

Fig. 5.15 is a timing diagram of this action. If the gates are CMOS, the pulse length is $t \approx RC$.

Figure 5.15 Timing diagram of the NAND monostable

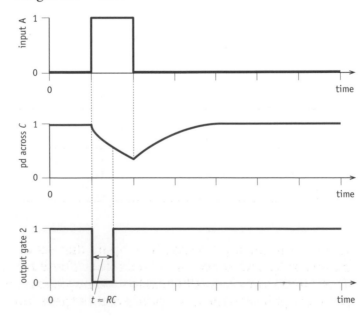

▮ Astable

The **astable** circuit in Fig. 5.16 has two cross-connected INVERT gates; it can also be built with NAND or NOR gates that have their inputs connected together. R and C are the timing components. R_1 is approximately ten times R and improves the performance.

Figure 5.16 Astable, using INVERT gates

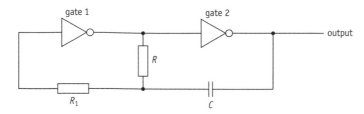

The astable automatically alternates between two unstable states. The action is:

▮ unstable with low output: output of gate 1 is high, charging C through R;
▮ unstable with high output: output of gate 1 is low, discharging C through R.

The output is close to a square wave, with frequency $1/2.2RC$.

▮ D-type flip-flop

Unlike the S-R flip-flop, in which a change of state occurs immediately, the **D-type flip-flop** changes state on the rising edge of its 'clock' input. At that instant, data present on the D (data) input is transferred to the Q output. There is also the $\overline{Q}$ output, which is the inverse of the Q output. Fig. 5.17 is the timing diagram.

Figure 5.17 Timing diagram of a D-type flip-flop

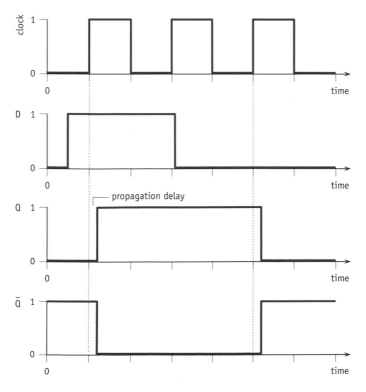

In addition, the flip-flop has two inputs that set or reset the flip-flop immediately, independently of the clock. These are called 'preset' and 'clear'. These inputs are normally held low. To set or reset the flip-flop, a brief high pulse is applied to the appropriate one of these inputs.

The flip-flop is made as an IC, containing two identical and independent flip-flops. There are also several ICs available which contain a number of flip-flops connected to make more complex circuits. Some of these are described below.

■ Divide-by-two circuit

This divider is made by connecting the $\overline{Q}$ output to the D input of a D-type flip-flop (Fig. 5.18a). At each rising edge of the clock input, the Q output follows the state of the D input. Since the $\overline{Q}$ output is the inverse of the Q output, the $\overline{Q}$ output changes state at every rising edge. Because there is a change at the rising edge but not at the falling edge, Q, $\overline{Q}$ and D change state at half the clock frequency. Fig. 5.18b shows the timing diagram. There is a **propagation delay** (see also Fig. 5.17) between the clock edge and the resultant change of Q, typically 22 ns.

Figure 5.18 Divide-by-2 circuit, based on a D-type flip-flop, and its timing diagram

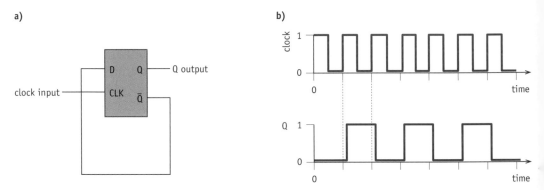

This circuit is called a divider because it divides the clock frequency by two. It illustrates one of the advantages of clocked logic. There is time for logic levels to settle between one rising clock edge and the next. Propagation delays have no effect, except at very high operating frequencies. In a system made up of several clocked logic ICs, clocking makes it much simpler to keep the action of each IC synchronised with that of the others.

The circuit is also known as a **toggle**, or **T-type flip-flop**.

■ Four-bit binary up counter

This is a pulse counter. Its output is a 4-bit binary value that is incremented (increased by 1) at each rising edge of the clock. The circuit consists of four D-type flip-flops, wired as T-type flip-flops and connected in a chain, as in Fig. 5.19. The $\overline{Q}$ output of one flip-flop is connected to the clock input of the next in the chain. The result of feeding a series of pulses into the chain is the sequence of outputs shown in Fig. 5.20. The input pulses may be regular clock pulses, as shown in the figure, or they may be irregular in length and spacing. An example of the latter would be the signal from a light sensor, detecting cars passing along a road. The output from the circuit counts the number of pulses received since the counter was last reset.

Figure 5.19 Four-bit binary up counter, based on D-type flip-flops

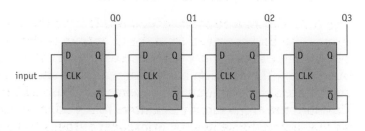

Figure 5.20 Timing diagram of the 4-bit up counter

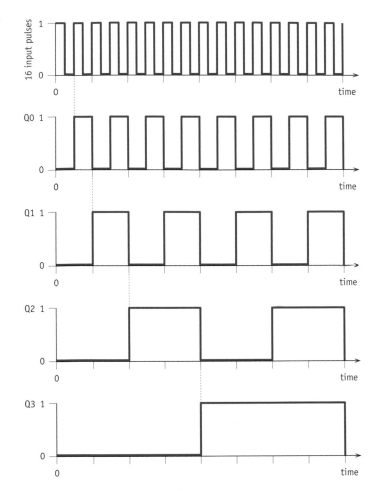

Fig. 5.20 shows the outputs of the counter during a sequence of 16 input pulses, assuming the counter has been reset to 0000 to begin with. The flip-flops are triggered on a positive-going edge, so Q0 changes to 1 as soon as the second pulse begins. Subsequent stages trigger when the $\overline{Q}$ output from the previous stage goes high. In other words, when the Q output from the previous stage goes *low*, as illustrated in the diagram. Sixteen pulses produce a sequence of outputs corresponding to the binary numbers 0000 to 1111 (0 to 15 in decimal, repeating).

■ Four-bit binary down counter

Figure 5.21 Four-bit binary down counter, based on D-type flip-flops

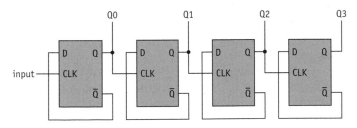

Fig. 5.21 shows a counter made from D-type flip-flops, in which each stage except the first is driven from the Q output of the previous stage. The 4-bit binary value is decremented (decreased by 1) at each rising edge of the clock, as in Fig. 5.22 overleaf. The timing diagram shows a downward counting sequence, assuming that the counter is set to 1111 to begin with. The flip-flops are triggered on a positive-going edge, so Q0 changes to 0 as soon as the second pulse begins. Subsequent stages trigger when the Q output

from the previous stage goes *high*. Sixteen pulses produce a sequence of outputs corresponding to the binary numbers 1111 to 0000 (15 to 0 in decimal, repeating).

Figure 5.22 Timing diagram of the 4-bit down counter

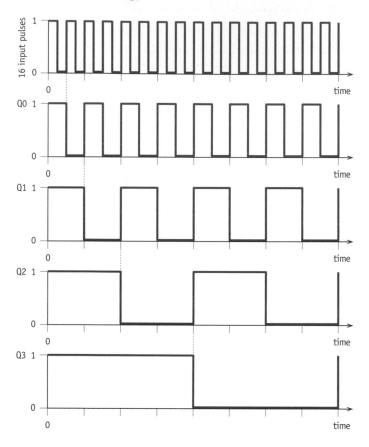

▊ Modulo-*n* binary up counter

A 4-bit up counter runs through a sequence from 0 to 15 (decimal), returns to 0 and then repeats. Sometimes we need a counter that has a shorter sequence. This is known as a **modulo-*n***, where *n* is the number of stages that it goes through before returning to zero and repeating. For example, a modulo-5 counter counts 0, 1, 2, 3, 4, 0, and so on.

Figure 5.23 Modulo-*n* counter

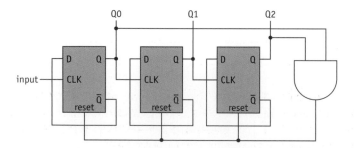

Fig. 5.23 shows the circuit. To make a modulo-5 counter, the AND gate is wired to detect when the counter reaches 5 (101 in binary) and immediately reset all the flip-flops to zero. While counting 0 to 4, no more than one input of the AND gate is high; its output holds the reset inputs low and the counter operates normally. As soon as the counter changes to 5, both inputs of the gate are high and its output goes high for the first time. Reset inputs are made high, resetting the flip-flops to 000 immediately.

Note that, because the count never has more than three binary digits, only three flip-flops are required for a modulo-5 counter.

■ BCD counter

In a BCD counter a modulo-10 counter is used to provide decimal output from a circuit. The counter runs from 0 to 9, then resets. The circuit is similar to that in Fig. 5.23, except there are four flip-flops, and the AND gate receives the Q1 and Q3 outputs. The output of the AND gate goes high for a count of 1010 (equivalent to 10 decimal) and resets the flip-flops. Fig. 5.24 is the timing diagram for a BCD counter.

Figure 5.24 Timing diagram of a BCD counter

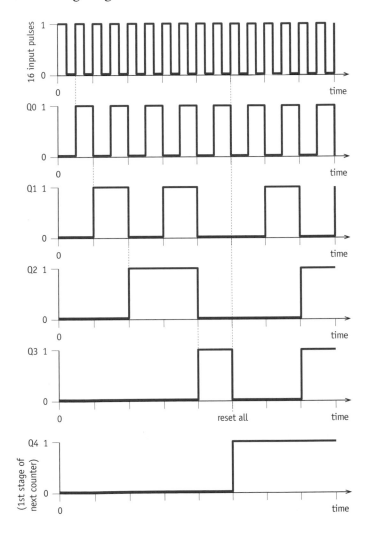

The output from the AND gate can also be connected to the input of another modulo-10 counter. This is incremented by 1 every time the previous counter is reset to 0. Three such modulo-10 counters cascaded in this way make up a BCD counter that runs from 0 to 999.

BCD counters are made as ICs. Some can count down as well as up. Some include decoders for driving a 7-segment display (see p. 66).

■ Synchronous counters

The counters described above are all examples of **ripple counters**, also known as **asynchronous counters**. Each stage triggers the next. But each stage takes time to respond (this is the propagation delay, which is usually a few tens of nanoseconds). The response of the counter ripples along the chain of flip-flops. This effect needs to be taken account of when several flip-flops need to change at once. For example, when the counter is changing from count 7 (0111) to count 8 (1000), the change ripples through from the least significant digit to the most significant digit, like this:

Outputs				Decimal equivalent
Q3	Q2	Q1	Q0	
0	1	1	1	7
0	1	1	0	6
0	1	0	0	4
0	0	0	0	0
1	0	0	0	8

The changed digits are printed in colour. In changing from 7 to 8 the output actually runs through the sequence 7, 6, 4, 0, 8. If the counter is driving a 7-segment display, these digits are displayed, but so rapidly that the eye does not have time to register them. A ripple counter is perfectly suitable for this kind of operation. However, if the counter outputs are being decoded by logic gates, the logic gate is able to detect these intermediate states and possibly respond to them. Another fault is that the propagation delay for the whole counter is the delay of a single stage multiplied by the number of stages. This limits the speed of circuits containing ripple counters.

To avoid these disadvantages, we use **synchronous counters**. The clock inputs of all the flip-flops are connected to a single line, so that they are all clocked at exactly the same time and all their outputs change state at the same time. There are no intermediate states like those shown in the table above. Because all flip-flops change together, the propagation delay of the counter as a whole equals the delay of only a single stage. A synchronous counter is better than a ripple counter for high-speed operation. Synchronous counters are described in more detail later (pp 75–79).

■ Shift registers

A shift register can be built as a chain of D-type flip-flops, with the Q output of each flip-flop connected to the D input of the next flip-flop in the chain (Fig. 5.25). Their clock inputs are all connected to the same line. At every rising clock edge, the data in one flip-flop is shifted on to the next flip-flop. Action is synchronous, so there are no glitches or disallowed states.

Figure 5.25 Shift register, built from D-type flip-flops

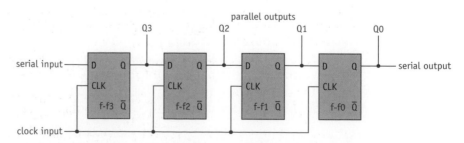

The shift register in Fig. 5.25 has a **serial input**, which transfers new data to flip-flop 3 when the clock goes high. On subsequent clock edges the data is shifted along the register and eventually appears at the **serial output**. The

register is therefore a 'serial-in-serial-out', or **SISO** register. The register in the figure also has **parallel outputs** from the flip-flops, so that data can be unloaded as a group of four bits. This register is thus also a 'serial-in-parallel-out', or **SIPO** register. Some registers have a 'parallel-in-parallel-out' ability and are called **PIPO** registers.

The following table describes the action of a 4-bit SISO register, as it is loaded with the data 1001.

Data at serial input	Data in flip-flops				Data at serial output
	Q3	Q2	Q1	Q0	
1	0	0	0	0	0
0	1	0	0	0	0
0	0	1	0	0	0
1	0	0	1	0	0
0	1	0	0	1	0
0	0	1	0	0	1
0	0	0	1	0	0
0	0	0	0	1	0
0	0	0	0	0	1
0	0	0	0	0	0

The first four lines of the table show the data being presented at the input, one bit at a time. After four clock pulses (line 5), the flip-flops hold all the data. It could be shifted out in parallel at this stage. Lines 6 to 9 show the data appearing at the serial output, one bit at a time. At line 10, the register is empty.

Shift registers are used for handling data. For example, in a telephone modem, a byte of data from a computer is parallel-loaded into an 8-bit PISO register and fed out to the telephone line bit by bit. At the receiving end, serial data is loaded into an 8-bit SIPO register, then unloaded as a byte of data to be sent to the receiving computer. Shift registers are also used in computation; for example, shifting binary data one step to the left multiplies it by 2. Shift registers are also the basis of several types of synchronous counter, as explained in the next subsection.

■ Modulo-*n* synchronous counters

Fig. 5.26a on p. 76 shows the basis of a modulo-6 synchronous counter, counting from 0 to 5. Only three flip-flops are needed to cover the six stages, 000 to 110, repeating. The Q output of each flip-flop is connected to the D input of the next, except for the last in the chain (f-f0), which sends the output from its $\overline{Q}$ output back to the D input of the first flip-flop (f-f2). Assuming that all flip-flops are reset to 000 to begin with, the sequence of outputs is as in Fig. 5.26b.

This type of counter is called a **walking ring counter**. It has useful properties. Only one output changes state at any one time; the result is that there are no glitches or intermediate states in its output. All stages have the same waveform, which has a frequency $1/n$ that of the clock, where n is the number of flip-flops. In this example, the frequency is $\frac{1}{3}$ of the clock frequency. The outputs have a mark–space ratio of 1. The phase difference between the waveforms in adjacent stages is $(360/n)°$.

Figure 5.26 Walking ring counter, modulo-6, and its timing diagram

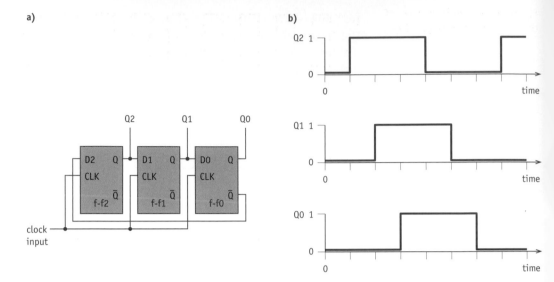

The walking ring counter does not provide binary outputs, but these are easily obtained by ANDing the outputs in pairs, as shown in the table.

Output	AND these outputs	
0	$\overline{Q0}$	$\overline{Q2}$
1	$\overline{Q1}$	$Q2$
2	$\overline{Q0}$	$Q1$
3	$Q0$	$Q2$
4	$Q1$	$\overline{Q2}$
5	$Q0$	$\overline{Q1}$

It is a useful property of walking ring counters that this decoding can always be done with 2-input gates. The result of this decoding is that the counter has *n* outputs, and only one output is high at each count. In the complete modulo-6 counter of Fig. 5.27, a sequence of six clock pulses produce a high output from outputs 0, 1, 2, 3, 4, 5, one at a time, in that order. Fig. 5.28 shows the timing diagram.

Figure 5.27 Walking ring counter with 1-of-6 outputs

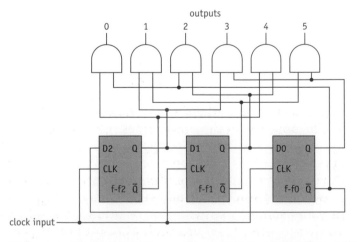

Taken as binary numbers, the outputs of the three flip-flops include every value from 000 to 111, except 101 and 010. These are **disallowed states**. Such states are not normally found as the logic goes through its cycles, but they

Figure 5.28 Timing diagram of the 1-of-6 counter (Fig. 5.27)

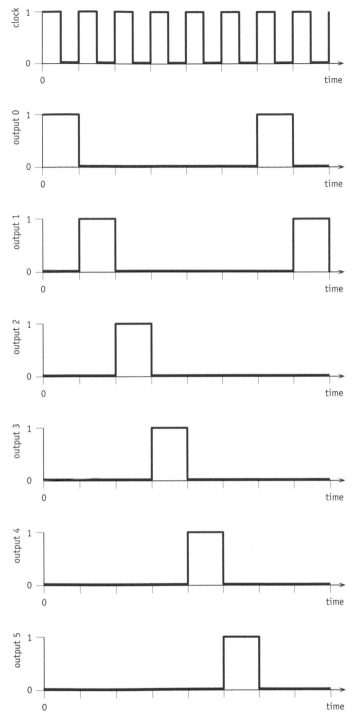

might occur accidentally when the counter is first switched on, or if a large 'spike' appears on the power lines. Examination of the logic of the chain of flip-flops shows that if 101 appears, the next clocking produces 010. If 010 appears, the next clocking gives 101. If either of these appears, from then on the counter alternates indefinitely between the two states. It is stuck.

Becoming stuck in disallowed states is a common problem with walking ring and similar counters. The solution is to add extra gates to detect the disallowed states and use their output to reset one or more of the flip-flops. In this example, a 3-input AND gate is used to detect $\overline{Q0}.Q1.\overline{Q2}$ (that is, 010). The gate output is connected to the reset input of f-f1. When the gate output goes high, f-f1 is reset instantly. This produces 000; the counter is back in its main sequence. If the disallowed state is 101, the outputs change to 010 at the next clocking, which is detected and reset to 000.

Fig. 5.29 is a block diagram of the complete counter system.

Figure 5.29 Block diagram of the 1-of-6 counter

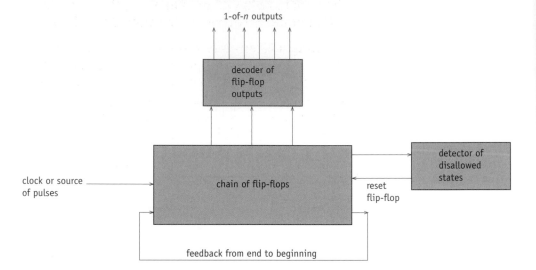

Designing a modulo-*n* synchronous counter   The stages in the design of the modulo-6 walking ring counter, shown in Fig. 5.26, are outlined below.

1 Set out a truth table for the required sequence of flip-flop outputs, using the columns headed Q2 to Q0:

State	Q2	Q1	Q0	D2	D1	D0
0	0	0	0	1	0	0
1	1	0	0	1	1	0
2	1	1	0	1	1	1
3	1	1	1	0	1	1
4	0	1	1	0	0	1
5	0	0	1	0	0	0

2 In the columns headed D2 to D0, enter the values that the data inputs need, so as to produce the output values of the next state. For example, data values for state 0 are the same as the output values for state 1.

3 Examine each data column in turn and try to find an output column that matches it or is logically derived from it. In this example, this is easy. D2 is the inverse of Q0, D1 equals Q2, and D0 equals Q1. The connections required to produce these results are as shown in Fig. 5.26a, inverses being obtained by using a $\overline{Q}$ output instead of the corresponding Q output.

4 Check the table for disallowed output values. These are 010 and 101. Use the logic equivalents found in paragraph 3 to find out what input data values these will produce after clocking. For 010, Q2 = 0, Q1 = 1 and Q0 = 0. Then D2 = $\overline{Q0}$ = 1, D1 = Q2 = 0 and D0 = Q1 = 1. The result is 101. Similarly, 101 leads to 010.

5 Work out gating to reset one or more flip-flops, to return them to one of the states listed in the table. The reasoning is outlined on p. 77.

6 The outputs of the flip-flops may be used directly (see below), or decoding gating may be used to produce the 1-of-*n* outputs. To do this, look through the table of flip-flop outputs to find unique pairs of outputs. For example, in state 0, both Q2 and Q0 are 0; this combination does not occur in any other state. So decoding for state 0 is $\overline{Q2} \cdot \overline{Q0}$.

Designing a Gray code generator A Gray code is a repeating sequence of outputs in which only one value changes at each clocking. The design example below shows how to produce a Gray code sequence at the outputs of the flip-flops, without a decoding stage. The design of other regular or of arbitrary sequences based on ring counters is similar. Many Gray code sequences are possible; the table below is an example.

State	Q2	Q1	Q0	D2	D1	D0
0	0	0	0	0	0	1
1	0	0	1	0	1	1
2	0	1	1	1	1	1
3	1	1	1	1	0	1
4	1	0	1	1	0	0
5	1	0	0	0	0	0

1 The truth table for flip-flop Q outputs is listed as above.

2 Entries for data inputs are made using the same procedure as before.

3 None of the data entries conforms to any easy logical pattern. Instead, either by testing out some possibilities or by using Karnaugh maps for each data column, work out the logical equations. The results are:

$$D0 = \overline{Q1} \cdot \overline{Q2} + Q0 \cdot Q1$$

$$D1 = Q0 \cdot \overline{Q2}$$

$$D2 = Q0 \cdot (Q2 + Q1)$$

These equations require four AND and two OR gates, as illustrated in Fig. 5.30.

Figure 5.30 Gray code generator

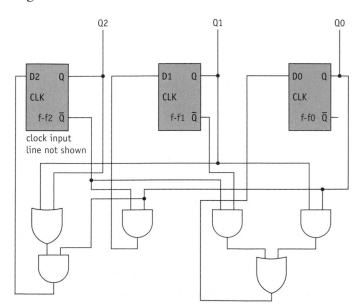

4 Disallowed outputs are 010 and 110. Checking the logic shows that both of these take the flip-flops to 000 at the next clock pulse. This is part of the main sequence so, normally, no state-detecting gates are required. If it is essential for the counter to correct itself immediately, additional logic gates are needed.

5 The outputs from the flip-flops are used directly, without decoding.

▮ Ten quick questions

1 If input A of a half adder is high and input B is low, what is the state of output S?

2 In a set-reset flip-flop built from NAND gates, what is the normal state of the inputs?

3 How is a D-type flip-flop connected to function as a T-type flip-flop?

4 What is the decimal equivalent of the BCD code 0010 1001?

5 What is the name for a counter that repeatedly counts from 0 to 4, then resets?

6 What is the name of a circuit that indicates the highest numbered input that is at logic high?

7 What is the distinctive feature of a synchronous counter?

8 Give another name for a data selector.

9 What happens when the 'clear' input of a D-type flip-flop is made high?

10 In what way are the flip-flops connected in a binary down ripple counter?

▮ Questions on digital circuits

1 With the aid of a circuit diagram, show how a switch is interfaced to a logic circuit with an active-high action. Give an example of a system in which such a switch could be used.

2 Describe how a named sensor can be interfaced to a logic circuit, to produce an active-low input. Give an example of an application of the circuit you describe.

3 Show how a solenoid may be switched on and off by the output from a logic circuit.

4 Draw diagrams to show how an LED may be switched by the output of a logic buffer, using the buffer as a) a source; b) a sink.

5 Write the truth table of a half adder. Draw a half adder circuit that uses two gates, and explain how it works.

6 This is part of the truth table of a full adder:

Inputs			Outputs	
C_i	B	A	C_o	S
0	1	0		
1	1		1	0
1		1		1

Copy the table and fill in the missing entries.

7 a) The full adder circuit of Fig. 5.5 (p. 63) shows that the carry output is found by majority logic. What is majority logic?
b) Write the truth table to show how the C_0 output is obtained when $A = 0$, $B = 0$ and $C_i = 1$; and when $A = 1$, $B = 1$, and $C_i = 0$. Include in the table the output states of all the gates involved.

8 a) What is the function of a priority encoder?
b) Write the full truth table of the encoder in Fig. 5.6 (p. 64), to show the outputs of all the gates.

9 Design a 3-input priority encoder built from NAND gates.

10 Write the truth table of the circuit shown in Fig. 5.31 as each of inputs A to E is made high, one at a time. What is its function?

11 Describe, words only, a 3-bit binary-to-decimal converter, built from gates.

12 Draw a block diagram of a surveillance system with six digital video cameras, each of which is connected in turn to the supervisor's monitor for 20 s.

13 a) How may a data selector IC be used to implement an arbitrary truth table?
b) In Fig. 5.32, what sequence of outputs is obtained as the 'select' inputs are run from binary 000 to binary 111?

14 Design a circuit for a 1-line-to-4-line data distributor, and describe how it works.

15 Write the truth table for a 2-bit BCD-to-7-segment display decoder, with active-high outputs, and counting from 0 to 3. Write the logic equations for each segment of the display.

16 Draw the circuit of the decoder in question 15. What type of LED display is driven by this circuit?

17 Write the truth table for a set-reset flip-flop based on a pair of NAND gates. The inputs of the gate are both high and the Q output is high. What happens to Q and $\overline{Q}$ when
a) a brief low pulse is applied to the reset input;
b) the low pulse is repeated?

18 What would be the action of the circuit in Fig. 5.14 (p. 68) if the NAND gates were replaced by NOR gates?

19 Analyse the behaviour of the circuit in Fig. 5.33. Draw a timing diagram showing an input pulse, the pd across C and the output pulse.

20 Describe an astable built from two NOR gates. If $R = 220\,k\Omega$ and $C = 470\,nF$, what is the approximate frequency of the astable?

21 List the input and output terminals of a D-type flip-flop. Draw its symbol.

22 Draw a timing diagram for a D-type flip-flop to illustrate the effect of the clock pulses on the transfer of data from the D input to the Q output. What is meant by the term 'propagation delay'?

23 What is meant by the term 'clocked logic'? Illustrate your answer with a circuit that has clocked logic.

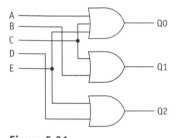

Figure 5.31

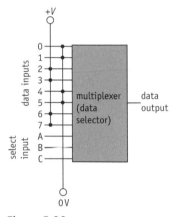

Figure 5.32

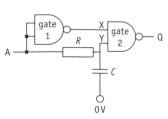

Figure 5.33

24 Draw a 2-bit up counter circuit built from D-type flip-flops, and its timing diagram.

25 Draw a 3-bit down counter circuit built from D-type flip-flops, and its timing diagram.

26 a) What is the output state of a 3-bit binary up counter, modulo-7, the instant before it resets?
   b) Draw a circuit diagram of the counter.

27 What is a synchronous counter? What are its advantages?

28 What is a shift register? Explain the difference between PISO and SIPO shift registers.

29 Design a synchronous down counter with an output sequence of 11, 10, 01, 00, repeating.

30 Design a 3-bit counter that produces an output for driving a display, consisting of three lamps. The lamps are to be turned on one at a time in sequence, as in the table below; the sequence is then repeated. Do not include gating for avoiding disallowed states.

Binary state	Q2	Q1	Q0
0	0	0	0
1	1	0	0
2	0	1	0
4	0	0	1

31 Check the circuit of question 30 for disallowed states, and add any additional gates needed to prevent the circuit from becoming stuck.

32 Design a synchronous counter to produce outputs for controlling a traffic light. The sequence is red, red and amber, green, amber, repeating. Check on disallowed states.

33 Analyse the action of the counter in Fig. 5.34.

Figure 5.34

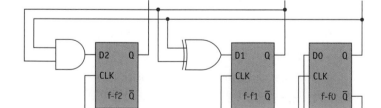

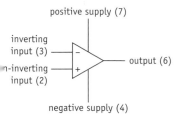

6 Operational amplifiers

In brief...
- An op amp has two inputs and one output (p. 83).
- Practical op amps differ from the ideal op amp in several ways (p. 83).
- Op amps have many applications, including: as a comparator, in amplifier circuits, as an adder, and in active filters (pp 84–88).
- A further application is in Schmitt triggers (p. 89).

Questions on operational amplifiers begin on p. 90, with answers from p. 169.

6•1 Inputs and outputs

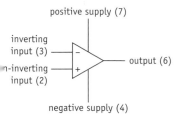

Figure 6.1 Symbol for an operational amplifier

An operational amplifier, or **op amp**, is a differential amplifier. It has two inputs, the **inverting input** and the **non-inverting input**. It has a single output. The drawing of the symbol for an op amp (Fig. 6.1) is marked with the pin numbers of a typical op amp, which is an integrated circuit in an 8-pin dual-in-line package. Pins 1, 5 and 8 may be used for offset nulling (see p. 84) or sometimes for other purposes.

A typical op amp requires a dual power supply, such as ± 12 V, but some types are able to operate on a single supply (0 V and $+V$).

If the input voltages at the non-inverting and inverting inputs are v_{in+} and v_{in-} respectively, the output is:

$$v_{out} = A(v_{in+} - v_{in-})$$

A is the **open-loop voltage gain**. Voltages are measured relative to the 0 V supply line.

6•2 Ideal and practical op amps

The properties of an ideal op amp are tabulated below and compared with the properties of a typical practical op amp.

Property	Ideal op amp	Practical op amp
open loop voltage gain	infinite	200 000 (= 106 dB)
effect of frequency on gain	independent	gain falls off above 10 kHz
input impedance, Z_{in}	infinitely high	2 MΩ or more
output impedance, Z_{out}	zero	75 Ω typical
speed of output swing	instant	limited by slew rate
input voltage offset	zero	a few millivolts

Some terms are now explained.

Output voltage swing The output can swing to within a few volts of the supply. Typically, the output of an op amp running on ± 15 V swings between -13 V and $+13$ V.

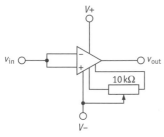

Figure 6.2 Offset nulling

Slew rate   This is the maximum rate at which the output voltage can swing, expressed in volts per microsecond. Different types of op amp vary widely in slew rate. A typical rate is 10 V/μs. An op amp with high slew rate should be used to avoid distortion of waveforms in high-frequency circuits.

Input voltage offset   When the inputs are equal, the output should be zero. In practice, a small voltage difference, called the input voltage offset, is needed to bring the output to zero. To **null** (compensate for) the offset, a variable resistor is connected as in Fig. 6.2. With the same voltage applied to both inputs, the variable resistor is adjusted to bring the output to 0 V.

Full-power bandwidth   This extends from dc up to the frequency (typically 10 kHz) at which the open-loop gain falls to half its dc power (the -3 dB point). Beyond the full-power bandwidth, the gain falls with frequency and the **gain–bandwidth product** is constant. The gain falls to 1 at the **transition frequency**, which is numerically equal to the gain–bandwidth product. For example, the transition frequency of a TL071 op amp is 3 MHz. The gain–bandwidth product is therefore 3 MHz. The open-loop voltage gain is 1 at 3 MHz, 2 at 1.5 MHz, 3 at 1 MHz, 30 at 100 kHz, and 300 at 10 kHz.

Note that the closed-loop gain of an amplifier cannot be greater than the open-loop gain.

6·3 Op amp applications

▌ Comparator

A comparator compares two voltages. The op amp comparator is wired as in Fig. 6.3. If there is more than about 70 μV difference between the input voltages, the output swings to saturation in one direction or the other.

An op amp comparator differs from a dedicated comparator (such as the 311) because:

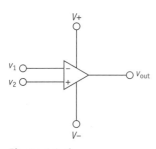

Figure 6.3 Op amp as a comparator

▌ it does not need a pull-up resistor at the output;
▌ its output can swing negative (when $v_1 > v_2$), but that of a comparator does not.

▌ Amplifier circuits

There are three basic amplifier circuits using op amps, as shown in the table opposite.

In the circuits of Figs 6.4 and 6.5, R_B is equal to R_A and R_F in parallel. R_B may be omitted in a low-precision circuit. Z_{out} is typically 75 Ω.

Note that power connections to the op amps are omitted to simplify the diagrams.

Some terms are now explained.

Virtual earth   In circuits with negative feedback, the output swings so as to make the voltages at the inverting and the non-inverting inputs equal. If the non-inverting input is connected to 0 V (directly or through R_B), the inverting input is held at 0 V, whatever input current is flowing toward it. It acts as a virtual earth.

Function	Circuit	Gain	Z_{in}
	Op amp amplifier circuits compared		
inverting	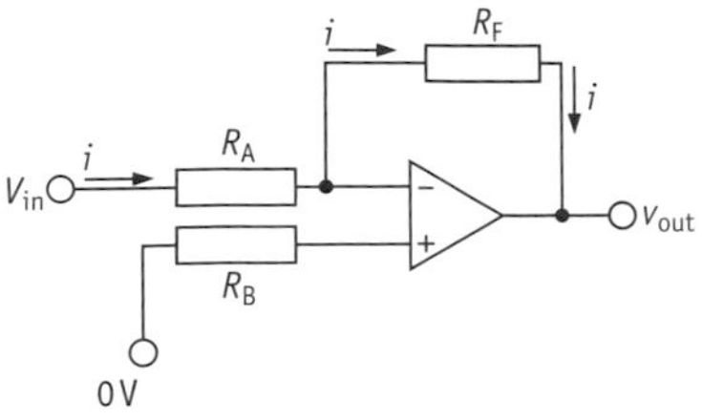 Figure 6.4	$-R_F/R_A$	low (R_A)
non-inverting	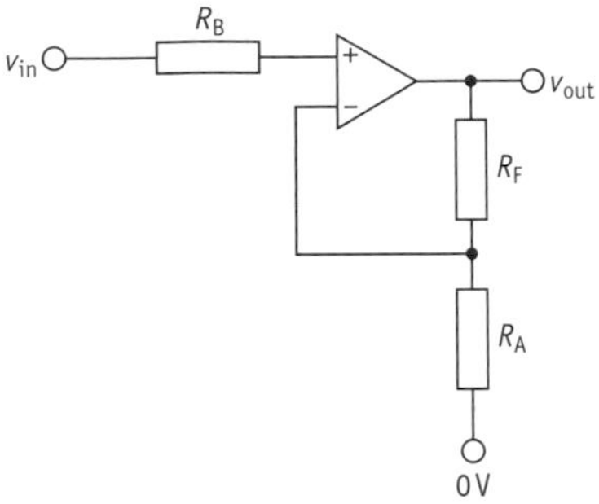 Figure 6.5	$(R_A + R_F)/R_A$	high (typically 2 MΩ for bipolar inputs, 1 TΩ for FET inputs)
voltage follower	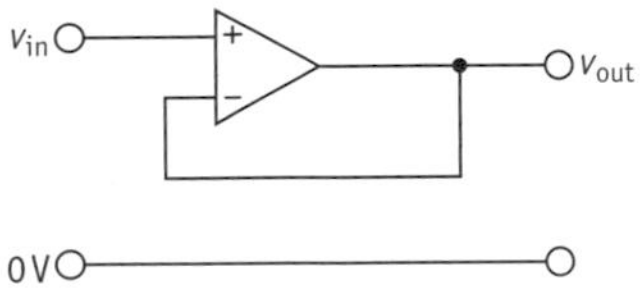 Figure 6.6	1	high, as above; used as a buffer for impedance matching

Gain of inverting amplifier   The current i through R_A is:

$$i = v_{in}/R_A$$

No significant current is able to flow into the inverting input because of its high Z_{in}. Therefore the same current, i, flows through R_F to the output terminal:

$$i = -v_{out}/R_F$$

The values of i are equal, and so:

$$v_{out} = -v_{in} \times \frac{R_F}{R_A}$$

$$\Rightarrow \text{gain} = \frac{v_{out}}{v_{in}} = \frac{-R_F}{R_A}$$

Gain of non-inverting amplifier   The circuit works by feedback of part of the output voltage. R_A and R_F make up a potential divider and the voltage at their junction is:

$$v = v_{out} \times \frac{R_A}{(R_F + R_A)}$$

This is fed back to the inverting input, so feedback is negative.

Because the current through R_B is very small, the voltage at the non-inverting input is very close to v_{in}. The amplifier adjusts v_{out} until the voltages at its inputs are equal:

$$v_{in} = v_{out} \times \frac{R_A}{(R_F + R_A)}$$

$$\Rightarrow \text{gain} = \frac{v_{out}}{v_{in}} = \frac{(R_F + R_A)}{R_A}$$

Closed-loop gain   This is the gain of the amplifier *circuit* and is determined only by R_A and R_F. It is independent of the open-loop gain of the op amp, provided that this has not been reduced because of high frequency.

Voltage follower   This is a non-inverting amplifier with $R_F = 0$ and $R_A = \infty$ (compare Fig. 6.6 with Fig. 6.5). It follows that $R_B = 0$. Using the equation for gain of a non-inverting amplifier:

$$\text{gain} = \frac{(R_F + R_A)}{R_A} = \frac{(0 + R_A)}{R_A} = 1$$

For highest Z_{in}, an op amp with FET inputs is used. Z_{out} is the Z_{out} of the op amp, which is low. The circuit is commonly used for **impedance matching** between a circuit with a high Z_{out} and a circuit with a low Z_{in}.

■ Adder

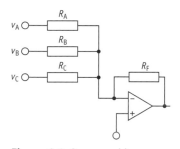

Figure 6.7 Op amp adder

An adder is alternatively known as a **summer**, or a **mixer**. Its function is to add voltages (though it does this by adding currents), and it is also used as a digital-to-analogue converter. The circuit (see Fig. 6.7, for example) is an inverting amplifier with two or more parallel inputs to the inverting input. In the voltage-adding circuit, all input resistors R_A, R_B, ... have the same value, R. Currents flow from different voltage sources to the virtual earth at the inverting input.

The pds across the resistors in Fig. 6.7 are v_A, v_B and v_C, so the currents are v_A/R, v_B/R and v_C/R. These combine at the virtual earth to give:

$$i = (v_A + v_B + v_C)/R$$

The combined current i flows on through R_F, so that the pd across R_F is:

$$v_{out} = -iR = -(v_A + v_B + v_C)/R \times R$$
$$\Rightarrow v_{out} = -(v_A + v_B + v_C)$$

The summation is limited by how close the output can swing towards the negative supply voltage.

■ Active filters

In contrast to passive filters, active filters incorporate active components so that additional signal power may be obtained from a power supply. The active component is usually an op amp. The table and diagrams on pp 87 and 88 compare some simple active filters.

The two **first-order active filters** in the table opposite each use one of the resistors of the amplifier circuit as part of the filter. The function of the op amp is to boost or cut the filtered signal.

Feedback in the **Sallen and Key filters** produces the equivalent of resonance near the cut-off point. The effect of this is to sharpen the 'knee' of the frequency response, so that there is a clearer distinction between the passband and the

		Op amp active filters compared			
Description	**Circuit**		**Frequency response**	**Voltage gain (magnitude) in passband**	**Cut-off (f_c) or centre (f_0) frequency**
first-order lowpass active filter	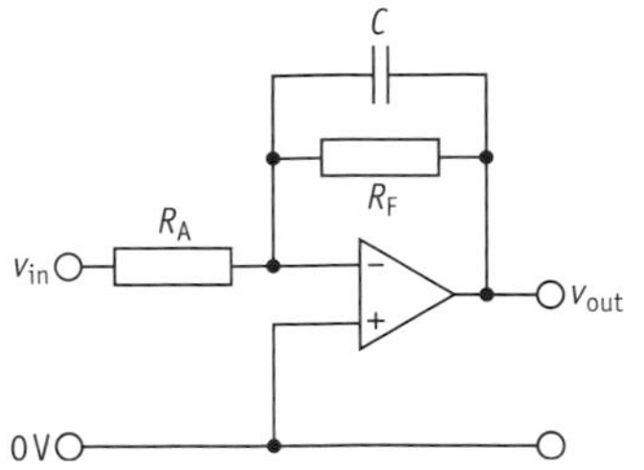 Figure 6.8		See Fig. 6.13	R_F/R_A	$f_c = 1/2\pi R_F C$
first-order highpass active filter	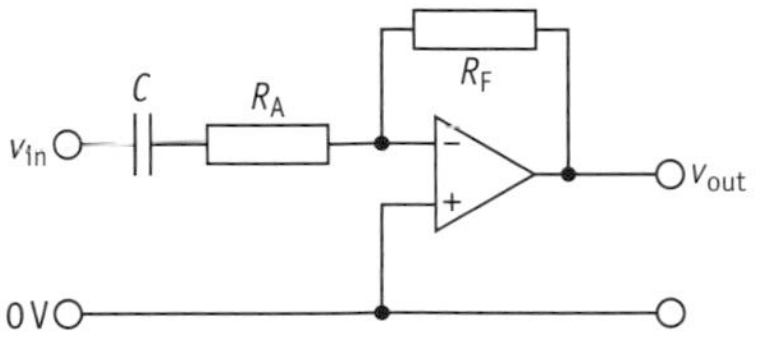 Figure 6.9		See Fig. 6.14	R_F/R_A	$f_c = 1/2\pi R_A C$
second-order lowpass active filter with feedback (Sallen and Key)	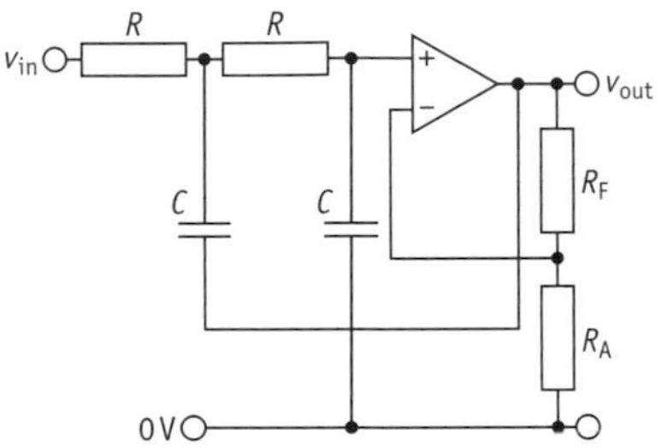 Figure 6.10		As Fig. 6.13 but with −12 dB/octave roll-off in transition region	$(R_A + R_F)/R_A$ must not be >3, for stability	$f_c = 1/2\pi RC$
second order highpass active filter with feedback (Sallen and Key)	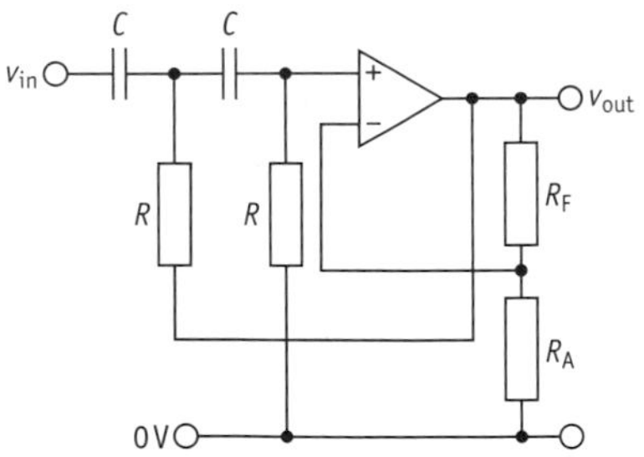 Figure 6.11		As Fig. 6.14 but with +12 dB/octave roll-off in transition region	$(R_A + R_F)/R_A$ must not be >3, for stability	$f_c = 1/2\pi RC$
bandpass active filter with multiple feedback	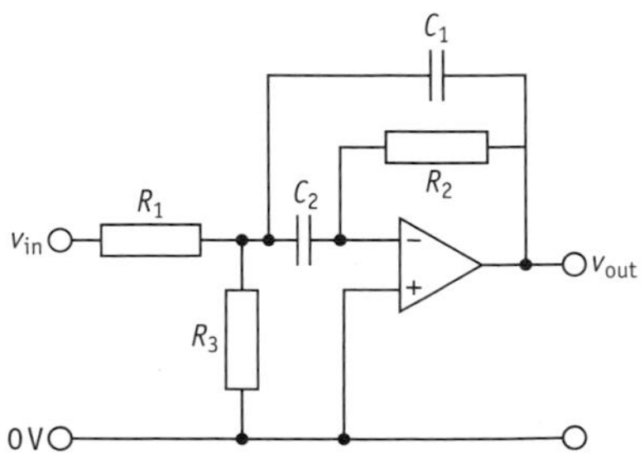 Figure 6.12		See Fig. 6.15	$\dfrac{R_2}{2R_1}$ at resonance	$f_0 = \dfrac{1}{2\pi C}\sqrt{\dfrac{(R_1 + R_3)}{R_1 R_2 R_3}}$

beginning of **roll-off** (the straight-line transition region). Gain is preferably not greater than 2. The exact shape of the response curve is controlled by choosing suitable values for R and C. Values are obtained from tables.

Figure 6.13 Frequency response of first-order lowpass active filter

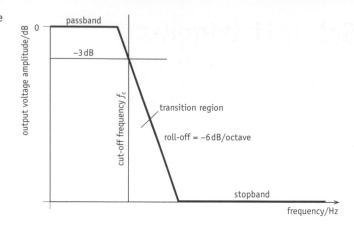

Figure 6.14 Frequency response of first-order highpass active filter

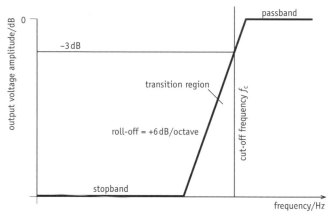

Figure 6.15 Frequency response of bandpass active filter with multiple feedback

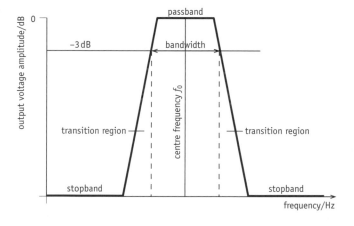

In the **multiple feedback bandpass filter** (Fig. 6.12), R_1 and C_1 form a highpass filter. The signal fed back to the inverting input through this filter cancels out the high frequencies in the signal. R_2 and C_2 form a lowpass filter, and the signals fed back to the inverting input through this cancel out the low frequencies. Intermediate frequencies pass through the circuit at full strength. This circuit produces a passband with narrow bandwidth. A bandpass filter with a wider bandwidth is built by following a lowpass filter with a highpass filter that has a lower cut-off frequency. Note that a *highpass* active filter based on an op amp has reduced output near the transition frequency of the op amp (see p. 84) and is therefore, in effect, a bandpass filter.

If f_L and f_H are the cut-off points of the lowpass and highpass filters, the centre frequency is given by:

$$f_0 = \sqrt{(f_L \times f_H)}$$

6•4 Schmitt triggers

Schmitt triggers are bistable circuits that have two triggering input voltages, the **lower threshold voltage** (LTV) and the **upper threshold voltage** (UTV). The circuit is triggered to change state when the input voltage rises above the UTV. Having done so, it is not triggered back to the other state until the input voltage falls below the LTV. The difference between the UTV and the LTV is known as the **hysteresis** (H) of the circuit.

Schmitt triggers can be built using transistors, op amps or logic gates. Those using op amps are summarised in the table below.

Op amp Schmitt triggers compared				
Type	**Action**	**Circuit**	**Calculating thresholds**	**Design**
inverting	output swings high when input falls below LTV	Figure 6.16	$V_{ref} = V_S R_2/(R_1 + R_2)$ Let $R = R_4/(R_3 + R_4)$ $UTV = V_{ref} + R(V_S - V_{ref})$ $LTV = V_{ref}(1 - R)$	Select UTV and LTV Let $V = (UTV - LTV)/V_S$ $V_{ref} = LTV/(1 - V)$ Let $R_2 = 1\,k\Omega$ $R_1 = R_2(V_S - V_{ref})/V_{ref}$ Let $R_4 = 100\,k\Omega$ $R_3 = R_4(1 - V)/V$
non-inverting	output swings high when input rises above UTV	Figure 6.17	$V_{ref} = V_S R_2/(R_1 + R_2)$ Let $R = R_4/(R_3 + R_4)$ $UTV = V_{ref}/(1 - R)$ $LTV = (V_{ref} - V_S R)/(1 - R)$	Select UTV and LTV $H = UTV - LTV$ Let $V = H/(H + V_S)$ $V_{ref} = UTV/(1 - V)$ Let $R_2 = 100\,k\Omega$ $R_1 = R_2(V_S - V_{ref})/V_{ref}$ Let $R_4 = 100\,k\Omega$ $R_3 = R_4(1 - V)/V$

Calculations are usually worked in kilohms. Initial values of R_2 and R_4 different from those used in the table can be used for calculating R_1 and R_3, if they produce more easily obtainable values. Note that, in the inverting trigger, the values of R_1 and R_2 must be only a few kilohms.

In the **inverting Schmitt trigger** (Fig. 6.16), the input goes to the inverting input of the op amp. If the input is high, the output is low. *Positive* feedback from the output pulls down the voltage V_{ref}, so that the input has to fall below LTV to cause the trigger to change state. A low input causes the output to go high, so raising V_{ref}. The input then has to rise above UTV to cause the trigger to change state.

In the **non-inverting Schmitt trigger** (Fig. 6.17), the input goes to the non-inverting input of the op amp, via R_4. If the input is high, the output is high. Positive feedback from the output raises the voltage V_{ref}, so that the trigger changes state when the input falls below UTV. The output falls, pulling down V_{ref}. The input then has to fall below LTV to cause the trigger to change state.

▌Ten quick questions

1 What is the name for the maximum rate of change of the output voltage of an op amp?
2 What do we call the procedure by which we adjust the output of an op amp to be exactly zero volts (with a dual supply) when the difference between inputs is zero volts?
3 What is the typical value of the output impedance of an op amp?
4 What do we call the difference between the threshold voltages of a Schmitt trigger circuit?
5 Define the transition frequency of an op amp.
6 What type of op amp amplifier circuit has the highest input impedance?
7 Give the equation for the cut-off frequency of an active first-order lowpass filter based on an inverting amplifier.
8 An inverting amplifier circuit has three parallel input resistors. The input resistors and the feedback resistor are equal. If the input voltages are 12 mV, 56 mV and 22 mV, what is the output voltage?
9 A bandpass filter is built by cascading a lowpass filter with a highpass filter. Which filter has the lower cut-off frequency?
10 What is the value of the roll-off of a second-order lowpass active filter?

▌Questions on operational amplifiers

1 An operational amplifier is connected as a comparator. When the voltage at the inverting input is $-24\,\mu V$ and the voltage at the non-inverting input is $31\,\mu V$, the output is $+5.5\,V$. What is the gain, A? Express this in decibels.

2 The full-power bandwidth of a CA3013 operational amplifier is 120 kHz. What is meant by this statement? If the transition frequency of the operational amplifier is 4 MHz, what is its open-loop gain at 1 MHz?

3 In a non-inverting amplifier (Fig. 6.5, p. 85), $R_A = 120\,k\Omega$ and $R_F = 56\,k\Omega$. What is the voltage gain? Calculate the value of R_B. What is a typical Z_{in} for the circuit if the operational amplifier has BJT inputs?

4 Calculate the voltage gain of an inverting amplifier (Fig. 6.4, p. 85) that has resistors of the following values:
   a) $R_A = 330\,\Omega$, $R_F = 1\,M\Omega$;
   b) $R_A = 10\,k\Omega$, $R_F = 100\,k\Omega$;
   c) $R_A = 470\,k\Omega$, $R_F = 2.2\,M\Omega$.
   In each case state the Z_{in} of the circuit.

5 Explain the meaning of the term 'virtual earth'. Use this term when deriving the equation for the closed-loop gain of an operational amplifier connected as an inverting amplifier.

6 Calculate the voltage gain of a non-inverting amplifier (Fig. 6.5, p. 85) that has resistors of the following values:
   a) $R_A = 270\,k\Omega$, $R_F = 1\,M\Omega$;
   b) $R_A = 10\,k\Omega$, $R_F = 100\,k\Omega$;
   c) $R_A = 820\,k\Omega$, $R_F = 390\,k\Omega$.

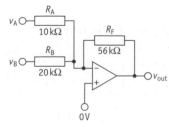

Figure 6.18

7 Derive an equation for the output of the circuit shown in Fig. 6.18. Calculate the output when $v_A = 200\,mV$ and $v_B = 150\,mV$.

8 Fig. 6.19 is a circuit for processing the output from an LDR light sensor. Describe the action of this circuit, including an explanation of the function of IC1. Derive an equation for the output of the circuit in terms of the five resistors and v_A. What change occurs in v_{out} when the amount of light falling on R_1 is increased? What is the purpose of the variable input v_A?

Figure 6.19

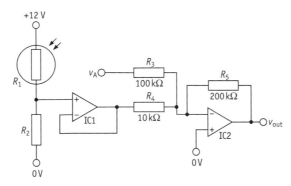

9 Design an operational amplifier circuit with gain of -24. What is its input impedance? If this is too low, what can be done to increase it?

10 Calculate the gain of a non-inverting operational amplifier if $R_A = 33\,k\Omega$ and $R_F = 470\,k\Omega$. Calculate the value of R_B. What is its Z_{in}?

11 Fig. 6.20a shows the circuit for a simple precision half-wave rectifier. Usually $R_1 = R_2$. The graph in Fig. 6.20b is a plot of v_{in}, a sinusoid of 0.75 V amplitude. Copy the graph and on the same grid plot the output v_{out} of the precision half-wave rectifier, and also the output (given the same input signal) of the simple half-wave rectifier in Fig. 4.22a (p. 56). Explain how the precision half-wave rectifier operates and state why it is preferred for rectifying signals of low voltage amplitude.

Figure 6.20

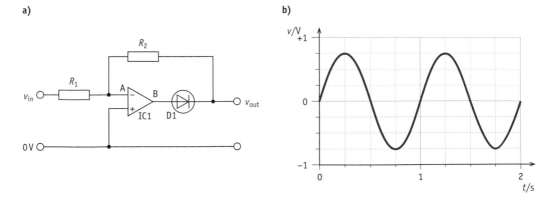

a)

b)

12 Draw the circuit of a first-order lowpass active RC filter, based on an op amp inverting amplifier. Calculate the cut-off frequency, given that $R = 180\,k\Omega$ and $C = 22\,nF$. Sketch the frequency response of this filter.

13 Design a first-order highpass active RC filter, with a cut-off frequency of 140 Hz and a passband gain of -2.4, based on an op amp inverting amplifier. Sketch the frequency response of this filter. What is the value of the roll-off?

14 Design a first-order lowpass active RC filter, based on an op amp inverting amplifier, with a cut-off frequency of 100 Hz and a passband gain of 1.5. What is its bandwidth?

15 Design a second-order lowpass active filter, with a cut-off frequency of 2 kHz and a passband gain of 2.

16 Sketch the frequency response of the filter in Fig. 6.21. Label it with its cut-off points and its centre frequency. What is its bandwidth?

Figure 6.21

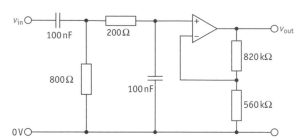

17 Design a broadband bandpass filter with the lower cut-off point at 500 Hz and a bandwidth of 2 kHz. What is its centre frequency? Draw a diagram of the circuit and mark the values of the components.

18 Draw a diagram of a multiple feedback bandpass filter and explain how it works. Explain how a highpass filter may have a frequency response similar to that of a bandpass filter.

19 A photodiode is used to detect the light from the headlamps of a car as it approaches a garage door. The signal from this sensor triggers the door to open. Draw the sensing circuit. The signal from this is processed by a filter to ensure that the circuit responds when the headlamps are shining continuously on the sensor, but does not respond to short flashes of light from cars passing by in the street or from lightning. Add the filter circuit to your diagram of the sensing circuit, marking the components with suitable values.

20 In a model railway system the locomotive is to be controlled by blowing a whistle. Design the input stage of such a system in which sound is detected by a microphone. Include in your design a circuit that filters the signal from the microphone, making the system most sensitive to high-pitched whistling sounds, while ignoring low-pitched sounds such as speech.

21 Describe the action of an inverting Schmitt trigger based on an operational amplifier. Use the terms *upper threshold voltage*, *lower threshold voltage*, *negative feedback* and *hysteresis*. Explain a practical application for such a trigger.

22 An operational amplifier is connected as an inverting Schmitt trigger. Calculate the upper and lower threshold voltages when:
a) $V_S = 15$ V, $R_1 = R_2 = 3.3$ kΩ, $R_3 = R_4 = 470$ kΩ;
b) $V_S = 15$ V, $R_1 = R_2 = 2.7$ kΩ, $R_3 = 330$ kΩ and $R_4 = 220$ kΩ;
c) $V_S = 12$ V, $R_1 = 2$ kΩ, $R_2 = 1$ kΩ, $R_3 = 330$ kΩ and $R_4 = 470$ kΩ;
d) $V_S = 9$ V, $R_1 = 1$ kΩ, $R_2 = 1.8$ kΩ, $R_3 = 100$ kΩ and $R_4 = 220$ kΩ.

23 An operational amplifier is connected as a non-inverting Schmitt trigger. Calculate the values of the resistors required when:
a) $V_S = 18$ V, UTV = 12 V and LTV = 10 V;
b) $V_S = 15$ V, UTV = 8 V and LTV = 7 V;
c) $V_S = 15$ V, UTV = 3 V and LTV = 2 V;
d) $V_S = 6$ V, UTV = 4.5 V and LTV = 4 V.
Hint: Assume that $R_2 = R_4 = 100$ kΩ, as suggested in the table on p. 89.

7 Signal processing

In brief...

■ Signal conditioning describes a group of simple signal processing techniques used for improving the quality of signals. It includes: clamping, clipping, use of a Schmitt trigger, eliminating contact bounce and precautions to eliminate noise (pp 93–94).

■ Signal processing also includes other techniques such as filtering and the use of differential amplifiers for extracting a signal from a background of noise (p. 94).

■ Analogue-to-digital converters are important for interfacing to logic circuits. These include: flash, counter, successive approximation and single-slope converters (pp 96–99).

■ Digital-to-analogue converters are used to convert the output from digital circuits; the op amp adder is used for this purpose (p. 99).

Questions on signal processing begin on p. 100, with answers on p. 172.

7•1 Signal conditioning

Signal conditioning means modifying a signal to make it more suitable for the circuit to which it is being applied, but without removing its information content. Some terms used in signal conditioning are explained below.

Clamping   This means altering the dc level on which the signal is based. See p. 43.

Clipping   This involves removing peaks and troughs of a signal, often to prevent the signal from overloading subsequent stages. Clipping is also used to remove unwanted spikes from signals. Fig. 7.1 shows how to use a Zener diode for clipping. In Fig. 7.1a the signal is clipped to V_Z, the Zener voltage. In Fig. 7.1b the signal is clipped to $\pm(V_Z + 0.7)$; this is because, in each half-cycle of the signal, the total voltage is the sum of the Zener voltage of one diode plus the forward voltage drop of 0.7 V across the other.

Figure 7.1 Zener diode clipping: **a)** of positive waveforms and pulses; **b)** of signals alternating above and below 0 V

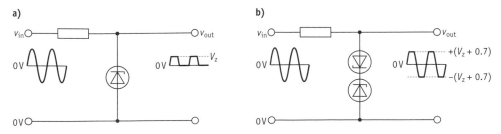

Schmitt trigger   A non-inverting Schmitt trigger (see Fig. 6.17, p. 89) is used to regenerate (or 'square up') a pulsed signal after its shape has been distorted during transmission.

Contact bounce   This occurs when contacts make and break several times as a switch is turned on or off, instead of only once. A train of short pulses is produced, which may be taken as multiple pulses by a logic circuit such as a counter.

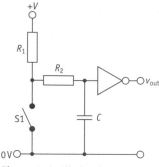

Figure 7.2 Eliminating contact bounce

Fig. 7.2 shows how to eliminate contact bounce. The basic INVERT gate may be replaced with the type that has Schmitt trigger inputs; or the gate may be replaced with an inverting Schmitt trigger circuit, like that in Fig. 6.16 (p. 89). The output is a rapid rising edge when S1 is closed.

Noise 'Noise' is an unwanted signal superimposed on the wanted signal. It may be caused by electromagnetic interference (EMI) from an external source, or it may arise from the random motion of electrons within the circuit itself. Noise is reduced or eliminated by a variety of precautions:

- screening of equipment and cables to shield from EMI (screening is earthed);
- keeping currents small to reduce electronic noise, particularly in the early stages of an amplifier;
- using low-noise versions of semiconductors and op amps;
- restricting bandwidth to that actually required for operation of the system.

7·2 Signal processing

Other signal processing techniques involve modifying a signal to increase its usefulness, often by removing certain parts of the information it contains. **Filtering** is an obvious example; certain frequencies are removed or attenuated in order to extract the frequencies of interest.

▐ Extracting a signal from background noise

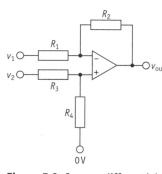

Figure 7.3 Op amp differential amplifier

When a wanted signal is superimposed on a dc or varying background signal, a **differential amplifier** is used to extract the signal. An op amp is a differential amplifier, so it is used as the basis of a differential amplifier circuit (Fig. 7.3). This circuit is also known as a **subtractor** because, if all the resistors have equal value:

$$v_{out} = v_2 - v_1$$

Sometimes the difference between the inputs produces a value for v_{out} higher than the op amp can deliver; the output needs to be scaled down. Often the input difference is so small that it needs to be scaled up. Scaling is done by making $R_1 = R_3$ and $R_2 = R_4$. When this is done:

$$v_{out} = (v_2 - v_1) \times R_2/R_1$$

There are two types of gain associated with this circuit:

- **differential mode gain**: this is the gain defined by the equation above; it is equal to R_2/R_1 and is usually high.
- **common mode gain**: this is the gain when the inputs are connected together, so that they both receive the same signal; it is usually very small.

From these we obtain the **common mode rejection ratio** (CMRR):

$$CMRR = \frac{\text{differential mode gain}}{\text{common mode gain}}$$

The CMRR ratio is most often expressed in decibels. Because CMRR refers to gains in *voltage*, the multiplying factor (see p. 6) is 20. The CMRR of a typical op amp is 100 dB; this means that the differential mode gain is 10^5 times greater than the common mode gain. As an example, consider an electroencephalogram apparatus that is measuring the pd between two probes placed on the patient's scalp. The probes also pick up signals from other equipment in the room, including 50 Hz EMI signals from mains cables. However, such signals are common mode signals as they are picked up equally by both probes. Amplification of the pd signal is 10^5 times that of EMI signals, so making it possible to pick out the very small pd signal against a background of larger EMI signals.

▌ Use of differential amplifiers for bridge measurements

Fig. 7.4 illustrates the principle of the **Wheatstone bridge** with a dc activation voltage V_A. If the bridge is taken to be two potential dividers (R_1 and R_2, R_3 and R_4), then the output voltages from these dividers are equal when:

$$R_1/R_2 = R_3/R_4$$

In this condition, V_{out} is zero and the bridge is said to be **balanced**. Given any three of the resistances, we can calculate the fourth. A differential amplifier is used to measure V_{out}, so as to detect the balance point ($V_{out} = 0\,V$) with high precision. The high CMRR means that common mode signals occurring on the bridge have negligible effect.

The bridge is used for measurement of:

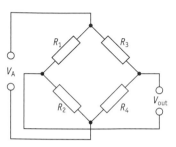

Figure 7.4 Wheatstone bridge

- **resistance**: R_1 is the unknown resistance. R_2 is a high-precision variable resistance, often a resistance box in which precision resistors are switched in series to build up a known resistance and so balance the bridge. R_3 and R_4 are known, so R_1 can be calculated. R_3 and R_4 are the **ratio arms**, switchable to give various ratios such as 1:100, 1:10, 1:1, 10:1 and 100:1. These extend the possible range of measurements.
- **temperature**: a platinum resistance thermometer is the unknown resistance. It consists of a coil of fine platinum wire. The temperature coefficient of resistance for metals is very small, but a bridge has sufficient precision to measure the small changes.
- **strain**: a strain gauge is the unknown resistance. It consists of thin metal foil, etched to produce an array of parallel and very fine metal conductors. The gauge is embedded in insulating film and is firmly fixed to the object (such as a girder) which is to be stressed. The conductors are parallel to the direction in which the object is to be stressed. Stress causes the object to become strained. The conductors become equally strained. They become longer and thinner and their resistance increases. The effect is small but the bridge is able to measure the change of resistance. Tables are used to convert this to a measurement of the amount of strain.

The sensor bridges described above are **quarter bridges**, with the sensor in only one arm. In a **half bridge**, there are two sensors at R_1 and R_4. Resistor R_2 is variable and R_3 is fixed or is a resistance box used to extend the range. The half bridge is more sensitive than a quarter bridge because when the output from R_1/R_2 rises the output from R_3/R_4 falls. V_{out} changes by double the amount, thus doubling the precision of the bridge.

Bridges can compensate for changes in the resistance of the lead connecting the sensor to the bridge. In this case, R_1 consists of the sensor and its lead in series. R_2 consists of the variable resistor and a dummy lead in series. As the lead to the sensor increases in resistance (perhaps because of a rise in room temperature), the dummy lead increases in resistance by the same amount.

7·3 Analogue-to-digital converters

Analogue-to-digital converters (ADCs) are used for interfacing signal sources to logic circuits.

∎ Flash ADC

See Fig. 7.5. The discussion here relates to a 3-bit converter having seven ($2^3 - 1$) comparators (see p. 84). A reference voltage V_{ref} is applied across the potential divider chain. Numbering the resistors as in the diagram, the voltage V_n at the junction of resistor n and resistor $(n + 1)$ is:

$$V_n = V_{ref} \times \frac{nR + R/2}{6R + R/2 + 3R/2}$$

R can be cancelled out, leaving:

$$V_n = V_{ref} \times \frac{2n + 1}{16}$$

Figure 7.5 Three-bit flash ADC

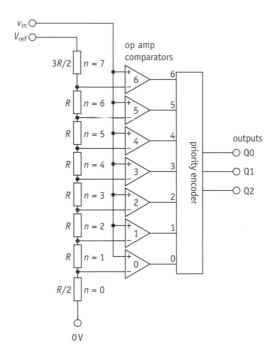

The exact value of R does not matter, provided that all Rs are equal and that the values of the $R/2$ and $3R/2$ resistors are in proportion. Because all the resistors are made on the same chip, this is easy to achieve and gives high precision to the converter.

The voltage V_n is applied to the inverting input of comparator n. The output of comparator n goes to logic high if:

$$v_{in} > V_n$$

At a given value of v_{in}, the highest-numbered comparator output that goes to logic high is the one for which:

$$V_{n+1} > v_{in} > V_n$$

The number of this highest-numbered comparator input is decoded by the priority encoder, as a binary output.

worked example

problem In a 7-comparator ADC, $V_{ref} = 8$ V. Comparators 0 to 3 have high outputs, the rest have low outputs. What is v_{in}?

working If n is the number of the highest-numbered comparator that has high output:

$$V_n = V_3 = 8 \times (2 \times 3 + 1)/16 = 3.5 \text{ V}$$
$$V_{n+1} = 8 \times (2 \times 4 + 1)/16 = 4.5 \text{ V}$$

solution v_{in} is between 3.5 V and 4.5 V. In other words, $v_{in} = 4$ V ± 0.5 V.

The example shows that if V_{ref} is 8 V, the converter gives the voltage to the nearest volt. Its **resolution** is ± 0.5 V.

Fig. 7.5 illustrates the fact that a flash converter with an m-bit binary output requires $(2^m - 1)$ comparators. This means that a counter with 8-bit output requires $(2^8 - 1)$ comparators, that is 255 comparators. A really precise ADC requires many more. This limits the usefulcss of flash ADCs. Their main advantage is their speed: the conversion time is the settling time of a single comparator plus the propagation time of the encoder. Typical conversion times are in the range 10 ns to 2 μs, depending on the number of bits.

In general, if a flash ADC has an m-bit output:

- it requires $(2^m - 1)$ comparators;
- they are numbered 0 to $(2^m - 2)$;
- the divisor in the equation for V_n is 2×2^m;
- the voltage steps are $V_{ref}/2^m$;
- the resolution is $\pm V_{ref}/(2 \times 2^m)$.

For example, for 4-bit output, $m = 4$, $2^m = 16$. The ADC requires 15 comparators, numbered 0 to 14; the divisor is 32; voltage steps are $V_{ref}/16$; and resolution is $\pm V_{ref}/32$.

■ Counter ADC

See Fig. 7.6a, p. 98. The binary counter is reset at the start of the conversion and the output from the digital-to-analogue converter (DAC, see p. 99) is 0 V. The output from the comparator is high, enabling the clock pulses to pass through the AND gate to the counter. As the count increases, the output of the DAC rises. As soon as the output of the DAC exceeds v_{in}, the output of the comparator swings low, disabling the passage of pulses through the AND gate. The counter stops and the digital value displayed represents v_{in}.

This is a simple and precise converter, but conversion time depends on the value of v_{in}.

■ Successive approximation ADC

See Fig. 7.6b. At each pulse of the system clock, the control logic generates a sequence of binary values that is sent to the successive approximation register (SAR). These are sent to a digital-to-analogue converter to produce an analogue voltage. This is compared with v_{in}, to determine whether the output from the SAR is greater than or less than v_{in}. Accordingly, a high or low logic signal is sent to the control logic. If the SAR output is greater than v_{in}, the output of the SAR is decreased; if it is less than v_{in}, the output of the SAR is increased.

Figure 7.6 ACDs compared:
a) Counter ADC; **b)** 4-bit
successive approximation ADC;
c) single-slope ADC

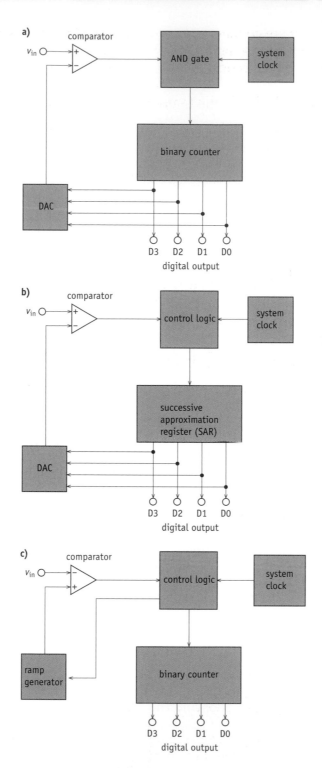

Working one bit at a time, starting with output D3 and working down to D0, the control logic gradually homes on the 4-bit value that is nearest to v_{in}. The use of a searching routine such as this requires that v_{in} does not alter during the conversion. Usually, v_{in} is held constant by a sample-and-hold circuit while conversion is performed. Then the 'end of conversion' output of the ADC is made high and the digital output appears on terminals D3 to D0.

The precision of this ADC depends on the number of bits in the SAR. Increasing the number of bits to obtain higher precision is no problem; 18-bit converters are common. However, conversion time is a clock cycle for each bit; the greater the precision, the longer the conversion time. An 18-bit ADC may have a conversion time as short as 20 μs, but a typical time is about 100 μs.

Compared with flash converters, successive approximation converters:

■ are slower, but still fast enough for many applications;
■ are more precise;
■ need a sample-and-hold device;
■ are generally cheaper, especially for high-precision versions.

■ Single-slope ADC

See Fig. 7.6c. When the start input is made low, the voltage output from the ramp generator (a constant current source charging a capacitor) begins to rise linearly from 0 V. At the same time pulses from the clock are counted. Counting stops as soon as the ramp voltage exceeds v_{in}. This ADC is simple and reliable, but not of high precision. This is because precision depends on the accuracy and stability of the capacitor.

7•4 Digital-to-analogue converter

Digital-to-analogue converters (DACs) are used to convert the output from digital circuits.

An op amp adder (see Fig. 6.7, p. 86) is adapted for use as a DAC by weighting its inputs. Instead of applying different input voltages, as in Fig. 6.7, standard input voltages (either 0 V or v_H) are applied and resistors of different values are chosen. The relationships between the resistors arc:

$$R_C = 2R_F$$
$$R_B = 2R_C = 4R_F$$
$$R_A = 2R_B = 8R_F$$

When an input is v_H (corresponding to logic 1), the current flowing to the virtual earth (the inverting input) is inversely proportional to the weighting resistor. This results in different currents flowing:

$$i_C = 2i_B = 4i_A$$

For example, if v_H is 6 V, $R_C = 10\,k\Omega$, $R_B = 20\,k\Omega$ and $R_A = 40\,k\Omega$:

$$i_C = 6/10\,000 = 600\,\mu A$$
$$i_B = 6/20\,000 = 300\,\mu A$$
$$i_A = 6/40\,000 = 150\,\mu A$$

If the input voltage is zero (corresponding to logic 0), the current through any of the input resistors is zero.

To convert a digital number, the input voltage is 0 V for the digits that are logic 0, and v_H for those that are logic 1. For example, to convert binary 110, we apply v_H volts to inputs v_C and v_B, and 0 V to input v_A. The current flowing to the virtual earth is:

$$i_{total} = i_C + i_B = 600 + 300 = 900\,\mu A$$

This is also the current flowing through R_F, the resistance of which is 5 kΩ, and:

$$v_{out} = -i_{total} \times R_F = -900 \times 5\,[\mu A \times k\Omega] = -4.5\,V$$

The output is scaled to the binary input, with an output of $-v_H$ being equivalent to an input of 1000. Thus v_{out} is multiplied by a **scaling factor** of $-8/v_H$ to give the equivalent in volts of the binary input:

$$-4.5 \times -8/6 = 6\,V$$

This exactly equals the binary input, but in volts.

▌ Ten quick questions

1 What is the name of the circuit that amplifies the difference between two input voltages?
2 What is meant by 'contact bounce'?
3 What term is used to describe altering the dc level of a signal?
4 Which type of ADC is the fastest?
5 If the feedback resistor of an op amp ADC is 12 kΩ, what is the value of the smallest of the input resistors?
6 What does 'clipping' do to a signal?
7 How many comparators are needed in a flash ADC with 4-bit output?
8 How many clock cycles are required by a successive approximation converter to convert the input to a 12-bit number?
9 What is the main advantage of a successive approximation ADC over a flash converter?
10 What do we call unwanted signals that are superimposed on a wanted signal?

▌ Questions on signal processing

1 **a)** List the properties of a Zener diode.
  b) Using a network diagram, explain the operation of a clipping circuit based on a Zener diode.

2 Draw a circuit used for eliminating contact bounce and explain how it works.

3 Op amps are used as comparators and as differential amplifiers. Explain the differences between these two types of circuit and their uses.

4 **a)** A differential amplifier like that in Fig. 7.3 (p. 94) has $R_1 = R_3 = 3.3\,k\Omega$, and $R_2 = R_4 = 10\,k\Omega$. If $v_1 = 1.25\,V$ and $v_2 = 1.04\,V$, what is the output?
  b) A differential amplifier like that in Fig. 7.3 has $R_1 = R_3 = 2.7\,k\Omega$, and $R_2 = R_4 = 15\,k\Omega$. If $v_1 = 3.42\,V$ and $v_{out} = -0.24\,V$, what is v_2?

5 Explain the terms *differential mode gain*, *common mode gain* and *common mode rejection ratio*.

6 If the differential mode gain of an amplifier is 130 and the common mode gain is 0.2, what is the CMRR?

7 Describe the principle of the Wheatstone bridge. What do we mean when we say that a bridge is balanced? Describe two applications for a Wheatstone bridge.

8 Explain the principle of a flash ADC, illustrating your answer with a diagram. Name a possible application for a flash ADC.

9 a) In a 7-comparator flash ADC, $V_{ref} = 10$ V, comparators 0 to 5 have high outputs and the rest have low outputs. What is v_{in}?

b) In a 7-comparator flash ADC, $V_{ref} = 12$ V, comparators 0 to 2 have high outputs and the rest have low outputs. What is v_{in}?

10 A flash converter produces an 6-bit digital output. How many comparators does it have? If $V_{ref} = 5$ V, comparators 0 to 20 have high outputs and the rest have low outputs, what is v_{in}?

11 What are the advantages of a successive approximation converter when compared with a flash converter?

12 Explain the principle of a named ADC, pointing out its advantages and disadvantages.

13 Draw a diagram of the ADC you described in question 12.

14 The clock of a successive approximation converter is running at 500 kHz. How long does it take to convert an input into a 12-bit output?

15 Draw a diagram of a digital-to-analogue converter based on an op amp.

16 Explain what is meant by 'weighting' resistors. How is this idea applied to an op amp DAC?

17 The feedback resistor of a 3-bit DAC is 12 kΩ. What are the resistances of the input resistors? Which of these is the input resistor for the least significant digit? Given the standard v_H is 5 V, calculate the currents and the output voltage when the digital input is 101.

18 What is the scaling factor in the DAC of question 17? What is the equivalent of v_{out}, given the input 101?

19 The feedback resistor of a 4-bit DAC is 10 kΩ. What are the resistances of the input resistors? Which of these is the input resistor for the least significant digit? Given the standard v_H is 8 V, calculate the currents and the output voltage when the digital input is 1011.

20 What is the scaling factor in the DAC of question 19? What is the equivalent of v_{out}, given the input 1011?

8 Power supply systems

In brief...

■ The essentials of a low-voltage dc power supply system are a step-down transformer, a rectifier and a smoothing capacitor (p. 102).

■ Load regulation and line regulation are the quantities that describe the performance of the system (p. 103).

■ Power supply systems usually include an input stage, a transformer, a half-wave or full-wave rectifier, a smoothing capacitor, and either a Zener stabiliser, a series regulator, an op amp series regulator or a 3-terminal regulator (pp 103–105).

■ Short-circuit protection is an optional but useful feature of a power supply (p. 105).

Questions on power supply systems are on p. 106, with answers from p. 172.

8•1 Power supply systems in outline

Most electronic circuits operate on low-voltage dc, which is obtainable from batteries. Batteries are essential for portable systems (except when solar cells are used). They are, however, whether rechargeable or not, expensive to use. If a circuit is to operate at high power or for lengthy periods, it is more economical to use the ac mains as a power source. The essentials of such a power supply system are illustrated in Fig. 8.1 and the stages are outlined below.

Figure 8.1 The main stages of a power supply system for electronic circuits

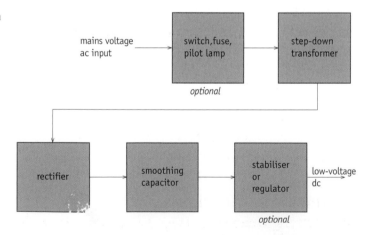

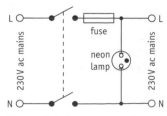

Figure 8.2 Input stage of a power supply system

1 The optional first stage, used in more expensive units, has a double-pole switch to isolate the system completely from the mains (Fig. 8.2). The fuse limits the current to a level that the transformer can safely conduct. The lamp indicates when the unit is operating and may be a neon lamp, as shown, or a filament lamp. Alternatively this pilot lamp may be an LED connected into the low-voltage side of the system. None of the items in this stage are an essential part of the power supply system.

2 A transformer steps down the mains voltage ac to a low-voltage ac that is slightly greater than the required output of the system (see p. 55).

3 A rectifier then converts the low-voltage ac to low-voltage dc (see pp 55–56).

4 The output from the rectifier is pulsed dc. A smoothing or 'reservoir' capacitor smoothes out the pulses (see below).

5 A power supply may be unregulated, in which case the final stabiliser/regulator stage is omitted, and the smoothed dc is fed directly to the load circuit. A stabilising stage is one that helps to minimise variations in output voltage caused by variations in load current. A regulator stage is a more complicated circuit (usually an IC) that uses feedback to hold output voltage constant when input voltage or load current changes.

8•2 Load and line regulation

The output voltage of a typical power supply falls as the amount of current drawn from it is increased. **Load regulation** is a measure of this effect. It is defined as the percentage change in output voltage as the current is increased from zero up to the maximum for which the circuit is designed.

The load regulation of a typical Zener stabiliser is several percent, while that of an IC regulator is only 0.1%.

The output voltage also varies with variations in the input voltage. **Line regulation** is defined as:

$$\frac{\text{change in output voltage}}{\text{change in input voltage}} \times 100\%$$

The line regulation of a Zener stabiliser is several percent, while that of an IC regulator is 0.01% to 0.3%.

8•3 Power supply systems in detail

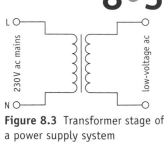

Figure 8.3 Transformer stage of a power supply system

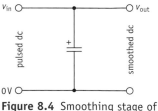

Figure 8.4 Smoothing stage of a power supply system

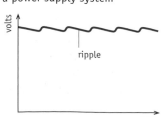

Figure 8.5 Smoothed dc, with ripple

▌ Input

See Fig. 8.2. The fuse, switch and pilot lamp are optional.

▌ Transformer

See p. 55 and Fig. 8.3.

▌ Rectifier

This may be a half-wave rectifier (see pp 55–56), or a full-wave rectifier (see p. 56). Its output is pulsed dc, with amplitude one or two diode drops below that of the output from the transformer.

▌ Smoothing capacitor

An electrolytic capacitor (Fig. 8.4) charges from the dc pulses, and discharges as current flows to the load or to the stabiliser/regulator. The charge begins to fall after after every peak of the pulse dc, causing **ripple** to appear on the smoothed dc (Fig. 8.5). This is typical of unregulated supplies but is mostly removed if smoothing is followed by a stabiliser or regulator stage.

In an unregulated power supply with a half-wave rectifier, if the peak voltage is V_p the mean voltage V_s after smoothing is:

$$V_s = V_p - I/2Cf$$

where I is the load current, C is the capacitance of the smoothing capacitor and f is the frequency of the mains ac (generally 50 Hz). This shows that the effect of ripple increases as load current increases. Ripple is reduced by making C large: capacitances used are typically 1000 µF or more. The frequency cannot be changed.

With a full-wave rectifier:

$$V_s = V_p - I/4Cf$$

There is '4' in the divisor instead of '2' because the frequency of the pulsed dc from a full-wave rectifier is double the mains frequency (see Fig. 4.23b, p. 56). Other factors being equal, a full-wave rectified supply has half the ripple of a half-wave supply.

■ Zener stabiliser

See p. 43. The network of Fig. 4.3 is suited to low-current output and when precise regulation is not required. By using a power Zener diode, it can provide an output of several amps. When the full load is not being drawn, a large current passes through the diode, which is wasteful. The load regulation of this stabiliser is poor because the output voltage falls with increase of load current.

■ Series regulator

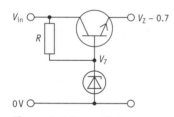

Figure 8.6 Zener diode stabiliser, with emitter follower to provide high-current output

The network of Fig. 8.6 has better load regulation than the simple stabiliser and also provides a high-current output without requiring a power diode. The network is known as a **series regulator**. The transistor is connected as a common-emitter amplifier. The base of the transistor is held at the constant Zener voltage V_Z and the output voltage is 0.7 V (the base–emitter voltage drop) less than the Zener voltage. The current through the Zener is small (5–10 mA), and is not affected by the amount of current (if any) being drawn by the load. This prevents the Zener voltage being affected by the amount of current through the Zener, and so provides good load regulation.

Component values for the series regulator are calculated as follows.

■ Select a 400 mW Zener diode with Zener voltage 0.7 V greater than the required output voltage.
■ Select a power BJT that will carry the required output current.
■ Assuming a current of 10 mA through the resistor, the required value of the resistor is:

$$R = (V_{in} - V_Z)/0.01$$

A Zener diode network may also be used to stabilise the dc supply from a battery, to obtain an output voltage that is not a multiple of the cell voltage.

■ Op amp series regulator

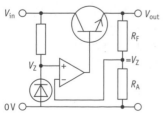

Figure 8.7 Op amp series voltage regulator

In Fig. 8.7 the Zener diode receives 5–10 mA through the series resistor under all load conditions, so the non-inverting input of the op amp is held at a constant Zener voltage. The actual output of the system is detected by using a potential divider network which feeds back a voltage that is proportional to V_{out}. Feedback is to the inverting input of the op amp, so this is negative feedback. If the load resistance decreases, the current increases, but the pd across the divider falls. The feedback voltage falls, too. This causes the output of the op amp to rise, so turning the transistor further on and supplying more current to the load.

This circuit uses the op amp as a non-inverting amplifier (see p. 85) and is stable when the voltages at the two inputs are equal:

$$V_{out} \times R_A/(R_F + R_A) = V_Z$$

Rearranging the equation gives:

$$V_{out} = V_Z(1 + R_F/R_A)$$

V_{out} can be regulated to any reasonable value, independently of the Zener voltage. A variable voltage regulator has a variable resistor in the feedback chain, to tap off the required feedback voltage.

■ Three-terminal regulator IC

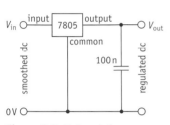

Figure 8.8 Network for a 3-terminal voltage regulator IC

The 7805 IC (see Fig. 8.8) is a typical 3-terminal regulator. The '05' in its type number indicates that it produces a regulated output of +5 V dc. Different types of regulator produce different regulated voltages with a precision of about ±4%. The regulation of any one type covers a wide range of supply voltages and output currents. For most types the supply voltage should be 2.5 V or more above the output voltage. The maximum supply voltage is 30 V to 40 V.

Regulators incorporate a **current-limiting** feature to protect the load from damage due to excess current. They also have **thermal shut-down**, by which the output current is cut off if the IC becomes overheated. This could happen as a result of a short circuit in the load circuit.

A 3-terminal regulator may also be used to regulate the dc supply from a battery, to obtain an output that is not a multiple of the cell voltage, and to protect the load from the effects of short-circuiting.

8·4 Short-circuit protection

Accidental short-circuiting of the output from a power supply unit may cause damage to the series transistor and possibly to other components. It may also cause damage in the load circuit. Output current may be limited to a safe maximum by the network outlined in Fig. 8.9.

Figure 8.9 Over-current protection

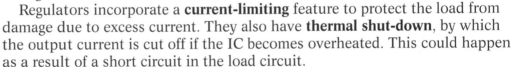
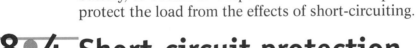

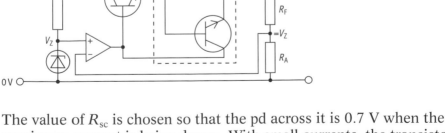

The value of R_{sc} is chosen so that the pd across it is 0.7 V when the maximum current is being drawn. With small currents, the transistor across which R_{sc} is connected is off. If the current exceeds the maximum, the transistor begins to turn on. This diverts current from the base of the series transistor, limiting the current it passes, even if the output of the circuit is shorted to ground.

The output voltage of the circuit is not affected by R_{sc} because the feedback is taken from a point nearer to the output terminals.

▌ Ten quick questions

1 What type of dc is produced by a diode rectifier?
2 When the mains is full-wave rectified, then smoothed, what is the frequency of the ripple?
3 What happens to ripple as the load increases?
4 A transformer is used to convert 230 V ac mains to 10 V ac. Its primary coil has 920 turns. How many turns has its secondary coil?
5 Name two safety features of a 3-terminal regulator.
6 If the load is fixed, what can be done to reduce ripple?
7 Why is the mains switch in a power supply a double-pole switch?
8 If the peak voltage of low-voltage ac is 12.5 V, what is its peak voltage after it has been full-wave rectified?
9 What is another name for a smoothing capacitor?
10 What quantity is used to express the amount by which the output voltage falls as load current increases?

▌ Questions on power supply systems

When selecting components that are made with a range of power ratings, choose the next higher rating for reliability.

1 Draw a diagram of a system to provide a 12 V, 0.5 A dc unregulated, half-wave rectified, smoothed supply, for powering a small model racing car. Suggest suitable component values.

2 Draw a diagram of a system to provide a 5 V, 1 A dc regulated supply for a small TTL logic circuit. Suggest suitable component values.

3 Draw a diagram of a power system to provide a 3 V, 400 mA dc Zener-stabilised power supply unit for powering a radio receiver. Suggest suitable component values.

4 **a)** Under no load, the mean output voltage of a power supply is 9 V. When the load is drawing the maximum current, the output voltage is 7.9 V. What is the load regulation of the system?

   b) Under no load, the mean output voltage of a power supply is 24 V. When the load is drawing the maximum current, the output voltage is 23.4 V. What is the load regulation of the system?

5 What are the advantages of an IC voltage regulator when compared with stabilisation by a Zener diode?

6 **a)** The output voltage of a Zener stabiliser increases with increased supply voltage, as shown in this table:

V_S	10	11	12	13	14	15
V_{out}	7.04	7.43	7.46	7.48	7.49	7.50

Calculate the line regulation over the useful output range.

   b) The output voltage of a Zener stabiliser increases with increased supply voltage, as shown in this table:

V_S	10	15	20	25	28
V_{out}	9.447	12.101	12.103	12.104	12.105

Calculate the line regulation over the useful output range.

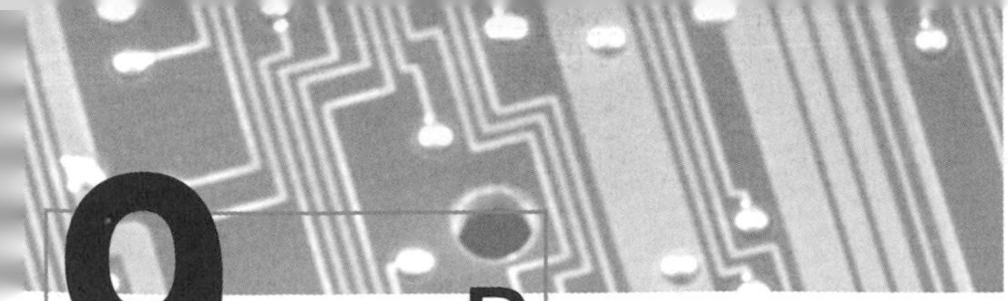

9 Power switching systems

In brief...

- Thyristors have several advantages for switching dc and ac (pp 107–109).
- Triacs switch ac in both half-cycles (p. 109).
- To isolate high voltages from low-voltage circuits we use pulse transformers and opto-isolators (p. 110).

Questions on power switching systems begin on p. 110, with answers on p. 174.

9•1 Thyristors

Thyristors and the way they work are described on pp 32–33. The advantages of a thyristor in switching dc or ac are:

- only a small positive pulse is needed to trigger it (about 1 V);
- only a fraction of a milliamp is needed to trigger it, so the triggering network can have fairly high output impedance;
- the thyristor has low resistance and the forward voltage drop when conducting is only about 1 V, so the driven device has almost the whole supply voltage across it;
- response is rapid (about 1 μs);
- it can be used for switching at high power (up to 1000 A at up to 1800 V, with a suitable thyristor). For safety, the switching control line runs from the gate of the thyristor back to a control panel, possibly in a separate control room. This carries only small triggering currents at low voltage.

■ Switching dc

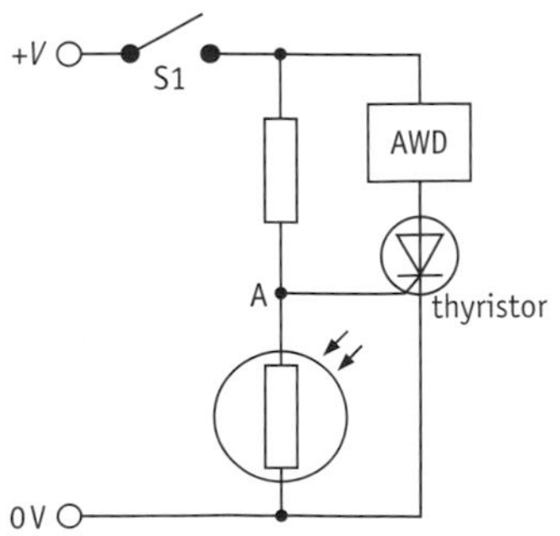

Fig. 9.1 shows an example of a network that uses a thyristor to switch on a dc-powered device. The circuit operates with S1 closed. If the LDR is briefly shaded, as when an intruder briefly breaks a beam of light directed at the LDR, its resistance increases and a high pulse is generated at A, triggering the thyristor into conduction. This switches on the audible warning device. Once triggered, the alarm sounds until S1 is opened.

The advantages of using a thyristor in this application are:

- rapid response to brief shading of the LDR;
- sensitivity to small drop in voltage;
- small triggering current required, so the high output impedance of the sensor network raises no problems.

■ Switching ac

Fig. 9.2 shows the circuit of a simple **half-wave controlled rectifier**. With ac, the thyristor is able to conduct only during positive half-cycles. It switches off at the end of every positive half-cycle, when the voltage across it is zero, so it has to be triggered to conduct at the beginning of every positive half-cycle. The circuit includes a potential divider that provides the triggering pulses. The voltage at point A is a sinusoid like the mains, but with a peak voltage

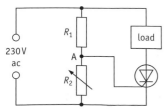

Figure 9.1 Triggering a thyristor by a fall in light level

Figure 9.2 Half-wave controlled rectifier

that is very much smaller and dependent on the setting of the variable resistor R_2. The voltage at A is zero when the half-cycle begins, then rises until the thyristor is triggered into conduction. The thyristor then conducts for the remainder of the half-cycle.

The time between the beginning of the half-cycle and triggering is known as the **firing angle** (Fig. 9.3). It is measured in degrees, the half-cycle being equivalent to 180°. The period for which the thyristor is conducting is known as the **conduction angle**:

conduction angle = 180° − firing angle

Figure 9.3 Typical output from a half-wave controlled rectifier

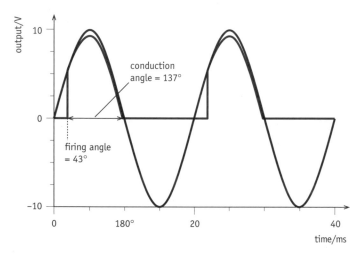

The firing angle is adjusted by setting R_2. If R_2 is set to a low resistance, it takes longer for the voltage at A to reach triggering level. The firing angle is greater, and less power is delivered to the load. The maximum firing angle is 90°.

A circuit such as this is used as a dimming control for a lamp or as a speed control for a motor. Its chief disadvantage is that it conducts only during the positive half-cycle and so can never deliver more than half power. Because of the maximum firing angle, it can never deliver less than a quarter power.

Fig. 9.4 shows a **full-wave controlled rectifier** circuit. The ac is full-wave rectified before coming under the control of the thyristor. All half-cycles are positive and the circuit can deliver up to full power to the load. The load is placed at either of two points in the circuit. A dc load is placed on the thyristor side of the rectifier. It receives pulsed dc, but the pulses begin at the firing angle (see Fig. 9.5 overleaf). As above, the maximum firing angle is 90°. It cannot deliver less than half power.

Figure 9.4 Full-wave controlled rectifier

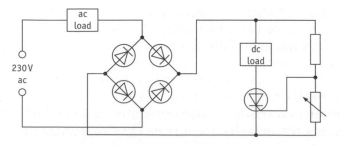

An ac load is placed on the mains side of the rectifier. It receives normal ac, but the half-cycles (both positive and negative) begin at the firing angle, with a maximum firing angle of 90°.

Figure 9.5 Typical output from a full-wave controlled rectifier

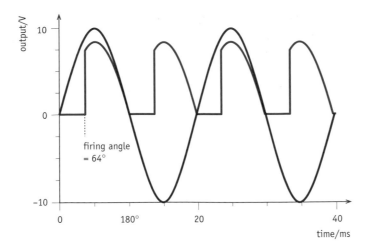

firing angle = 64°

Triggering with a potential divider, as in Figs 9.2 and 9.4, limits the maximum firing angle to 90° in each half-cycle. The power delivered to the load in each half-cycle can never be less than half the full power. Fig. 9.6 shows a way of triggering the thyristor so that the firing can occur at any time during the half-cycle. The resistor and the **commutating capacitor** produce a sinusoidal signal that lags behind the ac mains (compare with a lowpass filter network). The phase angle ϕ of the signal is given by:

$$\phi = \tan^{-1} R/X_C$$

where X_C is the reactance of the capacitor at the frequency at which the circuit is operating (50 Hz in this circuit).

The **diac** is similar in structure to a triac (p. 33) but has no gate terminal. It does not conduct at first, and voltage across it builds up to the threshold voltage (usually about 30 V). Then it suddenly begins to conduct, producing a pulse that triggers the thyristor. The pulse has a fast rise-time, is very short, and provides sufficient current; all these are ideal properties for triggering a thyristor. This circuit has the advantage over the potential divider networks of Figs 9.2 and 9.4 that the firing angle can be extended up to 180°. Because of this, the supply of power to the load is controllable over a wider range.

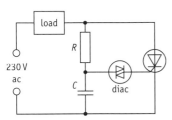

Figure 9.6 Triggering a thyristor with an *RC* network and diac

9•2 Triacs

Triacs and the way they work are described on p. 33. They are used in circuits similar to those described in subsection 9.1 above, though triacs are less often used in high-power circuits. The difficulty with triacs is that, since they conduct in both directions, there is only a short time while voltage is reversing for them to switch off. They may continue conducting and control of the triac fails. This can be overcome, but the circuits required are more complicated.

Fig. 9.7 shows a simple triac circuit. By varying R_1, the delay in the *RC* network can be set to trigger the triac at any time during the cycle. The diac produces a positive pulse during the positive half-cycle and a negative pulse during the negative half-cycle. The firing angle can be set to any value between 0° and 360°. This means that a lamp, for example, can be operated at any brightness from fully on to fully off.

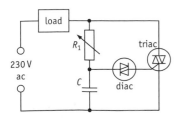

Figure 9.7 Triggering a triac with an *RC* network and diac

9·3 Isolation

Thyristors and triacs are triggered by low-voltage, low-current pulses, so they can easily be triggered by the output from a logic gate. Instead of the regular phase-controlled pulses used in the circuits described above, the thyristor or triac may switch high-powered circuits under the control of logic circuits, including computers. For example, such circuits control the speed of heavy-current motors in industrial machinery. The danger is that certain components may fail and result in high voltages finding their way into the low-voltage logic circuits. This may cause expensive damage to the logic circuit and possibly be hazardous to the operator. For safety, the control circuit must be electrically isolated from the high-power controlled circuit. This can be done by using a **pulse transformer** or an **opto-isolator**.

▌Pulse transformer

The output of the logic circuit is fed to the primary coil of a small transformer. The turns ratio is usually 1 : 1. The pulse from the logic circuit appears on the secondary coil, which is connected to the gate of the thyristor or triac. In a typical pulse transformer, the isolation between the primary and secondary coils can withstand 2000 V.

▌Opto-isolator

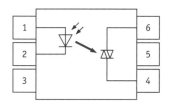

Figure 9.8 Opto-triac

An opto-isolator consists of an LED and a triac or thyristor, housed in a plastic package of the same kind as is used for integrated circuits (Fig. 9.8). The LED is switched on by a pulse from a logic or other low-power circuit. The light from the LED triggers the triac (or thyristor) into conduction. The triac controls the current in a high-power circuit. A typical 'opto-triac' can withstand 7500 V between the LED and the triac. The triac is rated at a maximum voltage of 240 V ac and a maximum current of 100 mA.

▌Ten quick questions

1. What term is used to describe the time difference between the start of a half-cycle and the time that a thyristor is triggered?
2. In a power-control circuit, when does the thyristor stop conducting?
3. What is the turns ratio of a typical pulse transformer?
4. If a thyristor is triggered by a 2-resistor potential divider, what is the maximum firing angle?
5. If the firing angle of a power control circuit is 75°, what is the conduction angle?
6. What is the purpose of a pulse transformer?
7. Name the 2-terminal component that is similar to a triac.
8. Name the terminals of a triac.
9. What is the forward voltage drop of a thyristor when it is conducting?
10. What is the advantage of using a resistance–capacitor network to trigger a triac, compared with using a potential divider?

▌ Questions on power switching systems

1 Describe a half-wave controlled rectifier circuit based on a thyristor, illustrating your answer with a circuit diagram.

2 Draw a graph of the output of the half-wave rectifier described in question 1, marking the firing angle and conduction angle on it.

3 Explain how **a)** a potential divider and **b)** a resistor–capacitor network are used to trigger a thyristor. Compare the advantages of the two techniques.

4 Design a sound-activated thyristor circuit to switch on a dc fan motor (component values not required). Describe how it works. The circuit should provide for switching off the motor manually.

5 Describe the structure and operation of a triac opto-isolator. What are the reasons for using this device?

6 Compare the action of **a)** a thyristor; **b)** a triac; **c)** a diac.

7 Explain the advantage of using an RC network to trigger a thyristor, instead of using a potential divider. If the frequency is 50 Hz, $R = 220\,\text{k}\Omega$ and $C = 15\,\text{nF}$, what is the phase delay?

8 Given that the capacitor in a thyristor circuit has a value 47 nF and the frequency of the ac is 60 Hz, what value of resistor is required to produce a phase lag of 60°?

10 Analogue control systems

In brief...

■ Analogue control systems are classified as open-loop systems (having no feedback, p. 112), closed-loop on–off systems (with negative feedback and on–off output switching, p. 112) and closed-loop proportional systems (with negative feedback and an output proportional to the error signal, p. 113).

■ Such systems are used for the control of temperature (p. 114), rotational speed and position (pp 114–115).

■ Some terms used when describing analogue control systems are defined and explained (pp 115–116).

Questions on analogue control systems are on p. 116, with answers on p. 174.

10·1 Types of analogue control system

■ Open-loop system

Fig. 10.1 shows the stages in an open-loop control system. As an example of this, Fig. 10.2 below it shows a system in which an operator is controlling an electric drill. The drill has a switch and, by closing or opening this, the operator activates the drill motor.

Figure 10.1 Open-loop control system

Figure 10.2 Controlling the speed of an electric drill; an example of an open-loop control system

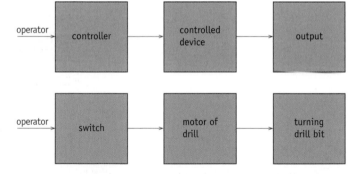

This is a simple, inexpensive on–off system. The drill might also have a variable resistor to control the speed of rotation of the bit.

■ Closed-loop on–off system

Fig. 10.3 shows a closed-loop on–off control system. A sensor measures the output. The comparator compares the voltage output v_o from the sensor with the set point (or reference) voltage v_s (previously set by the operator). The comparator sends a feedback signal to the processor, which results in the controlled device being turned either on or off. Feedback is negative:

■ if $v_o > v_s$, feedback acts to reduce v_o;
■ if $v_o < v_s$, feedback acts to increase v_o.

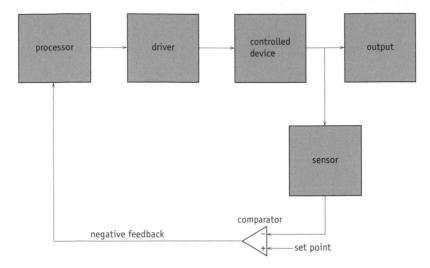

Figure 10.3 Closed-loop on–off control system

As an example of this, Fig. 10.4 shows an electronic thermostat system. This holds the temperature of a room (or oven, refrigerator, greenhouse) constant. The processor stage is a BJT or MOSFET used to switch a relay off or on, depending on whether the output from the comparator is high or low. This system is designed on the assumption that it continuously loses heat to the surroundings; it is not able to reduce the temperature if it is too high.

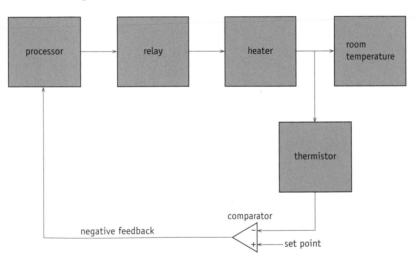

Figure 10.4 A thermostat system; an example of a closed-loop on–off control system

▌ Closed-loop proportional system

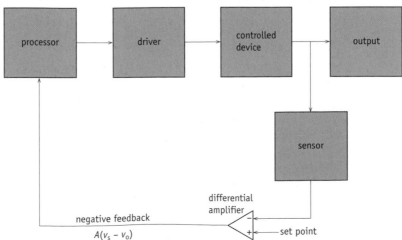

Figure 10.5 Closed-loop proportional control system

Fig. 10.5 shows a closed-loop proportional control system. The comparator of Fig. 10.4 is replaced by a differential amplifier. The magnitude of the negative feedback signal is proportional to the difference between the output and the set point. The greater the difference, the larger the signal sent by the processor to the controlled device, which is made to change the output more rapidly.

An example is a thermostat system with proportional control, illustrated in Fig. 10.6. The processor consists of a pulse generator. This produces pulses with a mark–space ratio proportional to the negative feedback signal. The relay and the heater are switched on by these pulses. If the room is cool (that is, if there is a relatively large difference between v_o and v_s), the mark–space ratio is raised, so that the heater is on for a larger proportion of the time. This means that it heats the room more rapidly. As the room gets closer and closer to the set temperature, the mark–space ratio falls and the rate of heating is gradually reduced. Gradually, the room temperature approaches the set point. Like the on–off system, this system is designed on the assumption that it continuously loses heat to the surroundings; it is not able to reduce the temperature if it is too high.

Figure 10.6 A thermostat system; an example of a closed-loop proportional control system

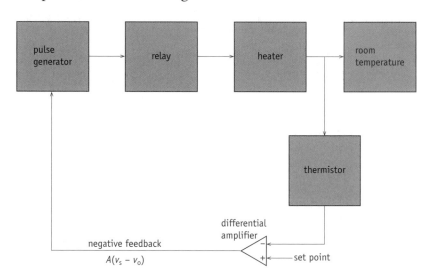

10·2 Further examples of analogue control systems

▌ Rotational speed control

An open-loop system has already been illustrated in Fig. 10.2. The problem with this system is the same as in most open-loop systems: there is no feedback. The control circuit has no way of responding to changes in external conditions. In this example, the rotational speed of the drill depends partly on the varying mechanical resistance that the bit has to overcome when drilling. This may vary according to the hardness of the material, the depth of the hole, and other factors.

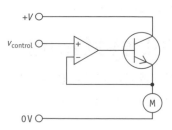

Figure 10.7 Motor speed-control system with negative feedback

The circuit in Fig. 10.7 shows a way of providing negative feedback. The transistor amplifies the output from the op amp, so that there is sufficient current to drive the motor. The voltage at the positive terminal of the motor is fed back to the inverting input of the op amp. This is negative feedback.

To control the speed of the motor, the operator varies the control voltage $v_{control}$. As in a non-inverting amplifier circuit, the op amp continuously adjusts its output so that the voltages at both its inputs are equal. The voltage across the motor is held equal to $v_{control}$, in spite of changes in back emf caused by variations in the mechanical load on the motor.

■ **Position control**

A potentiometer is used as in Fig. 3.13 (p. 35) to sense the linear position of an object. The object might be part of a machine, such as tool-holder on a lathe. The potentiometer wiper is mechanically linked to the tool-holder. A reversible motor moves the tool-holder along a fixed track. The position of the object on the track is represented by the voltage V_{out} from the potentiometer. This is fed back to a differential amplifier in an on–off closed-loop control system similar to that used in the thermostat with proportional control (Fig. 10.6). However, proportional control might not be appropriate in such an application. The only information the processor stage needs is whether V_{out} is greater than, less than or equal to $v_{control}$. If they are equal, no current is supplied to the motor. Current is supplied if they are unequal and its direction is such as to reduce the difference between V_{out} and $v_{control}$. This is negative feedback. The motor moves the tool-holder in one direction or the other until $V_{out} = v_{control}$.

In certain systems, a problem arises with overshoot. Owing to delays or inertia in the system, the tool-holder is moved past the intended position. Then the motor is automatically reversed to bring it back to the intended position. It may overshoot again several times. It oscillates about the intended position, perhaps indefinitely. This is called **hunting**. It is avoided if the system has a **dead band** on both sides of the intended position. The motor is switched off when V_{out} is close to $v_{control}$, even if it is not exactly equal.

A position control system such as this is called a **servo system**. It differs from a regulator in that the set point is not fixed (or at least fixed temporarily) but is continually being altered, either by an operator or automatically. As the set point changes, the system alters its output accordingly.

The same principles are applied to angular position control using a rotary potentiometer. A **servomotor** is a reversible electric motor with reduction gearing that moves a lever slowly through an angle of a few tens of degrees. The lever is mechanically coupled to the mechanism of the system being controlled.

Servomotors are often used in adjusting the angle of the flight control surfaces in aeroplanes, and are also used for moving the limbs of robots. The rotary potentiometer is on the same spindle as the lever, so its output voltage represents the position of the mechanism. The feedback from the rotary potentiometer is used in the same way as described above for the linear potentiometer, to bring the mechanism to the intended angular position.

10·3 Describing analogue control systems

Some terms used when describing analogue control systems are now explained.

Error signal   The voltage signal $(v_s - v_o)$ fed back from the comparator or differential amplifier to the processor.

Bang-bang control   An alternative name for on–off control.

Reference voltage   An alternative name for the set point.

Hysteresis A property of Schmitt trigger and similar circuits. The threshold voltage for change is higher when input is increasing, and lower when input is decreasing. This is a useful property in control systems as it avoids the system oscillating around the set point. Many systems have hysteresis built in to them, either by the use of Schmitt trigger circuits or logic gates with Schmitt inputs.

▌ Ten quick questions

1 What do we call the signal fed back from the comparator to the processor stage of a control system?
2 State another name for on–off control.
3 What is the 'dead band'?
4 What do we call the type of system in which the output is controlled by altering the set point?
5 What is the main characteristic of a proportional control system?
6 A heat-seeking missile gradually homes on its target. What type of control system does it have?
7 What is the essential feature of feedback in a closed-loop control system?
8 A motor is connected into the collector circuit of a BJT, and its speed is controlled by varying the base current. What type of control system is this?
9 What is an alternative name for the set point?
10 In what way does an open-loop system differ from a closed-loop system?

▌ Questions on analogue control systems

1 Describe an example of an open-loop control system, and how it works. What is the chief advantage of such a system?

2 What is meant by negative feedback? Illustrate your answer by references to a closed-loop control system.

3 Describe an example of a closed-loop proportional system to control the rotational speed of a motor. Suggest an application for such a system.

4 Describe *two* factors that might cause the output of a closed-loop system to oscillate rapidly about the set point. What can be done to avoid this?

5 **a)** What is a servo system? How does it differ from a regulator?
  b) Describe how a servomotor is used to control the angular position of the elevators in a model aeroplane.

11 Digital control systems

In brief...

- Hardwired systems are reliable for simple tasks, but are not easy to correct or amend (p. 117).
- Microprocessor systems are flexible and able to perform complex tasks. They comprise a central processing unit (CPU), a system clock, memory, and several input and output devices linked to the CPU by address, data and control busses (pp 118–120).
- Microcontroller systems, too, are flexible and able to perform complex tasks. Their structure is similar to that of microprocessor systems, except that the CPU, memory and some other units are all on the same chip (pp 120–121).
- The memory map of a system shows where data and programs are stored, and which areas are available for use in computations (p. 121).
- The CPU is the heart of the system. It receives input from the rest of the system, performs arithmetical and logical operations, and directs its output to other units in the system (p. 122).
- The actions of the system are directed by one or more programs. A program consists of a sequence of instructions to be executed by the CPU (pp 122–124).
- A person programming a system uses a special language, such as assembler, BASIC or ladder logic. Special software is used to convert these programs into machine code to be run by the processor (pp 124–125).
- Flowcharts are an important first step when writing a program (p. 125).

Questions on digital control systems and programming begin on p. 125, with answers from p. 174.

11·1 Hardwired systems

A hardwired control system is based on one or more active devices such as transistors and logic gates. It often has one or more sensors as its input, and an actuator as its output. The sensor may be an analogue device such as a light-dependent resistor, but its output is read in binary fashion, to find out if it is above or below a given set point, and not as an analogue quantity. The output of the system is usually binary. The actuator is switched either on or off.

There are many examples of hardwired control systems in this book:

- Fig. 4.25 (p. 57) is an intruder detection system;
- Fig. 5.12 (p. 67) controls a seven-segment display;
- Fig. 5.19 (p. 70) is a binary up counter, which forms part of many systems;
- Fig. A4.4 (p. 164) is a thermostat;
- Fig. A5.3 (p. 166) is a surveillance control system;
- Fig. A9.1 (p. 174) is a sound-sensitive motor switch.

Hardwired control systems perform a wide range of simple tasks (and those described in this book are simpler than average). Dishwashers, washing machines, sliding doors and automatic car-park barriers can be put under hardwired digital control. They rely on logic gates and other more complex logic ICs for their control functions.

Designing, building and testing a hardwired system takes time and is expensive. There is the disadvantage that, once it is designed and built, it cannot easily be altered. Part of the system might need to be redesigned if it proves unreliable in use, or if new improved features are to be added, or if it is decided to substitute a different type of sensor or actuator. Such modifications are likely to involve laying out the circuit board differently. This can be as costly and take almost as much time as producing the original design. This is much less of a problem with microprocessor systems, described below.

11·2 Microprocessor systems

In a microprocessor system, software replaces most of the hardware. The only hardware items required are the sensors, the actuators and their interfaces to the system. Fig. 11.1 illustrates the parts of a microprocessor system and how they are connected. This diagram is based on the items found in a typical microcomputer. In more specialist systems, for example an automatic pilot system for an aircraft, some of these items are not required but other types of unit, not shown in the diagram, may be necessary.

Figure 11.1 Main parts of a typical microprocessor system

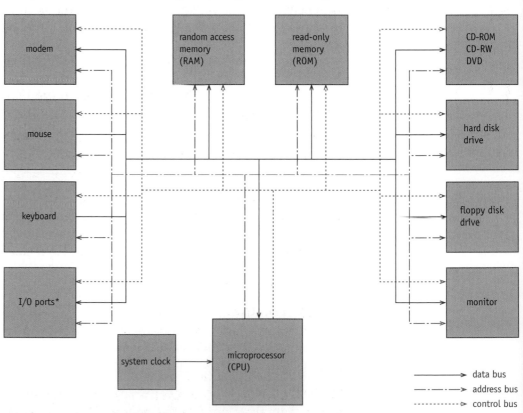

*printer port, serial ports, universal serial bus

The functions of the different parts of a microprocessor system are now described.

▌ Central processing unit (CPU)

The CPU consists of a microprocessor chip that performs all the logical and arithmetical operations of the system. Commonly used types are the Intel *Pentium 4* and the AMD *Athlon XP* processors. Operation of the processor is described in subsection 11.5.

■ System clock

The system clock is an astable that synchronises the actions of all parts of the system. The astable runs at frequencies up to 3 GHz, or sometimes higher.

■ Read-only memory (ROM)

The ROM consists of ICs containing numerous data registers that store data permanently. It is programmed either during its manufacture or in a special programming operation at a later stage (see subsection 11.6). In a general-purpose system such as a microcomputer, the ROM holds the program used to bring the system into operation when it is first switched on. In a specialist system such as a washing machine, the ROM holds the program for all the activities that the machine performs.

A microcomputer may have up to 512 MB (megabytes) of ROM, but systems with special abilities, such as fast 3D graphics, may have up to 1 GB.

■ Random access memory (RAM)

This consists of data registers that store data temporarily. The data is lost when the system is switched off. Data may be loaded into the registers (written) or read from the registers at any time. Data stored here includes programs or parts of programs currently being run, data generated during arithmetical or logical operations, and reference data (look-up tables).

■ Off-line data storage

The system may have one or more units used for the mass storage of data. The data is read from this store and placed into RAM when required for processing. Types of storage include the following.

Hard disk drive   This stores large amounts of data (up to 120 GB), with fast access. The drive contains a stack of disks coated with magnetic film, and is sealed to exclude dust. It is not usually removable from the system.

CD-ROM drive   This reads data stored on a compact disc, typically 650 MB. Data is represented by microscopic dimples in a thin metallic film. CD-ROMs cannot be written to, but CD-R (recordable) and CD-RW (re-writable) discs can be written to as well as read, if the system has a CD-RW drive. Some systems have drives that read data from digital versatile discs (DVDs). Access is fast with all of these.

Floppy disk drive   This stores 1.44 MB of data on a thin plastic disk coated with magnetic film. Access to this is relatively slow, and floppy disks are less often used than formerly.

■ Input peripherals

Peripheral devices interface the system to the outside world. Input peripherals accept data from outside the system. There is usually a keyboard and often a mouse. Some systems have input sockets that accept audio (analogue) signals from a microphone or an audio system. Systems may have special input peripherals. For example, a supermarket computer system has input from a laser bar-code reader and from a weighing platform at every checkout.

■ Output peripherals

The most important output peripheral is usually the video monitor or some form of LCD display. There may also be loudspeakers and an audio signal output socket.

■ Input/output (I/O) ports

These provide two-way communication with the outside world. A modem (modulator–demodulator), for example, makes a connection to a telephone line. I/O ports are data storage ICs connected to sockets by which they communicate with external equipment, such as a printer or external disk drives. These connections are usually parallel, so that data is transmitted and received a byte at a time. Serial sockets are used for equipment such as a digital camera or a scanner, for which the slower serial (one bit at a time) communication is acceptable.

■ Busses

All the units above are connected to the CPU by busses. These are sets of 8, 16, or more parallel lines, or conductors, along which data is transmitted in parallel. There are three types of bus, as illustrated in Fig. 11.1, p. 118.

Address bus This carries the address of a memory register, which the CPU puts on the bus by setting the appropriate lines to low (usually 0 V) or high (usually 5 V) logic levels. The addressed device then responds. The width of the bus (that is, the number of lines) is the number required to cover all the addresses on the memory map (see subsection 11.4).

Data bus This is used for one-way communication between the CPU and input units, such as the keyboard. It is also used for two-way communication between the CPU and memory, ports and data storage drives. It may happen that several units are trying to put data on to the bus at the same time. To avoid such **bus contention**, each unit is connected to the data bus by **three-state outputs**. When the three-state outputs are enabled (by a control signal from the CPU), they take up either a low or a high output state, in the usual way. When the outputs are disabled, the logic voltage does not appear at the output. Instead, the output pin goes to a **high-impedance state**, in which it is, in effect, disconnected from the bus. The operating system ensures that the outputs of only one device are enabled at a time. The width of the data bus is the same as the number of bits in a **word**. A word is the unit of data used in the system; it may be 8 bits (a byte), 12 bits, 16 bits (two bytes) or more long.

Control bus This carries control signals from the CPU to other devices in the system.

11•3 Microcontroller systems

Microcontroller systems have an architecture similar to that of computer systems, except that most parts of the system are on the same chip. The microcontroller is a single IC with perhaps 20 to 40 pins, some with as few as 8 pins, and some with more. It contains a chip that has on it the CPU, the clock, the memory (both ROM and RAM) and several other devices, such as an analogue-to-digital converter. The size of ROM and RAM are much smaller than in computer systems. Often they have only 1 or 2 kilobytes of ROM, and perhaps only 64 bytes of RAM.

A vast range of microcontrollers is available from manufacturers such as Microchip (the PIC family) and Atmel (the AVR family). They have different selections of on-chip devices, and differing amounts of ROM and RAM, so it is usually possible to find a controller suited to any given application. Usually a controller is supplied with its ROM blank, but it is possible to have a particular operating program put into ROM during manufacture. A manufacturer of electronic kitchen scales, for example, is able to buy quantities of a given type of microcontroller pre-programmed with the program written specifically for operating the machine.

During the development of a microcontroller system, the operating program is written using a microcomputer running special software. The microcontroller is plugged into a programming board that is connected to the computer. The programmer writes a section of program, then downloads it into the ROM of the microcontroller for testing. The ROM is electrically erasable. The program is run, step by step, to check that its action is correct. If alterations are needed, the program in the computer is modified, then the new version is downloaded to the ROM for testing again.

A variation on this procedure is to write the program using 'emulator' software. This software behaves just as the microcontroller would behave. All writing, testing and modifying is done on the computer. The program is downloaded into the microcontroller only when it is complete and fully tested.

The biggest difference between the architecture of microprocessor systems and that of microcontroller systems is in their input/output terminals. Microprocessors communicate through complex devices such as keyboards, modems, monitors and port ICs. Microcontrollers communicate through their I/O pins. Most of the pins of a microcontroller are I/O pins. They are configurable to act either as inputs or outputs. As inputs they are 1-bit inputs, capable of receiving signals from the 1-bit devices described on pp 61–62. As outputs, they provide 1-bit control of actuators and indicators. A typical output buffer can source up to 20 mA per pin, or sink up to 25 mA. A current of 20 mA is enough to drive actuators cither directly or through transistor switches.

Occasionally, the controller is connected to a 4-bit or 8-bit device and then it is possible to program a group of pins as a 4-bit or 8-bit port, instead of having to program the pins individually.

11•4 Memory map

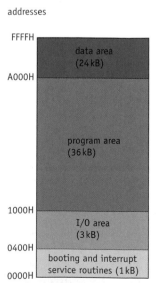

addresses

Figure 11.2 Memory map of a small microprocessor control system (not to scale)

The layout of memory is represented as a map. The details of a map vary widely from one microprocessor or microcontroller to another (we shall call them both 'controllers' from now on as they both operate in a very similar way). Fig. 11.2 shows the main features of a hypothetical memory map. The map covers hexadecimal addresses 0000H to FFFFH, that is, 64 kilobytes of memory space. The binary equivalent of FFFFH is 1111 1111 1111 1111, so 16 lines are required in the address bus.

In the example shown, the lowest 1 kB of memory is occupied by ROM. Here programs are stored for starting up the system. The processor automatically goes to this area when it is first switched on. The booting program tells it where to go next to find the first instruction in the main program. Interrupt service routines are also stored here (see p. 123).

Just above the ROM is an area reserved for input and output. This is not memory but modems, I/O ports, disk drives and similar devices have addresses within this area. The devices have data registers in them that can be written to or read from in a similar way to memory. The area is not fully occupied with devices, so leaving room for adding new devices to the system.

The program memory is usually the largest area. It may consist of blocks of ROM chips in systems that are dedicated to one particular application. In a microcomputer this area is RAM so that any program can be downloaded into this area and run. A new computer may not have RAM chips for the full range of addresses, leaving the option open to expand RAM in the future.

At the top of the memory map is the data area. This is RAM, and is used by the processor for temporary storage of data such as intermediate values in a calculation, and for tables of data required during the current program.

11·5 The CPU

The central processing unit (the microprocessor, or the CPU section of a microcontroller) contains data registers linked by internal busses. It works at a rate set by the system clock. Registers are 8, 16 bits wide, or wider. The registers are:

▌ **accumulator**: holds values (arithmetic or logic) that are to be operated on;
▌ **program counter**: its content is increased by 1 every time an opcode (see subsection 11.6 below) is read from memory, so it holds the address of the opcode that is to be read next;
▌ **instruction register**: holds the opcode that the CPU is working on;
▌ **stack pointer**: holds the address of the top of the stack (see opposite);
▌ **status register**: individual bits (called flags) indicate that certain events have occurred; for example, the **zero flag** is set to 1 if a calculation gives zero as its result;
▌ **general-purpose registers**: there may be several of these.

Microprocessors also have:

▌ **data bus register**: holds data on its way to or from the data bus;
▌ **address bus register**: holds an address ready to put on the address bus.

The **arithmetic/logic unit** (ALU) operates on data in the accumulator, often using data stored in other registers. The ALU is able to add, subtract, increment or decrement the values in the accumulator, and perform logical operations such as AND, OR and INVERT. Flags in the status register are set or reset as a result of some of its operations.

The description above applies to most types of controller, but many differ in detail.

11·6 Programs

A program is a sequence of binary codes, known as **opcodes**, stored in RAM or ROM. Opcodes may consist of a single byte (8 bits) but the more recent controllers operate on opcodes of 12, 16 or more bits. Each different code causes the controller to perform a particular operation. The CPU runs through the sequence of opcodes one at a time, in a **fetch–execute cycle**:

▌ put the address in the program counter onto the address bus;
▌ enable RAM or ROM to put the instruction (opcode) stored at that address on to the data bus;
▌ put the instruction on the data bus into the instruction register;
▌ execute the instruction.

Executing an instruction may involve reading further data from memory, performing operations in the ALU and storing data in memory.

Other terms connected with programs will now be explained.

Jump   Instead of working through the sequence of opcodes from one address to the next, a new address is placed in the program register, making the CPU jump to an address later or earlier in the sequence. It continues reading sequentially from the new address. A jump may be **non-conditional** or **conditional**. An example of a conditional jump is 'jump if zero'. If the previous calculation gave a zero result (that is, if the zero flag is 1), a new address is put in the program counter and the CPU jumps to a different part of the program and continues from the new address. Otherwise, the program counter is incremented in the usual way and the CPU goes to the next address in sequence. Jumping is sometimes referred to as 'branching'.

Stack   Microprocessors set aside a small area of RAM for use as a stack. Important data is stored here on a last-in-first-out basis. When data is put on the stack, it is added to the top of the stack (the highest address) and the stack pointer is incremented. When the top item of data is taken off, the stack pointer is decremented. The stack is often used for briefly storing an intermediate value in a calculation. It is also used to store the current state of certain CPU registers when the CPU goes to a subroutine or responds to an interrupt. The CPU 'pushes' the contents of its accumulator, the program counter and the status register onto the stack. When it returns, it 'pops' these items off the stack, in the reverse order, back into its registers.

Subroutine   This is a short program segment that is frequently used during the running of a program. For example, a program may need to read data at one of the input ports every few minutes. The routine for accessing the port and reading the data can be programmed once as a subroutine, instead of repeating the program segment every time it occurs. When data is to be read, the CPU is made to jump to the subroutine. However, before jumping, it saves its current data on the stack. It executes the subroutine, then recovers its data from the stack (including the address from the program counter) and jumps back to its previous step in the program.

Look-up table   This is an array of stored data that is accessed in a systematic way. For example, the table may be the ten codes for producing the numerals 0 to 9 on a 7-segment display. If the base address of the table is C100H and holds the code for '0', the CPU obtains the code for '7' by reading address C107H.

Direct and indirect addressing   In direct addressing mode, the instruction tells the CPU the actual address it is to access for data. In indirect addressing mode, the instruction tells the CPU to look in a given indirect address, where it will find the address that it is to access. A direct address is a fixed item in the program. However, the program can change the address stored in the indirect address by storing a new address there. In this way, the CPU is made to access different addresses on different occasions.

Interrupts   The normal operation of the program is interrupted when the CPU receives an interrupt signal along a line of the control bus. It receives interrupts from various sources:

▍ **clocked interrupts**: if the system includes a real-time clock, this can be set to interrupt the CPU at regular intervals (say, once a minute) or at a given time or date. The CPU saves its current data on the stack, then jumps to an interrupt service routine (ISR). There may be several of these; the one it jumps to depends on what source caused the interrupt.

▌ **peripherals**: the keyboard, the printer and other parts of the system can interrupt the main program. For example, the keyboard interrupts the program when a key-press is detected.

▌ **processing errors**: an example of this is when a calculation requires division by a given variable and on that occasion the variable is equal to zero. This is impossible to calculate, and an internal interrupt causes the CPU to stop operating. The ISR causes the display of an error message (such as 'Division by zero error').

Polling This is used in some systems instead of interrupts. In polling, each device that may need to send data to the CPU has a register containing an **interrupt flag**. When a device needs to interrupt the CPU, it sets this flag. At regular intervals, the CPU contacts each device in turn to find out if its flag is set. If it is set, the CPU goes to the appropriate ISR. If more than one device is trying to interrupt, the one with the highest priority is selected. Polling is a simple system but is slower than using interrupts, since the CPU has to access all the devices in turn. The delay may make the CPU too late to respond, and the system may crash because of this.

11•7 Programming languages

Controllers are generally programmed by inserting the IC into a socket on a programming board, which is connected to a computer. Software in the computer allows the user to key in the program and then download it into the memory of the controller. It may be run to check that it is working properly and, if it is not, it may be altered and rechecked until it works. The program is then permanently stored in the controller. After this, the controller is removed from the programming board, with the final version of the program permanently stored in its memory. It is plugged into its socket on the circuit board of the appliance that it is to control.

The program may be written using a number of different languages, depending on the software.

▌ Machine code

Machine code consists of the actual opcodes of the controller's instruction set. The code is usually expressed in hexadecimal and is keyed into the programming board in this form. This is the most direct form of programming but, because the codes bear little obvious relationship to the CPU actions they result in, writing programs in machine code is very difficult and subject to a high level of error.

▌ Assembler

An assembler program is written by using **mnemonics**, which are abbreviations of the programming commands. The code also includes **operands**, which are numerical values, addresses and other data that the CPU needs to act on. Mnemonics usually consist of 3 to 5 letters and are relatively easy to learn and remember. The software automatically converts the mnemonics and associated operands into machine code before downloading it into the memory of the controller.

▪ BASIC

BASIC is one of many **high-level languages**, so-called because they use familiar English words as commands. However, although the words are familiar, the syntax of the language must be strictly followed if the controller is to 'understand' the program. The software automatically converts the BASIC program into machine code before downloading it into the memory of the controller.

▪ Ladder logic

Ladder logic is a special language used for programming certain types of programmable logic controller. The sequence of operations is expressed by various symbols and by the way they are connected. A typical program has the appearance of a ladder. Ladder logic is relatively easy to learn; it was first devised for use by engineers who are not expert computer programmers.

11•8 Flowcharts

Setting out a flowchart is usually the first stage in writing a program. It provides a map of the different steps in the program and how they are linked. It helps clear thinking about what is the best approach, and it makes it easier to check that the program will do what is intended.

Flowcharts are built up from boxes connected by arrows to show the paths that may be taken through the flowchart. Different kinds of box are used for different types of operation (Fig. 11.3).

Figure 11.3 Types of box used in flowcharts

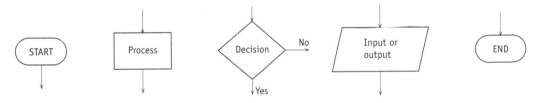

Examples of flowcharts are given in the questions and answers at the end of this section.

▪ Ten quick questions

1. What do we call a binary code that the CPU stores in its instruction register?
2. What is a 'flag'?
3. For what name is 'RAM' a short form?
4. What is the main difference between RAM and ROM?
5. Name *three* forms of off-line storage of data.
6. What is the name for a set of parallel lines that each carry one bit of a data word?
7. If the highest address in the memory of a system is 03FFH, how many lines are required in the address bus?
8. What is the main disadvantage of a hardwired system compared with a system based on a microprocessor or microcontroller?
9. Name the three states of a three-state output.
10. What is an ISR?

▌ Questions on digital control systems

1 Describe the operation of the stack of a microprocessor and its uses.

2 What happens when an interrupt occurs in a program? Compare the processing of an interrupt with 'polling'.

3 Explain what is meant by the terms *bit*, *byte* and *word*.

4 What is a 'look-up table'? Give an example of the use of a look-up table in a program.

5 Draw a diagram of a typical microprocessor system.

6 What is meant by 'bus contention'? How is this prevented?

7 Explain the difference between ROM and RAM in a microcontroller, and list their uses.

8 Describe the operation of the fetch–execute cycle in a microprocessor.

9 Draw the memory map of a typical microprocessor or microcontroller system and explain the functions of the different areas.

10 What is a program? Illustrate your answer by a short segment of a program, written in a language of your own choice.

Note The remaining questions are about programming, using flowcharts. In questions 11 to 16, you are asked to devise a program segment to perform a given function. Programs should be written so that they can be implemented on a microprocessor or microcontroller system. Only an outline program is required, not the details of machine-code operations. Use names (labels) to represent variables. Details of interfaces and external circuits are not required. In questions 17 to 20, you are given the flowchart and asked to comment on what it does.

11 Write a flowchart program for a security system that sounds a siren for approximately 5 minutes when any one of three infrared sensors is triggered.

12 Write a flowchart program to count the cars entering a car park and to switch on a 'Full' sign when there are 8 cars in the park. Assume that there are no cars to begin with, and that cars do not leave the park.

13 In a cheese-packing factory, blocks of cheese are passed along a conveyor belt. At one point on the belt there is a weighing platform. The weighing circuit has an 8-bit binary output to give the weight to the nearest gram. After leaving the platform, the blocks of cheese pass over an electrically operated flap. This can be lowered momentarily to divert a block into a reject bin. Devise a program to weigh each block as it passes along the belt and reject it if it weighs less than 200 g or more than 215 g, and to sound a 1-second 'beep' every time a block is rejected.

14 A wind direction vane has an optical encoder on its shaft (Fig. 11.4). This is a transparent disc with an opaque pattern printed on it. Three photodiodes receive light from the three LEDs on the opposite side of the disc. From information about which photodiodes are receiving light at any instant, the position of the disc is read to the nearest 45°. The pattern in which the sectors are marked conforms to a Gray code. Only one bit changes as the disc turns from one position to the next. This eliminates intermediate states.

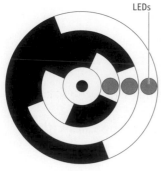

LEDs

Figure 11.4 Optical shaft encoder

The display consists of eight LEDs, labelled 'N', 'NE', 'E', and so on, to indicate wind direction. The function of the control system is to indicate the present wind direction by turning on the corresponding LED. A beeper sounds for 2 s when the wind changes direction. Design the program.

15 An on–off system for a greenhouse switches on a heater as the greenhouse cools below the set point and switches it off when the temperature exceeds the set point. It also switches on a warning lamp if the temperature falls below 4 °C. The temperature is measured by a thermistor network that feeds its voltage output to a DAC. Design the program for this system, assuming that the value of the set point is programmed into the system. Assume that the temperature is read in degrees Celsius. The program should include hysteresis.

16 When the control button is pressed, an electronic 'dice roller' displays the patterns for scores 1 to 6 repeatedly at high speed. The display consists of seven LEDs, and it changes too fast for the player to read the pattern. The display freezes when the same button is pressed a second time and held, giving in effect a random throw. Releasing the button starts the rapid display routine again. Design the circuit. There is no need to specify the codes used for obtaining particular patterns.

17 The flowchart of a system is shown in Fig. 11.5. p. 128. The input to the system is a button that gives a '0' output when not pressed and a '1' output when pressed. It is connected to a pin in Port B which has been labelled *button*. The outputs are three lamps, switched by BJTs, connected to data lines D0 to D2 of Port A. Describe the action of the system, and a possible application.

18 The flowchart of a system is shown in Fig. 11.6, p. 128. There is no input to the system. The output of the system is an 8-bit DAC connected to the 8 bits of Port A. Describe the action of the system.

19 The flowchart of a system is shown in Fig. 11.7, p. 128. The input to the system is a button that gives a '0' output when not pressed and a '1' output when pressed. It is connected to a pin labelled *button*. The output of the system is an LED turned on by a '1' to the pin labelled *LED*. Describe the action of the system.

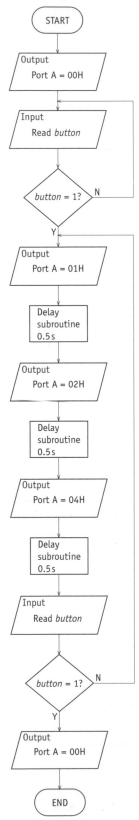

Figure 11.5

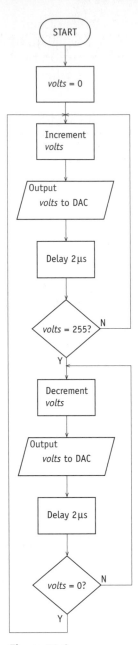

Figure 11.6

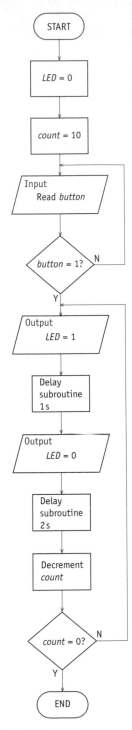

Figure 11.7

12 Audio systems

In brief... ■ A domestic audio system has signal sources, source selection, pre-amplifier, volume and tone controls, a power amplifier, and one or more speakers (pp 129–131).
■ Signal transfers may be for maximum voltage or for maximum power (pp 132–133).
■ A public address system is similar to a domestic system, but has more signal sources and the facility to mix them (p. 134).

Questions on audio systems are on p. 135, with answers on p. 179.

12•1 Domestic audio system

A typical domestic audio system is illustrated in Fig. 12.1. Except for the signal sources, the units are duplicated to carry the left and right stereo channels, but this is not shown in the diagram. The functions of the units are described below.

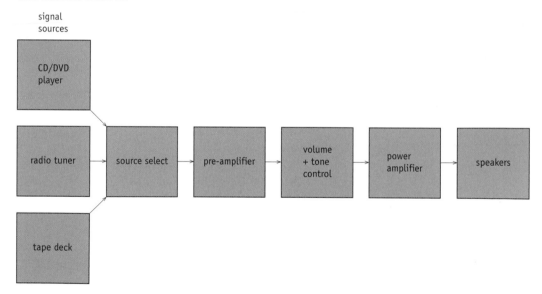

Figure 12.1 Domestic audio system

■ Signal sources

Signal sources in a domestic audio system include the following.

CD/DVD player   Stereo audio signals are stored on compact discs (CDs) or digital versatile discs (DVDs) in digital form. The player has digital-to-analogue converters, so the output signals are analogue.

Radio tuner   The tuner receives amplitude-modulated or frequency-modulated radio signals (see p. 141). The tuner demodulates these and produces analogue signals, often in stereo.

Tape deck   Audio signals are stored on magnetic tape in analogue form. A magnetic head (or a pair of heads in a stereo system) detects the varying magnetic field due to the arrangement of magnetic domains on the tape and converts this to an audio signal.

▌ Source select

A system of switches connects one of the signal sources to the pre-amplifier. In some systems, pressing one of a set of three or four latching push-buttons connects one source and disconnects the other sources.

▌ Pre-amplifier

The signal from the source is usually only a few millivolts and the current only a few milliamps. The pre-amplifier needs high input impedance to ensure maximum voltage transfer from the source (see subsection 12.2).

High input impedance is achieved if the first amplifying stage is a common-collector amplifier (emitter follower), a common-drain amplifier (source follower) or a non-inverting op amp (or its equivalent in a special pre-amplifier IC). This transfers the voltage signal with no amplification. The next stage or stages are based on common-emitter or common-source amplifiers, which amplify voltage. Often the first of these stages is a common-source amplifier because of its high input impedance; it can even accept the signal direct from the source without voltage loss. This is followed by a common-emitter stage, or two, because of the better linearity of BJT transistors.

Above the full-power bandwidth, the gain of an amplifier falls off as frequency increases (see p. 84). This is why it is better for the amplifier to have two or three stages, each of medium gain, rather than a single stage of high gain.

The low current in the early amplifier stages means that little noise is generated in the early stages of the system, which would be amplified along with the wanted signal by later stages.

▌ Volume and tone control

Volume control and tone control are different functions but the circuits responsible may be combined. The most important function of tone control is to compensate for unevenness in the frequency response of the system. Each signal source has its characteristic response, which is corrected by tone control (or **equaliser**) circuits. Passive or active filters are used for this purpose. In some systems, appropriate equalising circuits are switched in automatically as each different source is selected.

It is also important to be able to adjust both volume and tone to allow for personal preferences and for the acoustics of the room in which the system is being operated. Each channel has its own volume and tone control circuit but these have ganged controls so that they operate equally on both channels. Usually there is also a balance control that adjusts the relative volumes of the two channels.

▌ Power amplifier

As the signal emerges from the volume and tone control stages it has an amplitude of several volts. The power amplifier is a common-collector or common-drain stage that has a voltage gain of 1 (or slightly less) but a high current gain. The power amplifier is usually a Class AB or B amplifier with push–pull action, because of its higher efficiency (see p. 53). The amplifier must effect maximum *power* transfer to the speaker (compare with a pre-amplifier and see subsection 12.2). There are usually two power amplifiers, one for each stereo channel.

The maximum power output of the amplifier can be shown to be proportional to the square of the supply voltage V_S. Here we consider the negative rail (see Fig. 4.18, p. 53) to be at 0 V and the positive rail to be at V_S. The quiescent (no signal) voltage at the emitters of Q1 and Q2 is $V_S/2$. For maximum power dissipation, the output voltage is made to swing as widely as possible between the positive and negative rails. The voltage amplitude of the signal is $V_S/2$. The rms output amplitude is $V_{rms} = V_S/(2\sqrt{2})$. Given that the impedance of the speaker is Z_L, the maximum power output is then:

$$P_{max} = V_{rms}^2/Z_L = V_S^2/8Z_L$$

▌ Speaker

The frequency response of a loudspeaker depends mainly on its diameter. For good quality reproduction, a system requires two, three or more speakers for each channel. These might have frequency ranges as shown in the table below.

Speaker	Range
tweeter	2 kHz–20 kHz
mid-range	50 Hz–5 kHz
bass (woofer)	30 Hz–800 Hz
sub-woofer	20 Hz–200 Hz

A low-cost system has only a mid-range speaker. Sub-woofers are used only in the highest quality systems.

The audio signal from each power amplifier is fed to the speakers through a **crossover network**. This consists of passive filter circuits (mainly capacitors and inductors, including the inductance of the speaker coils) that separate the signal into different frequency bands and route them to the appropriate speakers. By routing the different frequency bands instead of simply passing the whole frequency range through a set of lowpass, bandpass and highpass filters, the network avoids waste of power.

A speaker is mounted on a **baffle** to prevent sound waves generated by the back of the cone from partly cancelling the sound waves generated by the front of the cone. Because these two sets of waves are 180° out of phase, cancelling would result in a serious reduction in volume. A baffle is a panel that has an aperture cut in it for mounting the speaker. The panel is made of a hard material and the speaker is firmly bolted to it. The panel may be flat (as when a speaker is mounted in a wall or ceiling) or it may be a box (an **enclosure**). In most systems the front of the box has apertures cut in it for mounting two or three speakers of different sizes. Sub-woofers usually have a separate enclosure. The box may have a vent to prevent the motion of the cone from being damped, but positioned so that the two sets of waves do not interfere.

The two sets of speakers in a stereo system are placed in the room so that they are to the front left and front right of the listener (or viewer in an audio-visual system). This is essential to obtain the stereo effect.

12•2 Signal transfers

There are two important transfers of signal in an audio system:

- maximum voltage transfer between the signal source and the pre-amplifier;
- maximum power transfer between the power amplifier and the speaker.

■ Voltage transfer

Fig. 12.2 shows the transfer of a signal from the source to the pre-amplifier. The source is represented by a voltage source v (for example, the output from a DAC in a CD player), which has an output impedance Z_{out}. This is connected to the pre-amplifier, which has an input impedance Z_{in}. The aim is to make v_{in} as great as possible.

The current in the circuit is given by:

$$i = \frac{v - v_{in}}{Z_{out}} = \frac{v_{in}}{Z_{in}}$$

Solving for v_{in} gives:

$$v_{in} = v \times \frac{Z_{in}}{Z_{in} + Z_{out}}$$

For v_{in} to be as large as possible, the value of $Z_{in}/(Z_{in} + Z_{out})$ must be as close as possible to 1. This happens only if Z_{in} is much greater than Z_{out}. The pre-amplifier must have a high input impedance, much higher than the output impedance of the source.

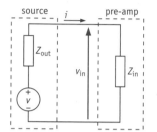

Figure 12.2 Transferring a signal from its source to the pre-amplifier

worked example

problem An electret microphone with $Z_{out} = 600\ \Omega$ produces a signal of amplitude 2.5 mV. It is connected to the input of a pre-amplifier which has $Z_{in} = 12\ \text{k}\Omega$. What is the amplitude of the voltage v_{in} across the input terminals of the pre-amplifier?

working Using the equation above:

$$v_{in} = 2.5 \times 10^{-3} \times \frac{12 \times 10^3}{(12 \times 10^3 + 600)} = 30/12\,600 = 2.38 \times 10^{-3}\ \text{V}$$

solution The amplitude of the voltage across the terminals is 2.38 mV.

■ Power transfer

Refer again to Fig. 12.2, but let the block on the left now represent a power amplifier, with voltage source v and output impedance Z_{out}. The block on the right now represents a speaker, impedance Z_{in}.

The voltage of the source equals the terminal voltage of either of the blocks, plus the voltage drop across Z_{out}:

$$v = v_{in} + iZ_{out} = iZ_{out} + iZ_{in} = i(Z_{out} + Z_{in})$$

Rearranging terms gives:

$$i = \frac{v}{Z_{out} + Z_{in}}$$

The power dissipated in the speaker is:

$$P = i^2 Z_{in} = \frac{v^2 Z_{in}}{(Z_{out} + Z_{in})^2}$$

It can be shown that this takes its maximum value when $Z_{in} = Z_{out}$. Since the speaker has low impedance (typically only 4 Ω or 8 Ω), the amplifier must have an equally low output impedance. This is the case for common-collector or common-drain amplifiers (see p. 53). Call this value Z. Then:

$$\text{maximum } P = \frac{v^2 Z}{(Z + Z)^2} = \frac{v^2 Z}{4Z^2} = \frac{v^2}{4Z}$$

This is the power dissipated in the speaker; an equal amount of power is dissipated in the transistors of the amplifier. The transfer of power is thus only 50% efficient.

worked example

problem 1   An operational amplifier with Z_{out} = 75 Ω drives a speaker with Z_{in} = 64 Ω. The rms signal voltage is 3.5 V. What is the rms power dissipation in the speaker?

working   Using $P = \dfrac{v^2 Z_{in}}{(Z_{out} + Z_{in})^2}$:

$$P = \frac{3.5^2 \times 64}{(75 + 64)^2} = 784/139^2 = 0.0406 \text{ W}$$

solution   The rms power dissipated in the speaker is 40.6 mW.

problem 2   A power amplifier with Z_{out} = 10 Ω drives an 8 Ω speaker. The rms signal voltage is 24 V. What is the power dissipation in the speaker? What is the maximum power dissipated in the speaker when the output impedance of the amplifier is reduced to 8 Ω?

working   Using $P = \dfrac{v^2 Z_{in}}{(Z_{out} + Z_{in})^2}$:

$$P = \frac{24^2 \times 8}{(10 + 8)^2} = 4608/324 = 14.2 \text{ W}$$

Maximum power (with equal impedances Z = 8 Ω) is:

$$\frac{v^2}{4Z} = \frac{24^2}{(4 \times 8)} = 18 \text{ W}$$

solution   The power dissipation is 14.2 W when Z_{out} = 10 Ω; this is increased to a maximum of 18 W when Z_{out} is reduced to 8 Ω.

12•3 Public address audio system

There are many ways in which a public address (PA) system can be assembled, a typical example being the system illustrated in Fig. 12.3. Compared with the domestic system, the one illustrated has several more signal sources and a mixer to allow input from two or more sources to be combined. However, a PA system used by a demonstrator in a department store would have only one microphone, no mixer and only one channel. All types of PA system tend to have more powerful output amplifiers than domestic systems.

Figure 12.3 Public address audio system

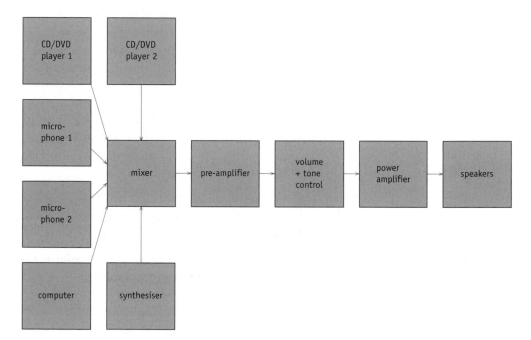

The system shown is suited for entertainment venues, such as clubs and pop concerts. The input units are:

▌ **CD/DVD players 1 and 2**: twin players allow fading from one track to another track on a different disc;

▌ **microphones 1 and 2**: for the compère, a singer or solo instrumentalist, or for use in a karaoke session;

▌ **computer with DAC output**: for pre-recorded tracks, possibly downloaded from the Web in MP3 or other formats;

▌ **synthesiser** or electronic keyboard;

▌ **mixer**: for mixing signals from two or more of the above sources.

Essentially, the circuit is based on the op amp adder circuit in Fig. 6.7, p. 86.

▋ Ten quick questions

1 Name the first amplifying stage in an audio system.
2 What is the function of a crossover network?
3 What is the essential requirement for maximum voltage transfer?
4 What is a woofer?
5 How do we prevent interference between sound waves produced by the front and back surfaces of the speaker cone?
6 What does an equaliser do?
7 What type of BJT amplifier would be used as the first stage in a pre-amplifier?
8 What is the essential requirement for maximum power transfer?
9 What is the benefit of using several low-gain amplifying stages instead of a single high-gain stage?
10 Why are currents kcpt small in a pre-amplifier?

▋ Questions on audio systems

1 List the main stages in an audio system intended for: **a)** a sports stadium; **b)** a supermarket; **c)** a different venue of your own choice. Draw a block diagram to illustrate each system.

2 Describe a named audio system and illustrate it by a block diagram. Describe the function and outline the circuit principles of any *two* of its parts, including at least one amplifier.

3 Explain why a multi-stage amplifier is preferable to a single-stage high-gain amplifier in a high-quality audio system.

4 List the sources used in audio systems, noting which are analogue sources and which are digital.

5 What is the function of a power amplifier? Compare the action and efficiency of Class A, AB and B amplifiers, illustrating one of these by a circuit diagram.

6 **a)** What is a mixer? Draw a circuit diagram of a simple op amp mixer and explain how it works.
  b) Give *two* instances of when two audio signals need to be mixed.

7 A power amplifier operating on 12 V delivers its signal into a 4 Ω speaker. What is the maximum power delivered to the speaker? What power is dissipated in the amplifier?

8 An audio system is to deliver a minimum of 20 W into an 8 Ω speaker. What is the minimum supply voltage for the power amplifier?

13 Communications systems

In brief...

■ All electronic communication systems have certain essential components (p. 136).
■ Transmission media include cable, optical fibre and radio (pp 136–139).
■ Noise and distortion must be minimised for reliable transfer of information (p. 140).
■ Most systems rely on modulation of a carrier wave. Types of modulation include: amplitude modulation, frequency modulation, pulse code modulation and other pulse modulation techniques (pp 141–143).
■ Frequency shift keying is used for sending digital information as an analogue signal (p. 143).
■ Bandwidth determines how much information may be carried on a channel (p. 143).
■ Multiplexing allows several signals to share a single channel. Time division multiplexing and frequency division multiplexing are the most commonly used techniques (p. 144).
■ Line transmitters and receivers include those designed for the RS-232 standard (pp 145–147).
■ Optical transmitters and receivers are ideal for digital signals (p. 147).
■ Radio transmitters and receivers allow signals to be broadcast, but can also be used for directional communication (pp 147–150).

Questions on communications systems begin on p. 150, with answers from p. 179.

13•1 The essentials

A communications system conveys information from one place to another. In electronic systems, the media of communication are cable, optical fibre and radio.

Fig. 13.1 illustrates the main features of a communications system, and is the reference map for the remainder of this section.

Figure 13.1 Essential features of a communications system

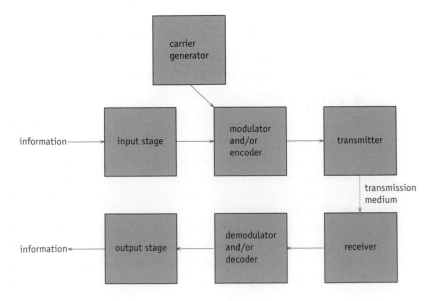

The terms associated with communications systems include the following.

Analogue and digital communication   The advantages of digital communication come from the fact that is it much easier and reliable for a circuit to operate with just two distinct voltage levels (low and high, 0 and 1) than with the continuous range of voltages in analogue communication. The main advantages of digital communication are:

▌ even if the signal is noisy or distorted, it is easy to distinguish between levels 0 and 1;
▌ processing of digital information is more reliable as a result of this;
▌ digital circuits are easily interfaced to computers for checking errors, coding, decoding and multiplexing;
▌ it is easy for a regenerating circuit (such as a Schmitt trigger) to reproduce well shaped digital pulses from a noisy or distorted signal, which is important for long-distance communications;
▌ consequently, the spacing between regenerators on digital lines can be wider than that of repeater stations on an analogue line.

Serial and parallel communication   These terms apply to digital systems. A serial system has a single channel along which data is sent one bit at a time. A parallel system has multiple channels, each carrying one bit at a time but together carrying a byte or larger group of bits. Parallel transmission is faster (8 times faster for an 8-line byte-wide system) but is more expensive. It is used over short distances when speed is important, for example between a computer and a printer.

Half and full duplex systems   A system with two-way communication is a **duplex** system. It is *half* duplex if communication is only in one direction at a time, and *full* duplex if communication is simultaneous in both directions.

Synchronous and asynchronous transmission   These terms apply to digital systems. In a synchronous system the transmitter and receiver run at the same clock rate so that they stay in time with each other. Timing pulses in the message help to keep them running at the same speed. In an asynchronous system, the receiver waits until it receives a 'start bit', then accepts data until it receives a 'stop bit' (for example the RS-232 system, see p. 146). Asynchronous systems are simpler to build and operate, but waste transmission time.

13•2 Transmission media

Electronic communications systems use one or more of three transmission media: cable, optical fibre and radio.

▌ Cable

The two most commonly-used types of cable are the **twisted pair** and the **coaxial cable**.

The twisted pair consists of two insulated wires twisted around each other. The wires are unshielded. Twisting minimises induction of signals from external magnetic fields because the currents induced in adjacent loops cancel each other out.

Coaxial cable consists of a single inner conductor of solid or stranded copper (the core), surrounded by a layer of insulator (dielectric), further surrounded by a screening layer of braided copper (the outer conductor), and all surrounded by a plastic sheath. The signal is carried in the core. The screening is usually earthed to prevent external fields from inducing currents in the core; it also prevents currents carried in the core from inducing currents in nearby circuits. Coaxial cable is often used for carrying radio-frequency signals.

Cable is used for both short- and long-distance communications, the longest being cables laid on the seabed. Although electromagnetic interference is minimised as explained above, it is not entirely eliminated.

▌ Optical fibre

Optical cable consists of a core of highly transparent glass of high refractive index, surrounded by a cladding of glass of lower refractive index. A light beam is directed along inside the core and is totally reflected where it strikes the surface between the core and the cladding. In this way the light is kept within the core, even though the fibre is curved. The fibre is protected by a plastic sheath. Although the glass is of high transparency, there is a gradual absorption of light, at the rate of about 0.15 dB per kilometre.

In a **graded index fibre**, the refractive index decreases smoothly from the centre of the core to the outside. Instead of being reflected, the light rays are gradually curved back toward the axis of the fibre. Pulses are less distorted in graded index fibre, which is therefore preferred for long-distance communication.

Optical fibre is used for both short- and long-distance communication. Glass fibres are more expensive than copper cable, but cheaper optical fibre made from polymer can be used for distances less than 100 m.

The advantages of optical fibre cable over conventional cable are:

▌ it is proof against electromagnetic interference (this makes it useful in industrial applications for sending control signals to machinery in an environment of strong fields due to the switching of heavy currents);
▌ it is secure against attempts to use electromagnetic means to read the data it is carrying;
▌ it has a higher bandwidth than other forms of communication, allowing many more signals to be frequency multiplexed on to a single channel (see p. 144);
▌ regenerator stations can be further apart;
▌ it does not cause a fire risk;
▌ it does not corrode.

▌ Radio

Electromagnetic waves are radiated from an antenna when electrons in the antenna are made to oscillate rapidly by the transmitter circuit. The frequency of the signal equals the frequency of the oscillations. Radio frequencies range from 30 Hz up to 3 GHz. The signal radiates in all directions in free space: it is **broadcast**. This makes radio transmission very different from cable and optical fibre transmission. It requires no material connection between sender and receiver, and it is not necessary for the sender to know the precise location of the receiver.

Radio signals travel in one of three ways.

Ground waves   For frequencies less than about 500 kHz the waves spread close to the Earth's surface. Nearest the ground the wavefronts are retarded so that they tilt over, following the curvature of the Earth. This allows reception over thousands of kilometres, though the strength of reception is greatly reduced by obstacles such as ranges of hills. This limits ground waves to relatively short distances in practice.

Sky waves At frequencies above 500 kHz the waves penetrate upward through the lower layers of the ionosphere but are gradually refracted down again to reach the Earth's surface some distance away. Returning sky waves skim the Earth's surface and re-enter the ionosphere again. In this way a powerful transmission can travel around the Earth. Sky waves are important for long-distance communication.

Space waves At frequencies above 25–30 MHz radio waves penetrate the ionosphere and pass into space. These high frequencies are used for communication between satellites and ground stations, and for communication with interplanetary missions. Because the frequency at which the waves fully penetrate the ionosphere depends on the sun-spot cycle and on atmospheric conditions, the frequencies used are generally greater than 100 MHz.

Broadcast radio has the advantages of reaching large numbers of recipients located at any place in a large area. However, signal strength falls off with distance and a powerful transmitter is needed to reach large numbers of people. If we want to communicate with just one receiver, this can be done more economically, and with a transmitter of lower power, if we use **directional transmission**.

The usual antenna for broadcast transmission is a dipole (Fig. 13.2). The two metal rods are fed with a signal from the transmitter. If the wavelength of the signal is about twice the length of the rods, a standing wave is set up in the dipole as shown. Given the frequency f of the transmission and that the velocity of electromagnetic waves (including radio waves) is 3×10^8 m/s, the wavelength $\lambda = 3 \times 10^8/f$. But because the velocity in a conductor is less than that in free space, the exact length of the dipole should be 0.46λ.

Figure 13.2 Dipole antenna

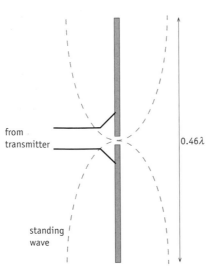

from transmitter

0.46λ

standing wave

A vertical dipole radiates equally strongly in all horizontal directions, so it is good for broadcast radio. It can be made directional by adding two or more **parasitic elements** to it, as in Fig. 13.3. These are simple metal rods which absorb some of the radiation from the dipole and resonate at the same frequency, emitting radiation. The result is that the signal is stronger in the direction of the director element (to the right in the drawing).

Dipoles as described above are used both for transmission and reception. A dipole with a larger number of director elements is used for reception in 'fringe areas' where signal strength is low, and where there are numerous other transmitters within range.

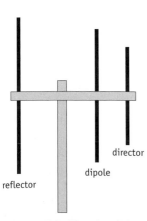

director

dipole

reflector

Figure 13.3 Directional dipole array

13·3 Noise and distortion in communications systems

Electronic noise originating within the circuit is a feature of all types of circuit, including communications circuits, and the remedies are the same (see p. 94). In this section we are concerned with noise due to interference from outside sources, particularly electromagnetic interference (EMI).

The further from the transmitter, the more the signal is weakened, or **attenuated**. A broadcast radio signal follows the inverse square law, so that doubling the distance reduces signal strength to one quarter. Unfortunately, EMI may be generated locally so that a signal weakened by distance is overcome by local EMI. The extent to which this occurs is measured by the **signal-to-noise power ratio**. If the rms of the signal voltage is V_S and the rms noise voltage is V_N, the signal-to-noise power ratio is:

$$\text{SNR} = 10 \log_{10}\left(\frac{V_S{}^2}{V_N{}^2}\right) \text{dB}$$

which may be simplified to:

$$\text{SNR} = 20 \log_{10}\left(\frac{V_S}{V_N}\right) \text{dB}$$

Distance increases the opportunities for picking up EMI in cables. Long-distance radio is subject to interference from lightning and from local radio stations. Optical fibre communications are not subject to EMI.

Attenuation may depend on frequency. For example, high frequencies are more attenuated than low frequencies in coaxial cables. Analogue signals thus become distorted by losing their higher frequencies. With digital signals, it is the highest overtones that give pulses their 'squareness'. If these are lost, the pulses become rounded and badly defined. This limits the maximum possible rate of transmission in coaxial cable, as pulses may become so distorted that they overlap. Optical signals are less affected by distance.

Attenuation on long routes is countered by **repeaters** or **regenerators**. A repeater station receives analogue signals, filters them to remove as much noise as possible, amplifies them and then transmits them to the next repeater station. A regenerator station receives digital signals, regenerates the pulses and transmits them to the next station as perfectly formed pulses. Repeaters improve the signal-to-noise ratio but slight distortion of the waveform is inevitable. Regenerators reproduce the original signal exactly, which is one of the advantages of digital systems.

Interference in analogue signals is avoided by using frequency modulation, as explained opposite.

Crosstalk is a form of interference in which signals present in one channel of a system find their way on to other channels. This can occur because of capacitance between lines running parallel with each other. In multicored cables it can be avoided by shielding each core in a separate earthed sheath. This is expensive and makes the cable heavy. Crosstalk may also occur between the lines in the ribbon cables used to connect computers to their peripherals, or between parallel tracks on a circuit board. A solution is to use only alternate conductors in the ribbon cable, and to earth the unused conductors between them. On a circuit board, earthed tracks are run between the used tracks. Crosstalk between optical fibres is negligible.

13•4 Modulation

On a short-distance low-fidelity transmission such as a local telephone circuit, or an office intercom system, the analogue signal from the microphone is amplified and sent direct to the receiver. In most other communications systems the signal is **modulated** on to a carrier signal. The frequency of the carrier is many times greater than that of the highest frequency to be transmitted.

There are three main kinds of modulation.

■ Amplitude modulation (AM)

Fig. 13.4 shows the signal, which begins with a short period at 0 V (no signal) then becomes a sinusoid. In Fig. 13.5, the signal is amplitude modulated on to a carrier, a sinusoid of higher frequency. The combined signal begins by alternating at constant amplitude (no signal), then its amplitude varies according to the voltage of the signal in Fig. 13.4.

Figure 13.4 Analogue audio signal before modulation

Figure 13.5 Carrier signal amplitude modulated with the audio signal of Fig. 13.4

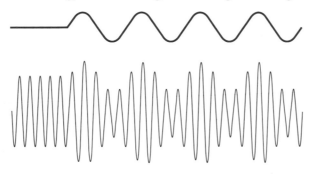

In practice, the carrier wave frequency is much higher with respect to the signal frequency than can be shown in the diagram. The **modulation depth** in Fig. 13.5 is 40%, meaning that the carrier amplitude is increased or reduced by 40% at the peaks of the signal. Noise and interference cause spikes that increase the amplitude, and so become superimposed on the signal.

■ Frequency modulation (FM)

In Fig. 13.6, the signal of Fig. 13.4 is frequency modulated on to the carrier. The combined signal begins by alternating at constant frequency (no signal), then its frequency varies according to the signal amplitude. Interference causes amplitude spikes as with AM, but an FM receiver is not affected by these as it is sensitive only to changes in frequency.

Figure 13.6 Carrier signal frequency modulated with the audio signal of Fig. 13.4

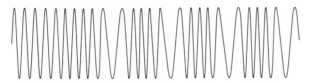

■ Pulse code modulation (PCM)

If the information to be transmitted as pulses is initially analogue, it is first put through a lowpass filter to remove noise, then sampled and converted into digital form using an ADC (Fig. 13.7). Typically, data is sampled 8000 times a second, and converted into bytes, with values from 0000 0000 to 1111 1111. These are passed into a PISO shift register and transmitted serially, a bit (0 or 1) at a time.

Figure 13.7 Pulse code modulation system

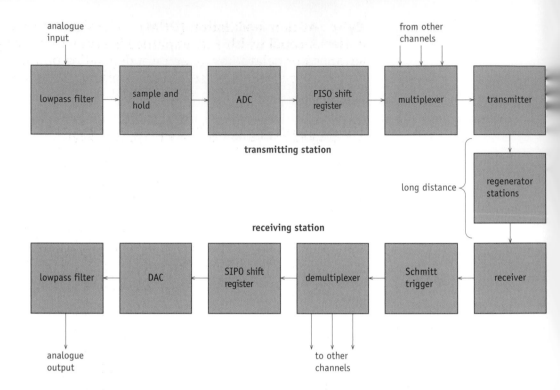

Digital data is transmitted by PCM in a similar system, beginning with the multiplexer and ending at the demultiplexer. PCM is the basis of the majority of digital communication systems. Additional bits are added to the message as it is sent; these aid error-checking on reception.

Sampling an analogue signal and converting it to a digital signal with a number of discrete levels gives rise to **quantisation noise**. This is because there is always a small difference between the resulting digital value and the exact value of the original analogue. For example, an 8-bit system has $2^8 = 256$ levels. If the original signal has 1 V amplitude, the difference between one digital value and the next is $1/256 = 3.9$ mV. During conversion, an analogue signal is rounded up or down to the nearest digital value, so the error in a conversion may be up to $3.9/2 = 1.95$ mV. This is equivalent to adding noise to the signal. Quantisation noise is reduced by increasing the number of bits in the conversion, so that the steps are smaller. It can generally be ignored if the system uses 12-bit converters. The effect of quantisation noise is worse when signal amplitude is low.

▮ Other pulse transmission methods

There are other methods of transmitting information as pulses, all of which rely on varying analogue quantities. They include the following.

Pulse amplitude modulation (PAM)   The signal is sampled and a series of pulses of equal width is sent with equal spacing, their amplitude varying with the voltage of the signal. PAM is used in time multiplexed transmissions, with other signals being sent in the gaps between pulses. PAM is subject to noise and interference. This system is not much used.

Pulse width modulation (PWM)   The signal is sampled and a series of pulses of equal amplitude is sent with their leading edges at regular intervals, their width varying with the voltage of the signal. The advantage of this system is that the transmission and reception circuits are simple.

Pulse position modulation (PPM)   The signal is sampled and a series of pulses of equal width and amplitude is sent with varying timing. Each pulse is advanced or delayed by an amount depending on the signal voltage. This system is immune to noise, but transmission and reception circuits are complicated and must be synchronised.

13•5 Frequency shift keying

Frequency shift keying (FSK) is a technique for transmitting digital information as an analogue signal. It is used, for example, in transmitting digital data from a computer to an Internet Service Provider over a public telephone line. The system is based on two audio frequencies, one of which represents '0' and the other '1'. In one version of FSK, a '0' is represented by a burst of 4 cycles at 1.2 kHz, and '1' is represented by 8 cycles at 2.4 kHz. Digital signals arc turned into FSK, and FSK turned back into digital signals, by a **modem** (*mod*ulator/*dem*odulator) which connects the computer with the telephone line.

13•6 Bandwidth

A pure sinusoid has only one frequency, but any other waveform can be considered to be a mixture of two or more sinusoids of different frequencies and amplitudes. If a carrier wave of frequency f_c is amplitude modulated with a pure sinusoid of frequency f_m, the frequency spectrum of the resulting signal is as shown in Fig. 13.8a. The signal now contains three frequencies: the carrier, and two 'sum and difference' frequencies, $(f_c - f_m)$ and $(f_c + f_m)$. These are referred to as **side frequencies**.

The **bandwidth** of a signal is the difference between the lowest and highest frequencies it contains. In the example of Fig. 13.8a, the bandwidth is $2f_m$. It does not depend on f_c.

Figure 13.8 Frequency spectrum of a carrier modulated by **a)** a single frequency; **b)** a range of frequencies

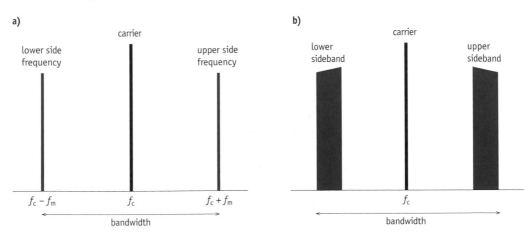

Typically, the signal modulated on to the carrier contains many frequencies. For each of these, the modulated signal contains the sum and difference frequencies, so that the frequency spectrum is as shown in Fig. 13.8b. There are two **sidebands**. The bandwidth of this signal is $2f_{max}$, where f_{max} is the highest modulating frequency that the original signal contains.

In an amplitude modulated signal the carrier itself contains no information, and the two sidebands each contain the same information. Also, the carrier has the largest amplitude and therefore the most power. It is wasteful of power to transmit the carrier and *both* of the sidebands. In single sideband (SSB) transmission, the carrier and one of the sidebands (usually the upper sideband) are filtered out before transmission, and only one sideband is transmitted. This is far more economical of power. It also restricts the bandwidth of the transmission, allowing transmitters to be more closely spaced with respect to frequency (see below).

A frequency modulated signal also has sidebands. Depending on the amount of modulation there may be one, two or several more. This gives FM signals a wider bandwidth than AM. Generally, for FM we use a high-frequency carrier, in the very-high-frequency (VHF) and ultra-high-frequency (UHF) bands, as this allows more room for the sidebands between carrier frequencies.

The term bandwidth is also applied to channels. The bandwidth of a channel is the difference between the lowest and highest frequencies that can be transmitted in that channel without significant loss. If the channel is thought of as a bandpass filter, the bandwidth is the difference between the lower and higher cut-off (-3 dB) points.

13•7 Multiplexing

Multiplexing is the name given to the use of a single channel to convey more than one signal simultaneously. There are two types of multiplexing: **frequency division** and **time division**.

▮ Frequency division multiplexing (FDM)

This is used mainly for analogue signals, and relies on the fact that the bandwidth of a channel is many times wider than the bandwidth of an AM signal, particularly a voice signal.

The frequencies needed for good speech recognition require a signal bandwidth of 3.4 kHz. This is the bandwidth of a standard telephone line. For long-distance communication by any of the three transmission media, the voice signal is modulated onto a carrier. If the voice signal is modulated on to 64 kHz, the lower sideband extends down to $(64 - 3.4) = 60.6$ kHz. With SSB transmission, the bandwidth of the signal is then 3.4 kHz. Transmission of other types of signal might require a wider signal bandwidth (20 kHz for high-quality music and more for video) but here we will discuss voice signals.

Given that 3.4 kHz is needed for a voice signal, it is possible to transmit a second signal on the same channel by modulating it on to a 68 kHz carrier. The bandwidth of this ranges from 64.6 kHz to 68 kHz, so does not overlap the previous signal. In this way, numerous signals can be 'stacked' on the same channel, on carriers 4 kHz apart. At the receiver, the individual signals are separated by tuning, demodulated and then routed to their intended recipients.

▮ Time division multiplexing (TDM)

This is used mainly for digital signals, or for analogue signals that have been sampled and converted into digital signals. It exploits the fact that digital signals consist of bits and bytes that can be handled at high speed by digital circuits.

In the system used in Europe (the North American system is similar) voice signals are sampled 8000 times per second and an ADC converts each sample into an 8-bit (= byte) value ranging from 0 to 255. At this sampling rate, a sample is obtained every 125 μs. It takes much less time than this to transmit the 8-bit value, so plenty of time is available to transmit samples of other signals along the same channel. If each channel is allocated a 'time slot' of 3.9 μs for transmitting its 8-bit value, for example, there is time for 30 signals to be transmitted, allowing also two time slots for transmitting synchronising and control data.

Transmission rates for TDM are rated in kilobits per second. In the system just described, each sample is a byte (8 bits) and 8000 samples per second are taken from each signal source. There are 32 sources (including the synchronising signals). The total bit rate is therefore $8 \times 8000 \times 32 = 2048$ kbit/s.

13•8 Line transmitters and receivers

For maximum transfer of power, the output impedance of the **line transmitter** (or **line driver**) must equal the characteristic impedance of the cable. Most coaxial cable has a characteristic impedance Z_0 of 50 Ω. (At high frequencies Z_0 of a cable depends on the capacitance and inductance per unit length of line, not on frequency.) With equal impedances, all power is transferred from the driver to the cable. Similarly at the other end of the line, if the input impedance of the **line receiver** equals Z_0, the signal is transferred from the cable to the receiver without loss of power. Line drivers and receivers are made as ICs and their impedances match the standard Z_0 values.

The types used for analogue transmissions are usually differential amplifiers with high slew rate and wide bandwidth. The driver has two outputs, operating in antiphase (Fig. 13.9). At the receiving end the signal appears across the load resistor, which has resistance equal to Z_0, so all the signal power is developed across it. The inputs of the differential amplifier have high impedance so the maximum voltage is transferred to it. This circuit uses a twisted pair.

Figure 13.9 Line driver and receiver for analogue signals

Line drivers and receivers for digital signals are gates with high slew rate. Their logic may be NOT, NAND (usually 2-input), or TRUE (output takes the same logic state as the input). Line drivers usually have buffer outputs, which are capable of supplying higher currents than regular logic gates. Line receivers often have Schmitt trigger inputs, useful for squaring up the pulses on arrival. Fig. 13.10 shows a typical digital line driver and receiver circuit, using a coaxial cable. The receiver has Schmitt trigger inputs, as indicated by the 'double-S' hysteresis symbol. Both ends of the coaxial cable are grounded. The load resistor equals Z_0 and all the signal power is developed across it.

Figure 13.10 Line driver and receiver for digital signals

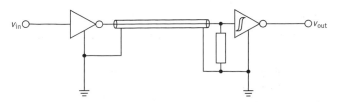

The RS-232 system is a standard for cable transmission of digital signals over distances up to 15 m. It is most often used for asynchronous serial transmission between a computer and a modem or other digital equipment. The most commonly used RS-232 system uses a 9-pin connector. In the case of a computer connected to a modem, the names and functions of the terminals are given in the table below.

Function	Pin name	Function	Direction
data transfer	TXD (or TD)	transmits data to modem	input
	RXD (or RD)	receives data from modem	output
	SG	signal ground	—
handshaking	RTS	ready to send: logic high when computer ready to transmit data	input
	CTS	clear to send: logic high when modem ready to receive data	output
	DTR	data terminal ready: logic high when computer operating correctly, modem may be connected to telephone line	input
	DSR	data set ready: logic high when modem is correctly connected to the telephone	output
indicators	DCD	data carrier detect: high when incoming data detected on telephone line	output
	RI	ring indicator: logic high when modem receives a call from telephone network	output

In the fourth column the directions are relative to the modem.

The standard also defines the logic levels to be used. A logic high is a voltage between $+3$ V and $+15$ V. A logic low is between -3 V and -15 V.

Special line drivers are made for RS-232 systems. They accept power supplies up to ±15 V and convert TTL input levels (0 V or $+5$ V) to RS-232 outputs. Some have NOT logic, so they invert the signal. One type of line receiver operates on a 5 V to 10 V supply, has Schmitt trigger inputs, NOT logic, and produces TTL outputs.

RS-232 does not specify the coding to be used, but data is usually transmitted according to the **ASCII code**. Letters, numerals and punctuation are coded into 7-bit groups. For instance, the letter 'A' is coded as '1000001'. When a device is waiting to receive a group, the logic level on the line is low. This is called **marking**. A transmission begins with a single '1' bit, as the line goes high. This is called the **start bit**, and is followed immediately by seven

data bits, starting with the least significant bit (D0). Next comes a **parity bit** (0 or 1), followed by a **stop bit**, which is low. The line then remains low (marking) until the next group arrives.

Whether the parity bit is low or high depends upon the parity rules of the system. With **even parity**, the parity bit is appended to the 7-bit code to make the total number of '1' bits even. For example, if the ASCII code is '1000001', with two 1s, the parity bit is 0. If the code is 0111011, with five 1s, the parity bit is 1 to give an even total of six 1s. Parity is checked automatically by the receiver and, if the received parity bit is wrong, this indicates an error in transmission. The transmitter is signalled to repeat the transmission.

13•9 Optical transmitters and receivers

▮ Optical transmitters

The light source is either an LED or a solid-state laser, usually producing infrared light. The source is clamped tightly against the highly polished end of the optical fibre. LEDs are cheaper and reliable, but have only low power output. Lasers are more powerful but more expensive.

With LEDs, the signal is sent by modulating the amplitude (intensity) of the emitted light. This is done by varying the current supplied to the LED. With lasers, it is possible to modulate amplitude, frequency, phase or polarisation. Light waves have very high frequencies compared with radio waves, and this gives optical systems the widest possible bandwidth, allowing many more voice channels (in the order of 100 000) to be carried on a single optical fibre. This is one of the main reasons why optical fibre is so widely used in telecommunications.

▮ Optical receivers

Three kinds of receiver are used.

Avalanche photodiodes   These are reverse-biased. When light strikes the diode a few electron–hole pairs are generated. These move in the electric field, hitting other atoms and liberating more holes and electrons. There is an avalanche effect and current through the diode rapidly increases. Avalanche photodiodes are sensitive and have a very short response time of 200 ps. This makes them suitable for operating at the highest frequencies.

PIN photodiodes   These have a layer of intrinsic (i-type) material between the p-type and n-type layers. The i-type material has few charge carriers and acts to separate the p-type layer from the n-type layer. This separation reduces the capacitance of the photodiode, making it much faster-acting. The wider gap allows more light to be absorbed, so increasing sensitivity.

Phototransistors   These are described on p. 34. They are very sensitive because of their amplifying action but are slower than the other types of sensor.

13•10 Radio transmitters and receivers

▮ Radio transmitter

In a simple radio transmitter (Fig. 13.11 overleaf) the input signal (audio or otherwise) is amplified and then mixed with the carrier signal. Modulation may be AM or FM. The modulated carrier is fed to a radio-frequency amplifier which selectively amplifies the radio-frequency signals. It may be a common-emitter amplifier (as in Fig. 4.14, p. 50) but with its collector resistor replaced by an inductor or by a capacitor–inductor resonant network. The input and output capacitors have values of a few nanofarads so that they pass high frequencies. The output of the rf amplifier goes to an antenna (p. 139) which radiates electromagnetic waves.

Figure 13.11 Block diagram of a simple radio transmitter

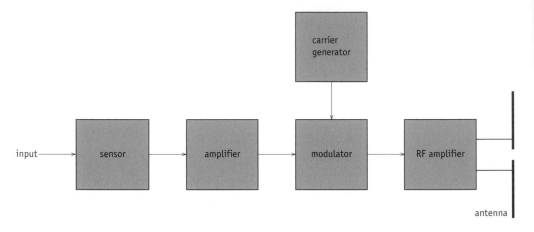

■ Simple AM radio receiver

In Fig. 13.12 electromagnetic waves reach the antenna and cause oscillations in a tuned network. The network is tuned to oscillate at the frequency of the carrier wave of the station that is to be received. The network oscillates strongly at this frequency but not at the frequencies of other stations. It is **selective**.

Figure 13.12 Block diagram of a simple radio receiver

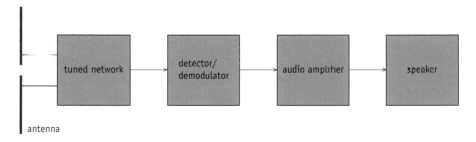

The oscillations pass to a detector circuit, where they are rectified. In the same stage, the carrier frequency is removed from the signal leaving only the varying voltage of the audio signal. This is amplified by an audio-frequency amplifier and drives a loudspeaker. Fig. 13.13 shows the half-wave rectified signal from Fig. 13.5 (black) and the demodulated signal (red).

Figure 13.13 The rectified signal before and after demodulation

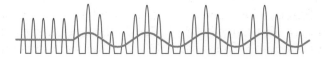

Fig. 13.14 shows the circuit diagram of this receiver as far as the demodulator stage. The tuned network is a capacitor and inductor in parallel, with resonant frequency $f = 1/(2\pi\sqrt{(LC)})$. The variable capacitor allows for tuning. The detector is a diode, usually a germanium diode because this has a lower forward voltage drop. The capacitor and resistor demodulate the signal and the output goes to an audio amplifier.

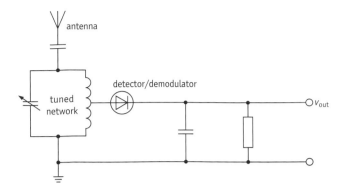

Figure 13.14 Circuit of a simple radio receiver

The stages shown in Fig. 13.14 have no power supply. They are powered solely by the power of the electromagnetic radiation received at the antenna. The circuit is suitable only for reception from nearby powerful transmitters.

■ Tuned radio-frequency (TRF) receiver

A TRF receiver has an rf amplifier in place of the tuned network of Fig. 13.12. The rf amplifier has already been described as part of the transmitter circuit. It may have the inductor coil wound on a ferrite rod, which then acts as an antenna. The ferrite rod concentrates the local electromagnetic field inside itself and therefore increases signal strength, coupling it directly to the amplifier. This, together with the fact that the amplifier has a power supply, makes the TRF receiver much more sensitive than the simple receiver described above. From the rf amplifier, the signal is detected (rectified) and demodulated before being passed to an audio amplifier and speaker.

Although it is sensitive, a TRF receiver is not selective. If there are several stations all of the same strength transmitting on frequencies that are close together, the receiver responds almost equally to all of them and they are all heard at the same time. This is due to the Q of the tuning circuit not being sufficiently high. One way to increase Q is to pass the signal through a series of rf amplifiers all tuned to the same frequency. The problem is to be able to tune all the amplifiers to the same frequency over the range of frequencies that the rf amplifier is intended to receive.

■ Superheterodyne (superhet) receiver

A superhet receiver (Fig. 13.15, p. 150) has only a single tuned rf amplifier, tunable to the carrier frequency. The modulated carrier wave signal from this is mixed with the signal from a tunable oscillator. The rf amplifier and this local oscillator are tuned together, so that the frequency of the oscillator is always a fixed amount greater than the carrier frequency. The frequency difference is often 455 kHz.

Beats are produced when the two signals are mixed; the beat frequency is the difference between the carrier and local oscillator frequencies. Thus, if the frequency difference is 455 kHz, the beat frequency is 455 kHz. This is called the **intermediate frequency** (IF) and the signal becomes modulated onto this. Whatever the original carrier frequency, the signal is now modulated onto 455 Hz.

The modulated IF then goes to an IF amplifier. This is designed to give its best performance at the IF frequency. With only one frequency to consider, the circuit designer is able to produce an amplifier with maximum gain and minimum distortion. The superhet thus has *high sensitivity*. The IF filter is a very narrow bandpass filter centred on 455 kHz. It removes other close-by

Figure 13.15 Block diagram of a superhet receiver

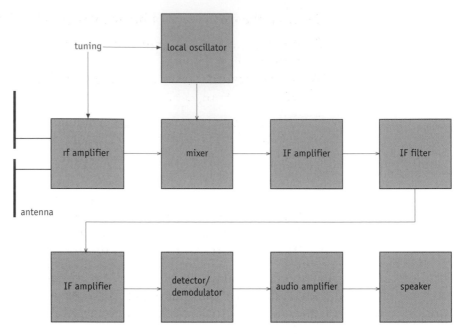

frequencies, giving the superhet *high selectivity* and removing noise. The signal is amplified again by a second IF amplifier, working at 455 kHz, again increasing the sensitivity and selectivity.

Finally, the signal is rectified and demodulated before being passed to an audio amplifier and speaker.

▌ Ten quick questions

1. What do we call the type of interference when signals on one channel are picked up on other channels?
2. What does 'FSK' stand for?
3. What is 'SSB'?
4. What is the characteristic impedance of a typical coaxial cable?
5. Which transmission medium has the greatest bandwidth?
6. What do we call a system that allows communication in both directions at the same time?
7. What happens at a regenerator station?
8. What is graded index fibre?
9. How is a PIN photodiode suited to fast data transmission?
10. What is meant by the 'intermediate frequency' of a superhet receiver?

▌ Questions on communications systems

1. List and explain the advantages of digital communication over analogue communication.

2. What is the difference between serial and parallel digital communication? State the advantages of each.

3. Describe the structure of coaxial cable and explain how electromagnetic interference is reduced when using this type of cable.

4. Explain how an optical fibre system works, including the transmitter and the receiver.

5. What are the main advantages of optical fibre communications?

6 Describe the three ways of broadcasting radio signals.

7 **a)** What is a dipole antenna and how does it operate as part of a radio transmitter?
  b) A UHF transmitter is operating at 800 MHz. What is the optimum length of the dipole?

8 Describe a dipole antenna suitable for directional reception in a fringe area. If the dipole is 150 mm long, what frequency is received most strongly?

9 **a)** Discuss the sources of noise in a named type of communications system, and how it may be minimised.
  b) What is the signal-to-noise ratio of a system if the rms signal voltage is 300 mV and the rms of the noise is 25 nV?
  c) What is the signal-to-noise ratio in a system if the signal voltage amplitude is 1.5 V and the rms of the noise is 7 nV?

10 Describe the differences between amplitude modulation and frequency modulation. What are the advantages of FM?

11 **a)** What is pulse code modulation? Describe the stages in the production of a PCM signal from an analogue signal source.
   b) Name and briefly describe two other types of pulse modulation.

12 What is 'quantisation noise'?

13 **a)** Explain the terms *carrier wave*, *sideband* and *single sideband*.
   b) An AM signal is based on a 2 MHz carrier. The audio frequencies present in the signal range from 40 Hz to 12 kHz. What is the bandwidth of the transmission?

14 What are the advantages of single sideband transmission? If the AM signal described in the previous question is transmitted as SSB, what bandwidth is required?

15 **a)** What is frequency division multiplexing? Illustrate your answer with a simple block diagram of an FDM system.
   b) If the frequency band of a cable system runs from 64 kHz to 108 kHz, how many voice channels can be transmitted simultaneously by FDM? Assume the bandwidth of a voice channel is 3.4 kHz.

16 What is time division multiplexing?

17 Describe the use of line driver and line receiver ICs in the transmission of digital data.

18 Describe the action of a superhet AM receiver. What are its advantages over a TRF receiver?

19 With the aid of a block diagram, describe an optical fibre link. Use and explain the terms *refractive index*, *laser diode*, *modulation*, *regenerator*, *avalanche photodiode* and *bandwidth*.

Answers

If the question or part-question simply requires recall, a full answer is not given here. Check your answers to these questions against the text and figures.

▌ Section 1

Ten quick questions

1 Potential difference.
2 They must be in the same units.
3 Superposition theorem.
4 Add them.
5 Quality factor.
6 When the impedances of L and C are equal.
7 Lags by $45°$.
8 It is zero.
9 Thévenin equivalent.
10 19.6 W.

Questions on analysing networks

Rules used are abbreviated in square brackets to: OL = Ohm's law, KCL = Kirchhoff's current law, KVL = Kirchhoff's voltage law, CR = current (division) rule, VR = voltage (division) rule, RS = resistors in series, RP = resistors in parallel. Note that there is often more than one way to analyse a network.

1 *Working:* 8 Ω and 10 Ω in parallel
  = (8 × 10)/(8 + 10) = 4.44 Ω.   [RP]
  Total resistance = 4 + 4.44 = 8.44 Ω
  Current through network = 12/8.44 = 1.42 A.   [OL, RS]
  Current through 8 Ω = 1.42 × 10/18 = 0.789 A.   [CR]
  Current through 10 Ω = 1.14 − 0.789 = 0.632 A.   [KCL]
  Pd across 10 Ω = 0.632 × 10 = 6.32 V.   [OL]
  Solutions: **a)** Effective resistance = 8.44 Ω;
  b) pd = 6.32 V; **c)** current = 789 mA.

2 *Working:* 7 Ω and 5 Ω in series = 7 + 5 = 12 Ω.   [RS]
  12 Ω and 10 Ω in parallel = (12 × 10)/(12 + 10) = 5.45 Ω.
  [RP]
  Pd across 7 Ω = 12 × 7/12 = 7 V.   [KVL]
  Pd across 5 Ω = 12 − 7 = 5 V.   [VR]
  Current through 5 Ω = 5/5 = 1 A.   [OL]
  Solutions: **a)** Effective resistance = 5.45 Ω; **b)** pd = 7 V;
  c) current = 1 A.

3 *Working:* All resistors in series = 6 + 10 + 2 + 10 = 30 Ω.
  [RS]
  Current through network = 12/30 = 0.4 A.   [OL]
  Current through 12 Ω = 0.4 A.   [OL]
  Pd across 10 Ω = 12 × 10/30 = 4 V.   [KVL]
  Solutions: **a)** Effective resistance = 30 Ω; **b)** pd = 4 V;
  c) current = 400 mA.

4 *Working:* 20 Ω, 30 Ω and 20 Ω in parallel = reciprocal of
  (1/20 + 1/30 + 1/20) = 7.5 Ω.   [RP]
  Add the 5 Ω in series with these, giving 12.5 Ω.   [RS]

Current through these is 12/12.5 = 0.96 A.   [OL]
Current through 5 Ω is 0.96 A.
Pd across 5 Ω is 0.96 × 5 = 4.8 V.   [OL]
Pd across the three parallel resistors is 12 − 5 = 7.2 V.
[KVL]
Pd across 20 Ω is 7.2 V.
Current through 20 Ω is 7.2/20 = 0.36 A.   [OL]
In lower branch, 3 Ω and 7 Ω = 10 Ω.   [RS]
Total network is 12.5 Ω and 10 Ω in
parallel = (12.5 × 10)/(12.5 + 10) = 5.56 Ω.
Solutions: **a)** Effective resistance = 5.56 Ω; **b)** pd = 7.2 V;
c) current = 360 mA.

5 *Working:* 30 Ω and 20 Ω in
  parallel = (30 × 20)/(30 + 20) = 12 Ω.   [RP]
  Add the other 20 Ω in series with these, giving 32 Ω.   [RS]
  Add the 5 Ω in parallel with
  these = (5 × 32)/(5 + 32) = 4.32 Ω.   [RP]
  Pd across the 30 Ω and 20 Ω in
  parallel = 12 × 12/32 = 4.5 V.   [VR]
  Pd across the 20 Ω in series with this = 12 − 4.5 = 7.5 V.
  [KVL]
  Current through the 20 Ω = 7.5/20 = 0.375 A.   [OL]
  Solutions: **a)** Effective resistance = 4.32 Ω; **b)** pd = 4.5 V;
  c) current = 375 mA.

6 *Working:* 20 Ω and 35 Ω in series = 20 + 35 = 55 Ω.   [RS]
  55 Ω and 100 Ω in
  parallel = (55 × 100)/(55 + 100) = 35.5 Ω.   [RP]
  Current through network = 12/35.5 = 0.338 A.   [OL]
  Current through 55 Ω = 0.338 × 100/155 = 0.218 A.
  [CR]
  Solutions: **a)** Effective resistance = 35.5 Ω; **b)** pd = 12 V;
  c) current = 218 mA.

7 *Working:* 50 Ω, 27 Ω, and 33 Ω in parallel = reciprocal of
  (1/50 + 1/27 + 1/33) = 11.5 Ω.   [RP]
  Current through network = 12/11.5 = 1.04 A.   [OL]
  Pd across each resistor = 12 V.
  Current through 50 Ω = 12/50 = 0.24 A.   [OL]
  Solutions: **a)** Effective resistance = 11.5 Ω; **b)** pd = 12 V;
  c) current = 240 mA.

8 *Working:* 30 Ω and 40 Ω in parallel =
  (30 × 40)/(30 + 40) = 17.1 Ω.   [RP]
  Add 10 Ω in series with this = 27.1 Ω.   [RS]
  20 Ω in parallel with this, giving
  (20 × 27.1)/(20 + 27.1) = 11.5 Ω.   [RP]
  Current through network = 12/11.5 = 1.04 A.   [OL]
  Pd across 10 Ω = 12 × 10/27.1 = 4.42 V.   [VR]
  Pd across 30 Ω = 12 − 4.42 = 7.58 V.   [KVL]
  Current through 30 Ω = 7.58/30 = 0.253 A.   [OL]
  Solutions: **a)** Effective resistance = 11.5 Ω;
  b) pd = 4.42 V; **c)** current = 253 mA.

9 *Working:* 3 Ω and 5 Ω in series = 3 + 5 = 8 Ω. [RS]
7 Ω and 2 Ω in series = 7 + 2 = 9 Ω. [RS]
These two effective resistances in
parallel = (8 × 9)/(8 + 9) = 4.24 Ω. [RP]
Pd across 3 Ω = 12 × 3/8 = 4.5 V. [KVL]
Pd across 2 Ω = 12 × 2/9 = 2.67 V. [KVL]
Current through 2 Ω = 2.67/2 = 1.34 A. [OL]
Solutions: **a)** Effective resistance = 4.24 Ω; **b)** pd = 4.5 V;
c) current = 1.34 mA.

10 *Working:* 30 Ω and 10 Ω in parallel
= (30 × 10)/(30 + 10) = 7.5 Ω. [RP]
25 Ω and 30 Ω in parallel = (25 × 30)/(25 + 30) = 13.6 Ω.
[RP]
These two effective resistances in series
= 7.5 + 13.6 = 21.1 Ω. [RS]
Pd across 25 Ω = (13.6 × 12)/21.1 = 7.73 V. [OL]
Pd across 10 Ω = 12 − 7.73 = 4.27 V.
Current through 10 Ω = 4.27/10 = 0.427 A. [OL]
Solutions: **a)** Effective resistance = 21.1 Ω;
b) pd = 7.73 V; **c)** current = 427 mA.

11 *Analysis:* First replace the 15 V source with a short circuit
(Fig. A1.1a). Arrows show the direction of the currents;
pds are in the reverse directions. R_1 and R_2 are in series,
totalling 30 Ω. R_3 is in parallel with these, giving
(30 × 50)/80 = 18.75 Ω. Add R_4 in series with this to
make a total network resistance of 28.75 Ω. Current
through network is 5/28.75 = 0.174 A. Current splits
between R_3 and (R_1 + R_2). Through R_3, it is
0.174 × 30/80 = 0.065 A. Through (R_1 + R_2) it is
0.174 − 0.065 = 0.109 A. Currents unite and become
0.174 A through R_4. Pds are (for R_1) 0.109 × 20 = 2.18 V,
(for R_2) 0.109 × 10 = 1.09 V, (for R_3) 0.065 × 50 = 3.25 V
and (for R_4) 0.174 × 10 = 1.74 V.

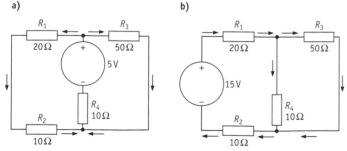

Figure A1.1

Next, replace the 5 V source with a short circuit (Fig.
A1.1b). R_3 and R_4 are in parallel, totalling
(50 × 10)/60 = 8.33 Ω, which is in series with R_1 and R_2,
totalling 38.33 Ω. Current through network is
15/38.33 = 0.391 A. This is the current through R_1 and
R_2. Current splits through R_3 and R_4: through R_3 it is
0.391 × 10/60 = 0.065 A. Through R_4 it is
0.391 − 0.065 = 0.326 A. Pds are 7.82 V for R_1, 3.91 V for
R_2, 3.25 V for R_3 and 3.26 V for R_4.

Solutions: Totalling currents and pds, taking opposing
directions into account where necessary:
R_1: Current = 0.391 − 0.109 = 282 mA.
Pd = 7.82 − 2.18 = 5.64 V.
R_2: Current = 0.391 − 0.109 = 282 mA.
Pd = 3.91 − 1.09 = 2.82 V.

R_3: Current = 0.065 + 0.065 = 130 mA.
Pd = 3.25 + 3.25 = 6.50 V.
R_4: Current = 0.326 − 0.174 = 152 mA.
Pd = 3.26 − 1.74 = 1.52 V.

Check: For each resistor, divide the pd by the current and
check that this equals the resistance.

12 *Analysis:* First replace the voltage source with a short
circuit (Fig. A1.2a). R_1 and R_2 are bypassed, so have zero
current and zero pd. Current in R_3 is 0.2 A. Pd across R_3 is
0.2 × 20 = 4 V.

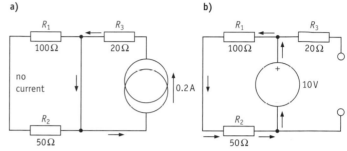

Figure A1.2

Next, replace the current source with an open circuit
(Fig. A1.2b). R_3 has zero current and zero pd. R_1 and R_2
in series total 150 Ω. Current through them = 10/150
= 0.0667 A. Pd across R_1 = 6.67 V. Pd across R_2 = 3.33 V.

Solutions: Totalling currents and pds:
R_1: Current = 67 mA. Pd = 6.67 V.
R_2: Current = 67 mA. Pd = 3.33 V.
R_3: Current = 200 mA. Pd = 4 V.

Check: For each resistor, divide the pd by the current and
check that this equals the resistance.

13 *Analysis:* First replace the voltage source with a short
circuit (Fig. A1.3a). R_1 and R_2 are in series, equivalent to
60 Ω. This is in parallel with R_3, making
(60 × 30)/90 = 20 Ω. This is in series with R_4, making
45 Ω. This is in parallel with R_5, giving a total effective
resistance of (45 × 15)/60 = 11.25 Ω. Pd across current
source = 0.5 × 11.25 = 5.625 V. Current through R_5
= 5.625/15 = 0.375 A. Current through R_1–R_4
network = 0.5 − 0.375 = 0.125 A. This is the current
through R_4, so pd across R_4 is 0.125 × 25 = 3.125 V.
Pd across R_1–R_3 network is 5.625 − 3.125 = 2.5 V.
Current through R_3 is 2.5/30 = 0.0833 A. Current through
(R_1 + R_2) is 0.125 − 0.0833 = 0.0417 A. Pd across R_1 is
0.0417 × 20 = 0.834 V. Pd across R_2 is 2.5 − 0.834
= 1.666 V.

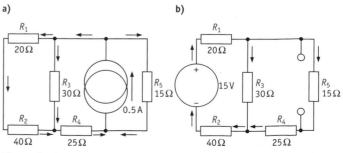

Figure A1.3

Next, replace the current source with an open circuit (Fig. A1.3b). R_4 and R_5 are in series, making 40 Ω. This is in parallel with R_3, making $(40 \times 30)/70 = 17.143$ Ω. This is in series with R_1 and R_2, making 77.143 Ω. Current through network is $15/77.143 = 0.1944$ A.
Pd across R_1 is $0.1944 \times 20 = 3.888$ V.
Pd across R_2 is $0.1944 \times 40 = 7.776$ V.
Pd across R_3 is $15 - 3.888 - 7.776 = 3.336$ V.
Current through R_3 is $3.336/30 = 0.1112$ A.
Current through R_5 and R_4 is $0.1944 - 0.1112 = 0.0832$ A.
Pd across R_5 is $0.0832 \times 15 = 1.248$ V.
Pd across R_4 is $0.0832 \times 25 = 2.08$ V.

Solutions: Totalling currents and pds, taking opposing directions into account where necessary:
R_1: Current = $0.1944 - 0.0417 = 153$ mA.
  Pd = $3.888 - 0.834 = 3.05$ V.
R_2: Current = $0.1944 - 0.0417 = 153$ mA.
  Pd = $7.776 - 1.666 = 6.11$ V.
R_3: Current = $0.0833 + 0.1112 = 195$ mA.
  Pd = $2.50 + 3.336 = 5.84$ V.
R_4: Current = $0.125 - 0.0832 = 41.7$ mA.
  Pd = $3.125 - 2.08 = 1.05$ V.
R_5: Current = $0.375 + 0.0832 = 458$ mA.
  Pd = $5.625 + 1.248 = 6.87$ V.

Check: For each resistor, divide the pd by the current and check that this equals the resistance.

14 *Working:* Leave AB as an open circuit and replace current source with an open circuit. No current can flow, so the voltage at AB, V'_{oc}, equals the pd across the voltage source, which is 6 V, with A positive. Leave AB on open circuit and replace voltage source by a short circuit. Current flows from the current source through R_2 and R_1, not through R_3. The voltage at AB is the pd across R_2, so $V''_{oc} = 0.1 \times 20 = 2$ V, with A positive. Summing pds, the Thévenin voltage $V_{Th} = 6 + 2 = 8$ V.
  Now short-circuit A and B and replace current source with an open circuit. Current flows from voltage source through R_2 and R_3, but not through R_1. Current is $I'_{sc} = 6/70 = 0.0857$ A, flowing from A to B. Leave A and B short-circuited and replace voltage source with a short circuit. Current flows through R_2 and R_3 in parallel and then R_1. Current through R_3 is the short-circuit current, I''_{sc}, which equals $0.1 \times 20/70 = 0.02857$ A, flowing from A to B. Summing currents, $I_{sc} = 0.0857 + 0.02857 = 0.11427$ A.

Solutions: Thévenin voltage $V_{Th} = 8$ V; Thévenin resistance $R_{Th} = 8/0.11427 = 70$ Ω.

15 *Working:* AB is an open circuit. Replace the 4 V source with a short circuit. Current flows through R_3, R_1 and R_2 in series. Pd across R_3 is $12 \times 80/330 = 2.91$ V, making the voltage at AB $V'_{oc} = 9.091$ V, with A positive. With AB still an open circuit, replace the 12 V source with a short circuit. Current flows through R_1, R_3 and R_2. Pd across R_3 is $4 \times 80/330 = 0.9697$ V, which is V''_{oc}. Summing, $V_{Th} = 9.091 - 0.9697 = 8.12$ V, with A positive.
  Now short-circuit AB. Replace the 4 V source with a short circuit. R_1 and R_2 in series are 250 Ω, R_4 and R_5 in series are 160 Ω. This is in parallel with $(R_1 + R_2)$, making 97.56 Ω. Add R_3 in series with this to make 177.56 Ω.

Current in network is $12/177.56 = 0.0676$ A. Part of this flows through $(R_3 + R_4)$, the amount being $I'_{sc} = 0.0676 \times 250/410 = 0.0412$ A, flowing from A to B. Leave AB short-circuited. Replace the 12 V source with a short circuit. Current flows through R_1, then through R_3 in parallel with R_4 and R_5 in series, and finally through R_2. The resistance of the $R_3/R_4/R_5$ sub-network is $80 \times 160/(80 + 160) = 53.33$ Ω. The total resistance of the circuit is $100 + 53.33 + 150 = 303.33$ Ω. The pd across the sub-network is $4 \times 53.33/303.33 = 0.703$ V. The current through R_4 and R_5 is $I''_{sc} = 0.703/160 = 0.0044$ A, flowing from B to A. Total current is $0.0412 - 0.0044 = 0.0368$ A.

Solutions: Thévenin voltage $V_{Th} = 8.12$ V; Thévenin resistance $R_{Th} = 8.12/0.0368 = 221$ Ω.

16 *Working:* AB is an open circuit. Replace the current source with an open circuit. Current flows through R_4 and R_3 in series. Pd across R_4 is $15 \times 50/125 = 6$ V. Pd across AB $= V'_{oc} = 15 - 6 = 9$ V, with A positive. Leave AB on open circuit. Replace the voltage source with a short circuit. Current flows through R_3 and R_4 in parallel. These are equivalent to 30 Ω, so pd across them is $2 \times 30 = 60$ V, with A positive. Summing, $V_{Th} = 9 + 60 = 69$ V.
  Now short-circuit AB. Replace the current source with an open circuit. Current flows through R_4, then through R_3 and R_5 in parallel. Total resistance $= 50 + (75 \times 220)/270 = 105.9$ Ω. Current in this network is $15/105.9 = 0.1416$ A. This splits to go through R_3 and R_5 in parallel. Current through $R_5 = 0.1416 \times 75/295 = 0.036$ A. This is I'_{sc}. With AB still short-circuited, replace the voltage source with a short circuit. Current flows through R_3, R_4 and R_5 in parallel, which totals 26.4 Ω. Pd across these, when total current is 2 A, is $2 \times 26.4 = 52.8$ V. Current through R_5 is $52.8/220 = 0.24$ A, that is, $I''_{sc} = 0.24$ A. Total current is $I_{sc} = 0.036 + 0.240 = 0.276$ A.

Solutions: Thévenin voltage $V_{Th} = 69$ V; Thévenin resistance $R_{Th} = 69/0.276 = 250$ Ω.

17 Given two parallel resistors, R_1 and R_2, their effective resistance is $R = (R_1 \times R_2)/(R_1 + R_2)$. If the total current flowing through the pair is I, then the pd across the pair (and across each resistor) is $V = IR$. The current through R_1 is I_1, so $V = I_1 R_1$.
$\Rightarrow IR = I_1 R_1$
$\Rightarrow I_1 = I \times R/R_1$
$\Rightarrow I_1 = IR_1 R_2/R_1(R_1 + R_2)$
$\Rightarrow I_1 = IR_2/(R_1 + R_2)$
Conversely, $I_2 = IR_1/(R_1 + R_2)$.
  The current through one resistor is inversely proportional to the resistance of the other resistor.

18 Given two or more series resistors, R_1, R_2, ..., R_n, the same current I flows through each of them. For a given resistor R_m the pd across the resistor is $V_m = IR_m$. The pd V_m is proportional to the resistance R_m.

19 a) $P = V^2/R = 15^2/470 = 479$ mW;
  b) $P = 25^2/2.2 = 284$ mW;
  c) $P = 3.5^2/5600 = 2.19$ mW.

20 a) $P = I^2R = 0.5^2/2200 = 550$ W;
  b) $P = 0.015^2 \times 33 = 7.43$ mW;
  c) $P = 5.5^2 \times 1.2 = 36.3$ W.

21 a) Without load, $V_{out} = 6 \times 390/610 = 3.84$ V.
With load, R_2 and R_3 in parallel are
$R = (390 \times 3300)/3690 = 348.8 \, \Omega$.
Then $V_{out} = 6 \times 348.8/568.8 = 3.68$ V. Current
through the load is $3.68/3300 = 1.11$ mA.
Power $= 3.68 \times 1.115$ [V × mA] $= 4.10$ mW.

b) Without load, $V_{out} = 24 \times 2200/3200 = 16.5$ V.
With load, R_2 and R_3 in parallel are
$R = (2200 \times 560)/2760 = 446 \, \Omega$.
Then $V_{out} = 24 \times 446/1446 = 7.40$ V. Current through
the load is $7.40/560 = 13.2$ mA.
Power $= 7.4 \times 13.2$ [V × mA] $= 97.7$ mW.

c) Without load, $V_{out} = 15 \times 33/1233$ [kΩ/kΩ] $= 401$ mV.
With load, R_2 and R_3 in parallel are
$R = (33 \times 3300)/3333 = 32.67$ kΩ.
Then $V_{out} = 15 \times 32.67/1232.67 = 397.6$ mV. Current
through the load is $397.6/3.3$ [mV/MΩ] $= 120.5$ nA.
Power $= 120.5 \times 397.6$ [nA × mV] $= 47.9$ nW.

22 a) Ratio of V_{in} to V_{out} is $12 : 4.8$ or $2.5 : 1$. Therefore, ratio
of voltage across R_1 to V_{out} is $1.5 : 1$. This is the ratio of
resistor R_1 to R_2. Possible E12 values are $150 \, \Omega$ and
$100 \, \Omega$, or $330 \, \Omega$ and $220 \, \Omega$. With $330 \, \Omega$ and $220 \, \Omega$,
loaded V_{out} is 4.67 V, which is 97% of unloaded V_{out}, so
drop is only 3%. Values ten times these result in a drop
larger than 10%. Values a tenth of these could be used
($15 \, \Omega$ and $10 \, \Omega$, or $33 \, \Omega$ and $22 \, \Omega$) but the network
would then take an unnecessarily large current.

b) Ratio of V_{in} to V_{out} is $5 : 0.9$ or $5.56 : 1$. Therefore, ratio
of voltage across R_1 to V_{out} is $4.56 : 1$. Possible E12
values are $100 \, \Omega$ and $22 \, \Omega$. With $100 \, \Omega$ and $22 \, \Omega$, loaded
V_{out} is 0.88 V, which is 98% of unloaded V_{out}, so drop is
only 2%. For the same reasons as in question 22(a),
values ten times or one tenth of these are not acceptable.

c) Ratio of V_{in} to V_{out} is $18 : 10.6$ or $1.7 : 1$. Therefore,
ratio of voltage across R_1 to V_{out} is $0.7 : 1$. Possible E12
values are $39 \, \Omega$ and $27 \, \Omega$, or $47 \, \Omega$ and $33 \, \Omega$, or $56 \, \Omega$
and $39 \, \Omega$, or $68 \, \Omega$ and $47 \, \Omega$, but $39 \, \Omega$ and $27 \, \Omega$ give
the output closest to 10.6 V. When loaded, V_{out} is
6.2 V, which is more than 10% below the unloaded
V_{out}. Reducing values to a tenth alters the effect of
loading so that the nearest output voltage is obtained
with $5.6 \, \Omega$ and $3.3 \, \Omega$, which produces a loaded output
of 10.3 V, 98% of the required value.

23 The output goes high when the transistor switches on.
This happens when the potential at A reaches 0.7 V (see
p. 31) and a base current begins to flow. The pd across R_2
is 0.7 V and the pd across R_1 is 5.3 V.
$R_1 = 19.8$ kΩ $\times 5.3/0.7 = 150$ kΩ. [VR]

24 When the MOSFET switches on, the pd across the LDR is
$9 - 3.5 = 5.5$ V. $R_1 = 12$ kΩ $\times 5.5/3.5 = 18.9$ kΩ. [VR]

25 R_3 and the MOSFET make up $100 \, \Omega$ and $0.5 \, \Omega$ in series,
totalling $100.5 \, \Omega$. When the MOSFET is fully on,
$V_{out} = 9 \times 0.5/100.5 = 0.045$ V.

a) When the MOSFET is off, no current flows through it
or through R_3, so no power is dissipated.

b) When it is fully on, the current through it (and R_3,
ignoring any load that might be connected) is
$9/100.5 = 89.55$ mA. Power dissipated in R_3 is
$0.089\,55^2 \times 100 = 802$ mW. Power dissipated in the
MOSFET $= 0.8955^2 \times 0.5 = 4.01$ mW.

26 a) Gain $=$ output/input $= 120/5 = 24$. In decibels:
$n = 10 \log_{10}(120/5) = 10 \times 1.380 = 13.8$ dB.

b) Gain $= 4.2/0.15 = 28$. In decibels:
$n = 10 \log_{10}(4.2/0.15) = 10 \times 1.447 = 14.5$ dB.

c) Gain $= 0.750/2 = 0.375$. In decibels:
$n = 10 \log_{10}(0.750/2) = 10 \times -4.26 = -4.26$ dB.

d) Gain $= 3.75/0.135 = 27.78$. In decibels:
$n = 20 \log_{10}(3.75/0.135) = 28.9$ dB.
[Calculating power gain based on voltage values
requires the multiplier 20 instead of 10.]

e) Gain $= 3.2/5.6 = 0.5714$. In decibels:
$n = 20 \log_{10}(3.2/5.6) = -4.86$ dB.
[Calculating power gain based on current values
requires the multiplier 20 instead of 10.]

27 a) Maximum current $= \sqrt{(V/R)} = \sqrt{(3/100)} = 173$ mA;
pd $= \sqrt{(3 \times 100)} = 17.3$ V.

b) Maximum current $= \sqrt{(25/4.7)} = 2.31$ A;
pd $= \sqrt{(25 \times 4.7)} = 10.8$ V.

28 Rms voltage $= 0.707 \times$ amplitude $= 8.13$ V.

29 Rms current $= 0.707 \times$ amplitude $= 297$ mA.

30 The rms voltage of the equivalent ac supply is 15 V, the same
as the dc supply. The peak voltage is $15/0.707 = 21.2$ V.

31 a) $X_C = 1/2\pi fC = 1/(2\pi \times 25 \times 100)$ [1/(kHz × nF)] $=$
$63.7 \, \Omega$;

b) $X_C = 1/(2\pi \times 50 \times 220)$ [1/(Hz × μF)] $= 14.5 \, \Omega$;

c) $X_C = 1/(2\pi \times 30 \times 12)$ [1/(MHz × pF)] $= 442 \, \Omega$;

d) $X_C = 1/(2\pi \times 500 \times 47)$ [1/(Hz × nF)] $= 6.77$ kΩ;

e) $X_C = 1/(2\pi \times 8 \times 2.2)$ [1/(MHz × μF)] $= 9.04$ mΩ;

32 a) $X_L = 2\pi fL = 2\pi \times 50 \times 10)$ [Hz × H] $= 3.14$ kΩ;

b) $X_L = 2\pi \times 200 \times 250$ [Hz × μH] $= 0.314 \, \Omega$;

c) $X_L = 2\pi \times 2 \times 50$ [MHz × μH] $= 628 \, \Omega$;

d) $X_L = 2\pi \times 6.7 \times 1$ [MHz × μH] $= 42.1 \, \Omega$;

e) $X_L = 2\pi \times 15.6 \times 2.5$ [Hz × H] $= 245 \, \Omega$.

33 All oppose the flow of current, and all are expressed in
ohms. Reactance is dependent on current frequency, but
resistance is not. Resistance causes dissipation of energy
(as heat) but reactance causes no energy loss.
   The value of resistance (R) depends on the dimensions
of the conductor and the resistivity of the material of
which it is made.
   The value of capacitative reactance (X_C) depends on the
dimensions of the plates or other conducting surfaces, the
amount they overlap, the distance between them and the
material (dielectric) between them. It decreases with
increasing frequency.
   The value of inductive reactance (X_L) depends on the
dimensions and materials of the former, and the number
and size of turns of the coil. It increases with increasing
frequency.
   Impedance (R, Z_C, Z_L) is a term that includes both
resistance and reactance, and is numerically equal to the
sum of these for any one device.

34 $X_C = 1/(2\pi fC) = 21.22$ kΩ
$V_{rms} = 0.707 \times 2.5 = 1.768$ V
$I_{rms} = V_{rms}/X_C = 1.768/21.22 = 83.3$ mA

35 $X_C = 1/(2\pi fC) = 0.241 \, \Omega$
$I_{rms} = 0.707 \times 0.120 = 0.0848$ A
$V_{rms} = I_{rms} \times X_C = 20.4$ mV

36 $X_L = 2\pi fL = 691\ \Omega$
$V_{rms} = 0.707 \times 325 = 230\ V$
$I_{rms} = V_{rms}/X_L = 230/691 = 333\ mA$

37 The mains voltage, 230 V, is the rms voltage; the peak voltage is $230/0.707 = 325\ V$, which is the maximum operating voltage. The minimum working voltage of the capacitor must therefore be 325 V.

38 Reactance $X_L = V_{rms}/I_{rms} = 6/0.4 = 15\ \Omega$
$f = X_L/2\pi L = 15/(2\pi \times 0.015) = 159\ Hz$

39 $Z = \sqrt{[R^2 + (X_L - X_C)^2]}$
$X_C = 1/(2\pi \times 27 \times 450)\ [1/(kHz \times nF)] = 13.10\ \Omega$
$X_L = 2\pi \times 27 \times 1.5\ [kHz \times mH] = 254.5\ \Omega$
$Z = \sqrt{[500^2 + (254.5 - 13.10)^2]} = 555.2\ \Omega$
$I_{rms} = V_{rms}/Z = 4/555.2 = 7.20\ mA$

40 $Z = \sqrt{[R^2 + (X_L - X_C)^2]}$
$X_C = 1/(2\pi \times 27 \times 250)\ [1/(kHz \times pF)] = 23\,579\ \Omega$
$X_L = 2\pi \times 27 \times 33\ [kHz \times mH] = 5598\ \Omega$
$Z = \sqrt{[110^2 + (5598 - 23\,579)^2]} = 17\,981\ \Omega$
$V_{rms} = I_{rms} \times Z = 2.5 \times 17\,981 = 45\ kV$

41 Charge $Q = VC = 6 \times 47\ [V \times nF] = 282\ nC$. Initial discharge current is $6/120 = 50\ mA$. The time constant is $RC = 120 \times 47\ [\Omega \times nF] = 5.64\ \mu s$. The capacitor is discharged for 1 time constant, so the pd is $0.37 \times 6 = 2.22\ V$. It takes 4 more time constants to almost fully discharge, that is $4 \times 5.64 = 22.56\ \mu s$.

42 a) The time constant for R_1 and C is $220 \times 180\ [\Omega \times \mu F] = 39.6\ ms$.
It takes $0.69 \times 39.6 = 27.3\ ms$ to charge the capacitor to 6 V (0.5 of 12 V).
b) 4.44 V is 0.37×12; it takes 1 time constant to discharge to this level. The time constant is therefore 70.2 ms, so $R_2 = 70.2/180\ [ms/\mu F] = 390\ \Omega$.

43 See Fig. 1.11, p. 8. The equation relating V_C to time is also given on p. 9. When $V_C = 0.5V_S$, it follows that $e^{-t/RC} = 0.5$. Taking natural logarithms of both sides of this equation gives $-t/RC = \ln 0.5 = -0.69$. From this we obtain $t = 0.69RC$.

44 See Fig. 1.13 and the explanation on p. 9.

45 Resonant frequency $f_R = 1/2\pi\sqrt{(LC)} = 16.4\ Hz$. The impedances of L and C are equal.

46 $Z_L = 2\pi fL = 27.65\ \Omega$. Given that Z_C equals Z_L at resonance, $C = 1/2\pi f Z_C = 1/2\pi f Z_L = 2.88\ \mu F$.

47 See the definition and equations on p. 11.
$f_R = 800\ kHz$; bandwidth $= 853 - 750 = 103\ kHz$
$Q = 800/103 = 7.77$

48 a) See pp 11–12.
b) *Working:* $f_c \approx f_R = 1/2\pi\sqrt{(LC)}$
$\Rightarrow\qquad f_c^2 = 1/4\pi^2 LC$
$\Rightarrow\qquad L = 1/4\pi^2 C f_c^2$
With a 10 nF capacitor and $f_c = 32\ kHz$, $L = 2.47\ mH$.
$R = \sqrt{(L/C)}/Q = 331\ \Omega$
Solutions: The filter network is shown in Fig. 1.16 (p. 11). $L = 2.47\ mH$, $R = 331\ \Omega$, $C = 10\ nF$. (Other solutions assuming other values of C are acceptable.)

■ Section 2
Ten quick questions

1. AND.
2. INVERT.
3. EX-OR.
4. A
5. $2^4 = 16$.
6. Only one of the variables changes state.
7. They are not equal.
8. $A + AB = A$
9. NAND or NOR.
10. De Morgan's theorem.

Questions on logic circuits

1. An electronic circuit with one or more inputs that accept logic high or low voltages. For any given combination of input levels the single output produces a logic high or low voltage, as set out in the truth table of the gate.

2. **a)** See the truth table on p. 19 (INVERT = NOT).
   b) Connect together all the inputs of the NOR gate. The gate then acts according to the first and last lines of the NOR truth table, which is equivalent to the INVERT truth table.

3. The outputs of a NAND is 0 when, and only when, all the inputs are high. The truth table for a 3-input NAND is:

Inputs			Output
C	B	A	Q
0	0	0	1
0	0	1	1
0	1	0	1
0	1	1	1
1	0	0	1
1	0	1	1
1	1	0	1
1	1	1	0

The symbol is:

Figure A2.1

4. IF A OR B, THEN Q. On Friday, Q = 0. See p. 19 for the OR truth table.

5. A = the door is open; B = food is cooking; Q = the lamp is on. IF A OR B, THEN Q. See p. 19 for the OR truth table. The last line (A = 1, B = 1) should never occur.

6 a) A = person detected; B = it is light; C = it is less than 30 s since the system was triggered; Q = light on. If A AND NOT-B AND C, THEN Q: $A\bar{B}C = Q$.

C	B	A	$\bar{B}$	Q
0	0	0	1	0
0	0	1	1	0
0	1	0	0	0
0	1	1	0	0
1	0	0	1	0
1	0	1	1	1
1	1	0	0	0
1	1	1	0	0

The lamp is on when the conditions or the sixth row of the truth table are in force. The logic circuit diagram is:

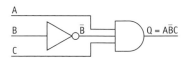

Figure A2.2

b) Use a PIR for moving person, and an LDR or photodiode for light level.

c) Use the 555 or 7555 timer IC wired as a monostable (see p. 47) with period 30 s.

7 By de Morgan,

$$\overline{ABC} = \overline{A} + \overline{B} + \overline{C}$$

Similarly,

$$\overline{A\bar{B}C} = \overline{A} + B + \overline{C}$$

Inverting both sides of the equation,

$$A\bar{B}C = \overline{\overline{A} + B + \overline{C}}$$

But $A\bar{B}C = Q$. So

$$Q = \overline{\overline{A} + B + \overline{C}}$$

The circuit includes a 3-input OR gate with inputs A and C inverted, and with input B not inverted. The output of this gate gives Q but we need $\overline{Q}$, so add a NOT gate to invert the output of the OR gate. In practice, to save a gate, we might replace the OR and NOT combination with a single NOR gate.

8 The lamp is on if A is closed. It is also on if B and C are closed. If '1' means 'switch closed' and 'lamp on', the truth table is:

C	B	A	Q
0	0	0	0
0	0	1	1
0	1	0	0
0	1	1	1
1	0	0	0
1	0	1	1
1	1	0	1
1	1	1	1

To obtain the table, enter binary values 0 to 7 in columns C to A. This gives all possible combinations of A, B and C. In column Q write '1' in every line which has A = 1. Then write '1' in any remaining cell in that column for which B = 1 and C = 1. Fill in any blank cells with '0' to complete column Q. The Boolean expression is Q = A + BC.

9 In the 3-bit (8-line) truth table, Q = 1 only when A = 0, B = 1 and C = 1 (C, B, A representing the binary number 110 = 6). The Boolean expression is $Q = \overline{A}BC$. The circuit is a 3-input AND gate, with input A inverted and the other two inputs not inverted.

10 Decimal 3 in 3-bit binary is 011, and decimal 5 is 101. If the digits of the binary number are identified as C, B and A from left to right, the Boolean expression is

$$Q = AB\bar{C} + A\bar{B}C$$

This can be simplified to

$$Q = A(B\bar{C} + \bar{B}C)$$

The expression in brackets is the EX-OR of B and C $(B \oplus C)$, so the circuit diagram is as shown in Fig. A2.3.

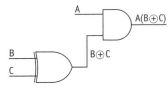

Figure A2.3

11 Output Q follows A in the top four rows of the table, and follows B in the bottom four.

S	B	A	Q
0	0	0	0
0	0	1	1
0	1	0	0
0	1	1	1
1	0	0	0
1	0	1	0
1	1	0	1
1	1	1	1

The Boolean expression is

$$Q = A\overline{B}\,\overline{S} + AB\overline{S} + \overline{A}BS + ABS$$

This type of equation (that is, one that ORs several terms, each of which contains all the variables) is often best simplified by drawing a Karnaugh map (Fig. A2.4). This shows three couples: $Q = AB + BS + A\overline{S}$. This can be represented by the circuit of Fig. A2.5.

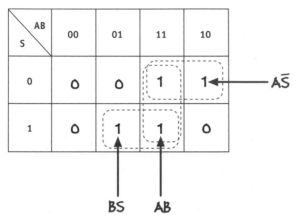

Figure A2.4

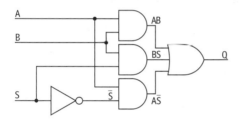

Figure A2.5

12 a) Use $A(B + C) = AB + AC$:

$$Q = (A + \overline{A})\overline{B}\,\overline{C}$$

Use $A + \overline{A} = 1$:

$$Q = \overline{B}\,\overline{C}$$

b) Use de Morgan on the first term:

$$Q = (\overline{A} + \overline{B})(\overline{A} + B)$$

Remove brackets:

$$Q = \overline{A}\,\overline{A} + \overline{A}B + \overline{A}\,\overline{B} + \overline{B}B$$

Use $AA = A$ and $B\overline{B} = 0$:

$$Q = \overline{A} + \overline{A}B + \overline{A}\,\overline{B} + 0$$

Use $A(B + C) = AB + AC$ on middle terms:

$$Q = \overline{A} + \overline{A}(B + \overline{B})$$

Use $A + \overline{A} = 1$:

$$Q = \overline{A} + \overline{A}$$

Use $A + A = A$:

$$Q = \overline{A}$$

13

Gate	1	2	3	4	5
B	A	$\overline{B}$	$\overline{A}$	$A\overline{B}$	$\overline{A}B$	$A\overline{B} + \overline{A}B$
0	0	1	1	0	0	0
0	1	1	0	1	0	1
1	0	0	1	0	1	1
1	1	0	0	0	0	0

Column 5 shows that Q is A EX-OR B. (This is another way of obtaining EX-OR.)

14 a)

B	A	AB	A + AB
0	0	0	0
0	1	0	1
1	0	0	0
1	1	1	1

The fourth column (A + AB) is identical to the second column (A), proving the identity.

b)

B	A	A + B	A(A + B)
0	0	0	0
0	1	1	1
1	0	1	0
1	1	1	1

The fourth column (A(A + AB)) is identical to the second column (A), proving the identity.

c)

B	A	$\overline{A + B}$	$\overline{B}$	$\overline{A}$	$\overline{A}\,\overline{B}$
0	0	1	1	1	1
0	1	0	1	0	0
1	0	0	0	1	0
1	1	0	0	0	0

The sixth column is identical to the third column, proving the identity.

d)

B	A	$\overline{AB}$	$\overline{B}$	$\overline{A}$	$\overline{A} + \overline{B}$
0	0	1	1	1	1
0	1	1	1	0	1
1	0	1	0	1	1
1	1	0	0	0	0

The sixth column is identical to the third column, proving the identity.

15

Gate		1	2	3	4
B	A	$\overline{AB}$	$\overline{A(\overline{AB})}$	$\overline{B(\overline{AB})}$	$\overline{\overline{A(\overline{AB})} \cdot \overline{B(\overline{AB})}}$
0	0	1	1	1	0
0	1	1	0	1	1
1	0	1	1	0	1
1	1	0	1	1	0

The entries for the output of gate 4 are identical with those in the EX-OR truth table, p. 19.

16 Use de Morgan: $Q = A(\overline{AB}) + B(\overline{AB})$
Use de Morgan again: $Q = A(\overline{A} + \overline{B}) + B(\overline{A} + \overline{B})$
Clear brackets: $Q = A\overline{A} + A\overline{B} + \overline{A}B + B\overline{B}$
Use $A\overline{A} = 0$ twice: $Q = A\overline{B} + \overline{A}B$
This is the expression for A EX-OR B.

17 See Fig. A2.6.

a)

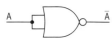

b)

c)

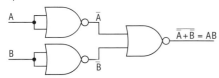

Figure A2.6

18 a) Insert brackets:
$$A(B + \overline{B}) + \overline{A}B$$
Use $A + \overline{A} = 1$:
$$A + \overline{A}B$$
Use $A + \overline{A}B = A + B$:
$$A + B$$

b) Remove brackets:
$$ABA + AB\overline{B} + A\overline{A} + AB + \overline{A}B + BB$$
Use $AA = A$ and $A\overline{A} = 0$:
$$AB + 0 + 0 + AB + \overline{A}B + B$$
Use $A + A = A$:
$$AB + \overline{A}B + B$$
Insert brackets:
$$B(A + \overline{A}) + B$$
Use $A + \overline{A} = 1$:
$$B + B$$
Use $A + A = A$:
$$B$$

c) Use de Morgan on first term:
$$(\overline{A} + \overline{B})(\overline{A} + B)$$
Remove brackets:
$$\overline{A}\,\overline{A} + \overline{A}B + \overline{A}\,\overline{B} + B\overline{B}$$
Use $AA = A$ and $A\overline{A} = 0$:
$$\overline{A} + \overline{A}B + \overline{A}\,\overline{B} + 0$$
Bracket last two terms:
$$\overline{A} + \overline{A}(B + \overline{B})$$
Use $A + \overline{A} = 1$:
$$\overline{A} + \overline{A}$$
Use $A + A = A$:
$$\overline{A}$$

19 Two variables NORed together equal their inverts ANDed together. Conversely, two variables NANDed together equal their inverts ORed together.

20 Gate outputs are:
gate 1 = $\overline{A}$, gate 2 = $\overline{B}$, gate 3 = $\overline{C}$, gate 4 = $\overline{A}\,\overline{B}\,\overline{C}$,
gate 5 = $A\,\overline{B}\,\overline{C}$, gate 6 = $\overline{A}\,\overline{B}\,\overline{C} + A\,\overline{B}\,\overline{C}$.
Applying logic to the output of gate 6:
Insert brackets: $(A + \overline{A})(\overline{B}\,\overline{C})$
Use $A + \overline{A} = 1$: $\overline{B}\,\overline{C}$
The circuit of Fig. 2.13 can be replaced by Fig. A2.7.

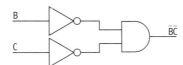

A ——— unconnected

Figure A2.7

21 All the output conditions have a high output (1) for one combination of A and B, and a low output (0) for the other three. This suggests using AND gates for the outputs.

For output '0' to produce 1 when A = 0 and B = 0, invert A and invert B and use an AND gate.
For output '1' to produce 1 when A = 1 and B = 0, invert B and use an AND gate.
For output '2' to produce 1 when A = 0 and B = 1, invert A and use an AND gate.
For output '3' to produce 1 when A = 1 and B = 1, use an AND gate.
Fig. A2.8 shows the circuit.

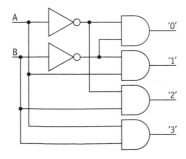

Figure A2.8

An alternative gate with one 1 and three 0s in its truth table output column is NOR. See question 26.

22

D	C	B	A	Gate 1	Gate 2	Gate 3	No. of 1s
0	0	0	0	0	0	0	0
0	0	0	1	1	0	1	1
0	0	1	0	1	0	1	1
0	0	1	1	0	0	0	2
0	1	0	0	0	1	1	1
0	1	0	1	1	1	0	2
0	1	1	0	1	1	0	2
0	1	1	1	0	1	1	3
1	0	0	0	0	1	1	1
1	0	0	1	1	1	0	2
1	0	1	0	1	1	0	2
1	0	1	1	0	1	1	3
1	1	0	0	0	0	0	2
1	1	0	1	1	0	1	3
1	1	1	0	1	0	1	3
1	1	1	1	0	0	0	4

The right-hand column gives the number of 1s in the DCBA input. The output of gate 3 is 1 whenever there is an odd number of ones. The value of the output of gate 3 can be used as a parity bit, appended to the 4-bit input, so that the total number of 1s in the 5-bit result is even. This gives even parity.

23 a) See Fig. A2.9a. The solution is $A + \overline{B}$.
   b) See Fig. A2.9b. The solution is $\overline{B}\,\overline{C}$.
   c) See Fig. A2.9c. The solution is A.
   d) See Fig. A2.9d. The solution is $A + \overline{B}C$.

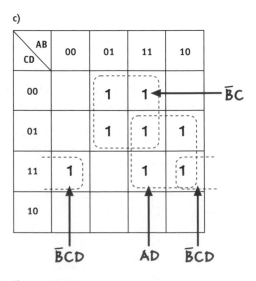

Figure A2.9

24 a) See Fig. A2.10a. The solution is $\overline{A}BD + \overline{A}CD$.
   b) See Fig. A2.10b. The solution is $\overline{A}D + BCD$.
   c) See Fig. A2.10c. The solution is $B\overline{C} + AD + \overline{B}CD$.

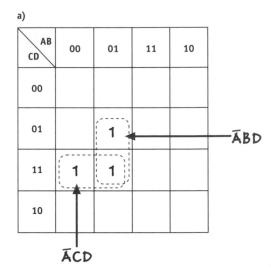

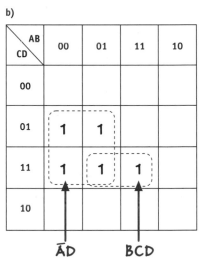

Figure A2.10

25 Q = 1 if the input corresponds to any of the four binary numbers, 010, 011, 101 or 110. The digits are represented by CBA in that order, with A = 1 and $\overline{A}$ = 0, and the same for B and C. The expression is:

$$Q = \overline{A}B\overline{C} + AB\overline{C} + A\overline{B}C + \overline{A}BC$$

This is mapped in Fig. A2.11 and simplifies to $\overline{A}B + B\overline{C} + A\overline{B}C$.

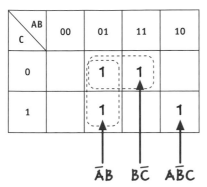

AB C	00	01	11	10
0		1	1	
1		1		1

$\overline{A}B$ $B\overline{C}$ $A\overline{B}C$

Figure A2.11

26 Replace the INVERT gate with a NAND gate with its inputs tied together. Replace the AND gate with a NAND gate. Then use another NAND, wired as an INVERT to invert the output of the 3-input NAND to produce AND. The result is shown in Fig. A2.12.

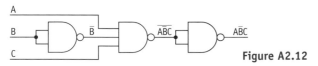

Figure A2.12

27 Set out the light sequence as a truth table:

Inputs		Outputs		
B	A	red	amber	green
0	0	1	0	0
0	1	0	1	0
1	0	0	0	1
1	1	0	0	1

Red: this is the same as a NOR gate truth table, so use a NOR gate for red.
Amber: there are three 0s and one 1 in this column, suggesting that the output is from a NOR gate. However, the entries in the first two lines are inverted, so invert the A input to this NOR gate.
Green: this column is identical with the B input column, so the B input drives the green lamp directly.
The result is shown in Fig. A2.13.

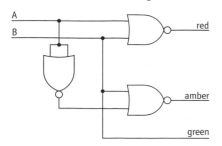

Figure A2.13

28 The expression with the same logic as these gates is Q = AB + BS + A$\overline{S}$. This has three AND terms that are ORed together. This means that the gate combining the three terms would use a 3-input OR gate, which we need to replace with a 3-input NAND gate. We use de Morgan's theorem, which converts NOR to AND, but first the expression needs to be put into NOR form. Invert both sides of the equation:

$$\overline{Q} = \overline{AB + BS + A\overline{S}}$$

Now we are able to use de Morgan:

$$\overline{Q} = \overline{AB}\cdot\overline{BS}\cdot\overline{A\overline{S}}$$

There are now three terms in NAND form so these can be represented by NAND gates, with a fourth NAND gate to produce the inverse of S.
Inverting both sides of the equation to get Q again gives:

$$Q = \overline{\overline{AB}\cdot\overline{BS}\cdot\overline{A\overline{S}}}$$

All expressions are in NAND form so the circuit may be built with five NAND gates, as in Fig. A2.14. Note that simply making the substitutions for each of the original gates (using Fig. 2.9, p. 24) requires eleven gates. Here, because the equation has been turned into NAND statements *before* trying to realise it in NAND, it needs only five gates. This is one more than in the original circuit, but the advantage is, if we use a NAND to invert S, that all gates are of the same type.

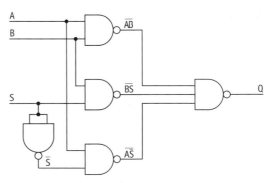

Figure A2.14

▌ Section 3

Ten quick questions

1 Drain.
2 4
3 Forward biased.
4 Large signal current gain of a BJT.
5 It falls.
6 Negative temperature coefficient.
7 The equivalent of two thyristors connected anode to cathode.
8 Siemens.
9 Zener diode.
10 Electret microphone.

Questions on components

1 Any three of: resistor, capacitor, inductor, diode.
Resistor: resists flow of current, resulting in a fall of potential along the length of the resistor; $R = V/I$.
Capacitor: stores energy (charge) in the form of the electric field between its plates; $V = Q/C$.
Inductor: stores energy in the form of a magnetic field threading the coil.
Diode: conducts current in one direction only, from anode to cathode.

2 *Forward bias*: the anode is made positive of the diode; current flows if the forward bias exceeds about 0.6 V.
Forward voltage drop: the fall in voltage across a conducting diode from anode to cathode; depends on the current flowing, but is typically 0.7 V.
Leakage current: the small current passing through a diode from cathode to anode when the diode is reverse biased.

3 **a)** Any three of: signal diode, power diode, Zener diode, light-emitting diode (LED), photodiode.
Signal diode: low current (100 mA); moderate reverse pd (75 V).
Power diode: high power rating (1 W, 5 W, 10 W or more); robust package; intended for mounting on heat sink; high reverse pd (several hundred volts).
Zener diode: when reverse biased, conduction occurs at specified voltage.
LED: produces visible light or infrared when forward biased.
Photodiode: package admits light (or infrared); leakage current when reverse biased is proportional to light intensity; fast response compared with LDR.
b) *Signal diode*: low-power rectification, including demodulation in radio receivers; protective diode.
Power diode: high-power rectification, such as in power supply units.
Zener diode: voltage regulator circuits; standard voltage in comparator circuits.
LED: indicator; opto-isolator; opto-coupler; high-speed light source in fibre-optic systems.
Photodiode: detector in security systems and fibre-optic systems; measuring light intensity.
Circuits for many of these applications are found in section 4 (pp 42–44 and pp 55–56).

4 **a)** Switch set to B: filling valve is powered during negative half-cycles, so it opens. No current through emptying valve, which stays closed.
b) Switch set to C: no power to valves, which both stay closed.
c) Switch set to A: emptying valve is powered during positive half-cycles, so it opens. No current through filling valve, which stays closed.
d) The indicator LED is powered during positive half-cycles, so comes on when emptying. There are two forward voltage drops in the supply to each valve, so they receive ac of amplitude $12 - 1.4 = 10.6$ V. In the circuit containing the LED, there are forward voltage drops of 0.7 V and 2 V (for the LED), total 2.7 V. Voltage across resistor is $12 - 2.7 = 9.3$ V. Current = $9.3/390 = 23.8$ mA.

5 Power dissipated in the diode is the current through it multiplied by the voltage across it.
a) Power = 0.4 W and voltage = 6.8 V; current = power/voltage = $0.4/6.8 = 58.8$ mA.
b) Power = 5 W and voltage = 12 V; current = power/voltage = $5/12 = 417$ mA.

6 **a)** Collector, base, emitter. The emitter is made most negative.
b) A BJT amplifies base current. The base–emitter voltage is approximately 0.7 V.

7 **a)** If a change in the base current of i_b results in a change in the collector current of i_c, then $h_{fe} = i_c/i_b$.
b) If the collector is 10 V positive of the emitter, the BJT is biased for operation. Using the equation from **a)**, the change in collector current is $i_c = i_b \times h_{fe} = 1.2 \times 260 = 312$ mA. Then the change in emitter current is $i_e = i_b + i_c = 313.2$ mA.

8 Working in amps, $h_{FE} = I_C/I_B = 8.16/0.024 = 340$.

9 **a)** Voltage across resistor is $V = IR = 0.002 \times 3000 = 6$ V. $V_{out} = 15 - 6 = 9$ V.
b) $I_B = I_C/h_{FE} = 0.002/200 = 10$ µA.
c) Voltage across base resistor = $IR = 10 \times 27$ [µA × kΩ] = 0.27 V. Voltage at base terminal is approximately 0.7 V, so $V_{in} = 0.7 + 0.27 = 0.97$ V.

10 **a)** The terminal by which current enters the MOSFET.
b) The change of drain current per unit change of gate–source voltage, $g_m = i_d/v_{gs}$.
c) The gate–source voltage at which the MOSFET just begins to conduct.
d) The current flowing through the transistor from drain to source.
(Note: in these answers, currents are taken to be conventional current.)

11 $v_{gs} = i_d/g_m = -5.6/800$ [mA/mS] = -7 mV

12 A MOSFET converts changes in input voltage to changes in output current; a BJT is a current amplifier. The advantages of a MOSFET are: extremely high input impedance; low 'on' resistance to drain current. The disadvantages are: non-linear forward transfer characteristic, causing distortion of large-amplitude signals; liability to destruction of gate insulation by electrostatic charge.

13 See p. 32.

14 See the description of a thyristor on p. 32. A triac is the equivalent of two thyristors connected anode to cathode. The triggering pulse of a thyristor is positive, but that of a triac may be either positive or negative.

15 The resistance of a *light-dependent resistor* (LDR) decreases with increasing light intensity. It is able to respond to a wide range of intensities, but its response is non-linear and relatively slow. The leakage current through a reverse-biased *photodiode* increases linearly with increasing light intensity. It is sensitive to low light intensities. The collector current of a *phototransistor* is linearly proportional to light intensity. Its response is slower, but is more sensitive than a photodiode.
a) Use a photodiode because of its fast response.

b) Use an LDR because of its wide operating range, or use an infrared photodiode because an infrared beam is invisible.

c) Use a phototransistor because of its sensitivity to low light.

16 Many circuits can be used. The basic circuit is a transistor switch, as in Fig. 4.4 (p. 45), but with the load replaced by a resistor (say 10 kΩ). The output of the switch is taken at the collector or drain terminal of the transistor and goes to the input of a logic gate.

17 See p. 34 and Fig. 4.14.

18 See p. 34. The advantages are that its small size makes it easy to measure temperatures in small spaces, and results in rapid response to changes of temperature.

19 a), b) See p. 35. LEDs are preferred because they: take less current; rarely burn out; are available in a wide range of shapes, sizes and colours; can be fabricated into special displays such as 7-segment displays and bar-graphs.

20 a) Assuming a 2 V drop across the LED, the resistor required is $(9 - 2)/0.02 = 350\,\Omega$. Nearest E24 value is $360\,\Omega$.

b) Voltage drop across LED is $18 - 2 = 16\,\text{V}$. Current $= 16/680 = 23.5\,\text{mA}$.

21 See Fig. A3.1. Transistor switches are discussed in subsection 4.2.

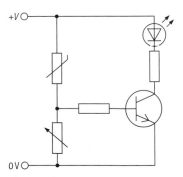

Figure A3.1

22 See Fig. A3.2. The protective diode is needed because the relay coil is inductive (see p. 42).

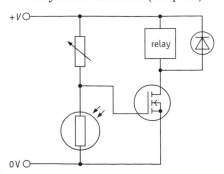

Figure A3.2

23 The resistance decreases as temperature increases, but the relationship is not linear.
a) 9 kΩ;
b) 16 °C.

24 See Fig. A3.3. The resistance of the thermistor at 18 °C is 20.3 kΩ (from the graph in question 23). To obtain 3 V at the gate of the MOSFET, the lower resistor must have a value $3 \times 20.3/(12 - 3) = 6.8\,\text{k}\Omega$. This is in the E24 series. The 'on' resistance of the MOSFET is so low that we can ignore the voltage drop across it. For the LED to run at 20 mA, the series resistor must be $(12 - 2)/0.02 = 500\,\Omega$. The nearest E24 value is $510\,\Omega$.

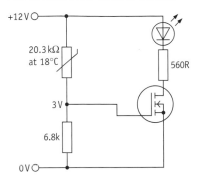

Figure A3.3

25 See p. 37 for the description. One revolution is 360/15 = 24 steps. 5 rpm requires 120 steps in 1 minute, or 2 steps per second. The advantages are that its direction of rotation and its angular position can be controlled by a digital circuit; its rate of rotation is precisely controlled by the system clock; it is not affected by variations in the mechanical load that it is driving.

26 Any three of: solenoid, relay, motor, speaker. See pp 36–38.

▍Section 4

Ten quick questions

1. Monostable.
2. The product of the current gains of the individual transistors.
3. Approximately 1.
4. Common-collector.
5. MOSFET.
6. $1.44/(R_1 + 2R_2)C$
7. $-6\,\text{dB/octave}$, or $-10\,\text{dB/decade}$.
8. $f_c = 1/(2\pi RC)$
9. Emitter follower.
10. Class B amplifier.

Questions on analogue networks and circuits

1. See p. 42.
2. See Fig. A4.1.

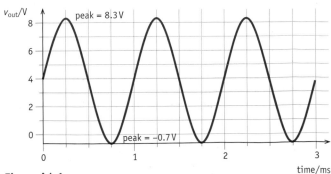

Figure A4.1

3 For the diagram see Fig. 4.3, p. 43. Use a 5.6 V Zener.
$R = (18 - 5.6)/(0.275 + 0.005) = 44.3\ \Omega$. Next lower E24 value is 43 Ω.
For the diode, power $= 5.6(0.275 + 0.005) = 1.57$ W.
For the resistor,
power $= (18 - 5.6)(0.275 + 0.005) = 3.47$ W.

4 Current through load $= 12/27 = 0.444$ A.
$R = (24 - 12)/(0.444 + 0.005) = 26.7\ \Omega$. Use 24 Ω.
For the diode, power $= 12(0.444 + 0.005) = 5.39$ W.
For the resistor, power $= (24 - 12)(0.444 + 0.005) = 5.39$ W.

5 When the intruder walks between the lamp and R_2, the beam of light is broken. R_2 is an LDR. When it receives less light, its resistance increases, the voltage at A increases, the base current to Q1 increases, Q1 is turned on, current passes through the siren and it sounds.

6 See Fig. A4.2. The variable resistor R_1 allows the switch-on temperature to be set. The protective diode D1 is essential.

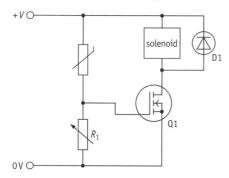

Figure A4.2

7 See p. 45.

8 The sensor could be an LDR, a photodiode or a phototransistor.
$I_B = I_C/h_{FE} = 0.03/120 = 250\ \mu A$

9 See Fig. A4.3. The photodiode D1 is reverse biased. Leakage current generates a pd across R_1, which can be adjusted so that the circuit is triggered when the darkroom light is on. Darkness reduces leakage current, reducing the pd across R_1, and turning Q1 off. The relay coil is switched off, and the normally closed contacts close. This switches on L1, to illuminate the 'Busy!' sign. The reverse happens when the darkroom light is on. D2 is a protective diode, needed because the relay is inductive.

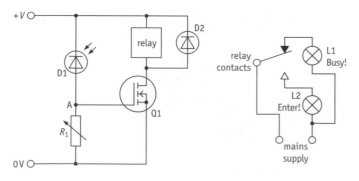

Figure A4.3

10 a) A Darlington pair. The emitter current of Q1 becomes the base current of Q2, so the total gain is the product of the two individual gains.
For Q1: $I_E' \approx I_C' = h_{FE} \times I_B'$
For Q2: $I_E'' \approx I_C'' = h_{FE} \times I_B''$
$= h_{FE} \times h_{FE} \times I_B'$

b) The h_{FE} of the two is $120^2 = 14\ 400$.

c) $I_B' = 0.01/14\ 400 \approx 0.7\ \mu A$

11 See Fig. A4.4. The sensor and heater can be run from the same 12 V supply. A power MOSFET with low 'on' resistance is preferred, as the current through the heater is $15/12 = 1.25$ A.

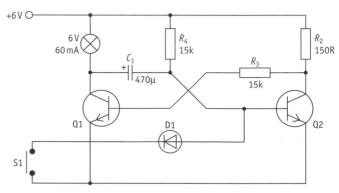

Figure A4.4

12 See p. 47.

13 The circuit in Fig. A4.5 is based on Fig. 4.6, p. 46. The lamp has low resistance and moderate current, so it can replace R_1 or R_2. Q1 goes 'on' when the monostable is triggered, so the lamp must replace R_1. Output from R_2 or Q2 is not needed. If C_1 is 470 μF, then for a 5-second pulse, $R_4 = 5/0.69C_1 = 5/(0.69 \times 470 \times 10^{-6}) = 15.4$ kΩ. Use 15 kΩ for R_3 and R_4. A push-button switch S1 has been added to the circuit to trigger it when pressed.

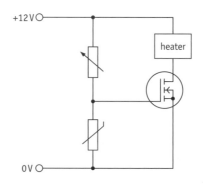

Figure A4.5

14 Use the circuit of Fig. 4.8 (p. 47), replacing R_1 and R_2 by LEDs, each with a series resistor to limit current. The mark–space ratio should be 1, so make $C_1 = C_2$ and $R_3 = R_4$. For a frequency of 1 Hz, and assuming 220 μF capacitors, $R = 1/1.38C$ (see p. 47), so $R = 1/(1.38 \times 220 \times 10^{-6})\ \Omega = 3.29$ kΩ. Use 3.3 kΩ resistors. Other combinations of R and C are possible.

15 See Fig. 4.10 (p. 47). $t = 1.1RC = 0.290$ s.

16 a) $f = 1.44/(R_1 + 2R_2)C$
$R_1 = 1.44/(450 \times 1 \times 10^{-6}) - (2 \times 1000) = 1.2\,\text{k}\Omega$
b) R_1 increases and frequency is reduced.
c) Supply voltage has no effect on frequency.

17 $f_c = 1/2\pi RC = 10.3\,\text{kHz}$. Phase change is $-45°$. See Fig. 4.12c (p. 49).

18 See p. 49. $f_c = 1/2\pi RC = 12.9\,\text{kHz}$

19 Phase difference is zero at 0 Hz, lagging as frequency increases until 100 kHz (f_c), when it is $-45°$, lagging further until it eventually reaches $-90°$ at high frequencies.

20 a) $f_c = 1/2\pi RC = 265\,\text{kHz}$
b) The region between the passband region and the stopband region, in which the rising frequency response curves over and becomes flat-topped. It includes the -3 dB point.

21 See Fig. 4.14 (p. 50).
Voltage gain $= -R_C/R_E = -3300/820 = -4.02$

22 See p. 51.

23 They form a highpass filter in which the resistors pass signals to the supply lines, effectively acting in parallel. Putting 4.7 kΩ and 22 kΩ in parallel gives
$(4.7 \times 22)/(4.7 + 22) = 3.87\,\text{k}\Omega$.
$f_c = 1/(2\pi \times 3.87 \times 4.7)\ [1/(\text{k}\Omega \times \mu\text{F})] = 8.75\,\text{Hz}$

24 See table on p. 53.

25 Emitter follower amplifier. See description on p. 52 of why it has unity gain. Because of its high input impedance and low output impedance, it is used as a buffer between a high-impedance source and a low-impedance load.

26 See Fig. 4.16, p. 52. The gate is biased to just above the threshold voltage, which is usually between 2 V and 4 V.

27 Very high input impedance, high frequency operation, non-linear gain.

28 See Fig. 4.17, p. 52. Gain ≈ 1; source follower amplifier.

29 'Complementary' because it is based on two transistors of opposite polarity (npn and pnp BJTs, or n-channel and p-channel MOSFETs); 'push–pull' because one transistor produces a positive voltage output (push) and the other a negative output (pull).

30 a) 50% efficiency because the transistor is conducting when there is no signal.
b) See Fig. 4.20, p. 54. The transistors are off when there is no signal. The diodes bias the transistors so that they are ready to turn on as the signal deviates from 0 V.

31 See Fig. 4.19, p. 53. Class B amplifiers. The transistors do not conduct as the input signal crosses between $+0.7$ V and -0.7 V.

32 A device to increase the rate transfer of heat from an electronic component to the air around it. When a component such as a transistor has a large current flowing through it and/or a large voltage across it, much power is dissipated in the component so that it becomes hot, and it may suffer permanent damage.

33 Metallic for good conduction and high heat capacity, fins for convection cooling, dull black surface for radiation.

34 To reduce the thermal resistance between the two surfaces, *or* to increase conduction of heat from the transistor to the heat sink.

35 Total resistance $= 1.5 + 0.1 + 17 = 18.6\,°\text{C/W}$.
At overheating temperature, the temperature difference $= 150 - 27 = 123\,°\text{C}$.
Maximum safe power $= 123/18.6 = 6.6\,\text{W}$.

36 Power dissipated in transistor is $P = I^2R = 1.2^2 \times 5 = 7.2\,\text{W}$.
Temperature difference at overheating $= 150 - 30 = 120\,°\text{C}$.
Thermal resistance $= 120/7.2 = 16.7\,°\text{C/W}$. Preferably use a sink with lower resistance, such as 8.5 °C/W.

37 When an alternating current passes through the primary coil, an alternating current (usually of different amplitude) is induced in the secondary coil.
Secondary voltage $=$ primary voltage $\times n_s/n_p$
$= 6 \times 550/120 = 27.5\,\text{V rms}$.
Secondary current $=$ primary current $\times n_p/n_s$
$= 0.4 \times 120/550 = 87.3\,\text{mA rms}$.

38 Secondary turns $= 450 \times 18/230 = 35.2$; wind 35 turns.

39 The diagram is similar to Fig. 4.22b (p. 56), but with a period of 8.33 ms. Input peaks are at ± 27.5 V, output peaks are at 26.8 V.

40 Double the efficiency and a more continuous supply of current; a diode bridge. See Fig. 4.23b, p. 56.

▍ Section 5
Ten quick questions
1 High.
2 High.
3 Its $\overline{Q}$ output is connected to its D input.
4 29
5 Modulo-5.
6 Priority encoder.
7 All its flip-flops are clocked at the same time.
8 Multiplexer.
9 Q output goes low, $\overline{Q}$ output goes high.
10 Q output of one connected to clock input of next.

Questions on digital circuits
1 See Fig. 5.1a, p. 61.

2 There are many possible answers, including answers based on Figs 4.4a and b, p. 45.

3 The current required is too large to be provided directly by the output. Use a MOSFET, as in Fig. A5.1.

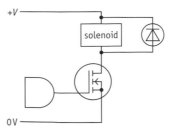

Figure A5.1

4 See Figs 5.2a and b, p. 62.

5 See p. 62 and Fig. 5.3, p. 63.

6

Inputs			Outputs	
C_i	B	A	C_o	S
0	1	0	0	1
1	1	0	1	0
1	1	1	1	1

7 a) A majority logic circuit has an odd number of inputs and one output. The output equals the majority of the inputs.

b)

C_i	B	A	$\overline{AB}$	$\overline{BC_i}$	$\overline{AC_i}$	C_o
1	0	0	1	1	1	0
0	1	1	0	0	1	1

8 a) The output shows the number of the highest priority input that is at logic 1.

b)

Inputs					Q1 =	Q0 =	Priority
3	2	1	$\overline{2}$	$\overline{1 \cdot 2}$	2 + 3	$(\overline{1 \cdot 2}) + 3$	
0	0	0	1	0	0	0	nil
0	0	1	1	1	0	1	1
0	1	0	0	0	1	0	2
0	1	1	0	0	1	0	2
1	0	0	1	0	1	1	3
1	0	1	1	1	1	1	3
1	1	0	0	0	1	1	3
1	1	1	0	0	1	1	3

9 First find Q0 in terms of NAND, working with input numbers. Then use de Morgan on the equation for Q0 in the table for question 8.

$$Q0 = (1 \cdot \overline{2}) + 3 = \overline{\overline{1 \cdot \overline{2}} \cdot \overline{3}}$$

This expression contains only NAND and INVERT (which can be obtained with a NAND gate).
For Q1, using de Morgan we find

$$Q1 = 2 + 3 = \overline{\overline{2} \cdot \overline{3}}$$

The inverted values are already required for Q0, so Q1 is obtained by using only one NAND gate. Fig. A5.2 shows the circuit.

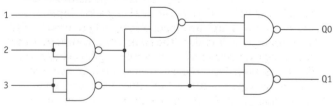

Figure A5.2

10

Inputs					Outputs		
E	D	C	B	A	Q2	Q1	Q0
0	0	0	0	1	0	0	1
0	0	0	1	0	0	1	0
0	0	1	0	0	0	1	1
0	1	0	0	0	1	0	0
1	0	0	0	0	1	0	1

It is a decimal-to-binary converter for 1 to 5.

11 There are three inputs, A, B and C, each with an invert gate to produce $\overline{A}$, $\overline{B}$, and $\overline{C}$. There are eight outputs, numbered 0 to 7, each coming from a 3-input NOR gate. The three inputs are connected to either A or $\overline{A}$, either B or $\overline{B}$, and either C or $\overline{C}$. The NOR gates thus decode all the binary values 000 to 111 applied to the three inputs. For example, the gate that produces output 5 receives inputs $\overline{A}$, B, and $\overline{C}$, so that its output goes high for input 101, when all three of its inputs are low.

12 See Fig. A5.3.

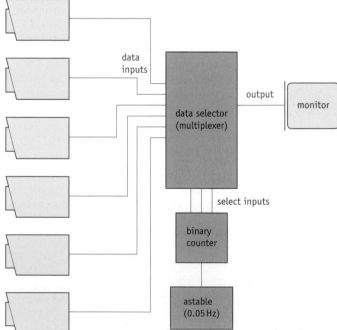

Figure A5.3

13 a) Its inputs are connected either to the positive line or the 0 V line. For each combination of 'select' inputs the appropriate logic level appears at the output.

b) Output sequence is 0, 0, 1, 1, 0, 0, 1, 1.

14 See Fig. A5.4. Data is fed to all four AND gates. Gates can pass the data to the output only if both of their other inputs are high. By feeding these with A or $\overline{A}$ and with B or $\overline{B}$, we can select which one of these will pass the data to its output.

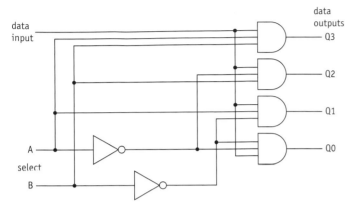

Figure A5.4

15

Inputs		Outputs						
B	A	a	b	c	d	e	f	g
0	0	1	1	1	1	1	1	0
0	1	0	1	1	0	0	0	0
1	0	1	1	0	1	1	0	1
1	1	1	1	1	1	0	0	1

$a = d = \overline{A}\overline{B}$
$b = 1$
$c = \overline{AB}$
$e = \overline{A}$
$f = \overline{A + B}$
$g = B$

16 See Fig. A5.5. The circuit drives a common-cathode LED display.

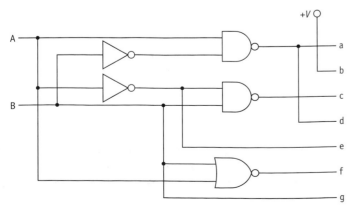

Figure A5.5

17

Inputs		Outputs	
S	R	Q	$\overline{Q}$
0	0	not allowed	
0	1	1	0
1	0	0	1
1	1	no change	

a) Q goes low and $\overline{Q}$ goes high;
b) nothing happens to either output.

18 a) The output would be normally low, but a high pulse would be produced on a falling input edge.
   b) See Fig. A5.6. Stable when input high and output low, with *C* discharged. A low input pulse makes Q go high instantly and *C* begins to charge. When its charge reaches logic high level, gate 2 changes state and Q becomes low. This ends the output pulse. *C* continues to charge until the input returns to high, when *C* begins to discharge again. The output stays low.

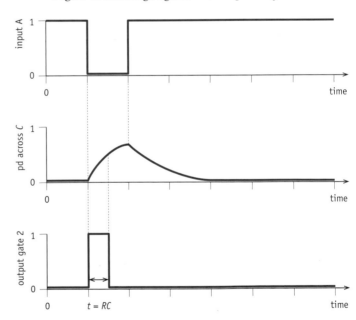

Figure A5.6

19 The output is normally high but with a low pulse on a falling edge. It is stable with input A and output Q high, X low, Y high, and with *C* fully charged. A low input makes output Q go low instantly, because gate 1 makes X high, and Y is still held high by the charge on *C*. Now *C* begins to discharge exponentially through *R*. As soon as the pd across *C* falls to the half-way point, Y counts as receiving a low input. Gate 2 now has input X high and input Y low, so Q returns to high. The output pulse is ended. The pd across *C* continues to fall for as long as A remains low, or until the pd reaches zero. When A is made high, *C* charges exponentially until the pd reaches the supply value, but this does not result in any further changes in Q. The timing diagram is as in Fig. A5.6 but with the two lower curves inverted.

20 The circuit is like that in Fig. 5.16 (p. 69), except that the INVERT gates are replaced by NOR gates, with the inputs of each connected together. The frequency is $1/2.2RC = 1/(2.2 \times 220 \times 470)[1/(k\Omega \times nF)] = 4.40$ Hz.

21 Inputs: clock, data (D), set (or preset), reset (or clear). Outputs: Q and $\overline{Q}$. See the symbol in Fig. 5.18a, p. 70.

22 See Fig. 5.17, p. 69. Propagation delay is the time taken by the gates in the flip-flop to change state after the rising edge of the clock input.

23 The output(s) of the circuit change only when the clock input rises from low to high (or in some devices, only when it falls from high to low). Any of the circuits using D-type flip-flops (pp 69–79) can be used as an illustration.

24 See Fig. 5.19, p. 70) (first two flip-flops only), and Fig. 5.20 (first three plots only).

25 See Fig. 5.21, p. 71 (first three flip-flops only), and Fig. 5.22 (first four plots only).

26 a) The output is 110 (decimal 6).
b) The circuit is as in Fig. 5.23, p. 72, except that all three outputs are ANDed using a 3-input gate.

27 The stages are driven by a common clock, so that changes in state all occur at exactly the same time. There are no glitches and no spurious output values. Synchronous counters are able to count faster than ripple counters.

28 See p. 74.

29 The outputs and required data inputs are:

Q1	Q0	D1	D0
1	1	1	0
1	0	0	1
0	1	0	0
0	0	1	1

The input to D1 is the invert of the EX-OR operation; in symbols:

$$D1 = \overline{Q0 \oplus Q1}$$

It may be obtained by feeding the output of an EX-OR gate to an INVERT gate. In practice, a ready-made exclusive-NOR gate can be used (Fig. A5.7). As shown, the symbol for an EX-NOR gate is the symbol for an EX-OR gate with the negating 'circle' at its output.

An answer showing an EX-OR gate followed by an INVERT gate is equally correct.

$$D0 = \overline{Q0}$$

There are no disallowed states.

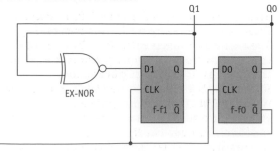

clock input

Figure A5.7

30 The full truth table is:

Binary state	Q2	Q1	Q0	D2	D1	D0
0	0	0	0	1	0	0
1	1	0	0	0	1	0
2	0	1	0	0	0	1
4	0	0	1	0	0	0

$$D2 = \overline{Q0} \cdot \overline{Q1} \cdot \overline{Q2}$$
$$D1 = Q2$$
$$D0 = Q1$$

See Fig. A5.8 for the circuit.

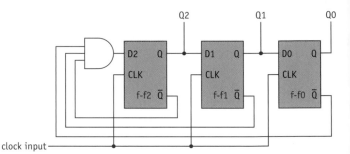

clock input

Figure A5.8

31 In this application, there is no need to correct the disallowed states immediately. The disallowed states, their effect on data inputs, and the change at the next clocking are:

Binary state	Q2	Q1	Q0	D2	D1	D0	Goes to state	Result
3	0	1	1	0	0	1	1	allowed
5	1	0	1	0	1	0	2	allowed
6	1	1	0	0	1	1	3	goes to 1, then allowed
7	1	1	1	0	1	1	3	goes to 1, then allowed

32 The states are:

Binary state	Red Q2	Amber Q1	Green Q0	D2	D1	D0
4	1	0	0	1	1	0
6	1	1	0	0	0	1
1	0	0	1	0	1	0
2	0	1	0	1	0	0

$$D2 = Q1 \oplus Q2$$
$$D1 = \overline{Q1}$$
$$D0 = Q1 \cdot Q2$$

See Fig. A5.9 for the circuit.

Disallowed states are 000, 011, 101 and 111. At the next clocking, these go to 010, 100, 110 and 001 respectively, which are all allowed states. No gating is needed.

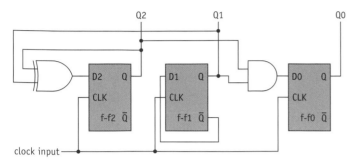

Figure A5.9

33 Inspection of the gates and connections in the diagram shows that:

D2 = Q0•Q1

D1 = Q0 ⊕ Q1

D0 = $\overline{Q0}$

Listing all possible states of Q, and using the equations above to obtain the corresponding D inputs:

Initial state	Q2	Q1	Q0	D2	D1	D0	Next state
0	0	0	0	0	0	1	1
1	0	0	1	0	1	0	2
2	0	1	0	0	1	1	3
3	0	1	1	1	0	0	4
4	1	0	0	0	0	1	1
5	1	0	1	0	1	0	2
6	1	1	0	0	1	1	3
7	1	1	1	1	0	0	4

The output cycles through 1, 2, 3, 4. This is a 1-to-4 binary up counter. The disallowed states of 0, 5, 6 and 7 all change to an allowed state at the next clock pulse.

■ Section 6

Ten quick questions

1 Slew rate.
2 Offset nulling.
3 $75\,\Omega$.
4 Hysteresis.
5 The frequency at which its open-loop gain falls to 1.
6 Non-inverting amplifier (extra point: one built from an op amp with FET inputs).
7 $f_c = 1/2\pi R_F C$
8 -90 mV (Note the negative sign.)
9 The highpass filter.
10 -12 dB/octave

Questions on operational amplifiers

1 Voltage difference at inputs (in microvolts) is
$31 - (-24) = 55\,\mu\text{V} = 0.000\,055\,\text{V}$.
$A = 5.5/0.000\,055 = 100\,000$
$n = 20\log_{10}(100\,000) = 100$ dB

2 The open-loop gain of the amplifier is above the -3 dB level from dc to 120 kHz. The gain–bandwidth product is 4 MHz, so the open-loop gain at 1 MHz is $4/1 = 4$.

3 Working in kΩ, voltage gain $= (120 + 56)/120 = 1.47$.
$R_B = (120 \times 56)/(120 + 56) = 38.1$ kΩ (Use nearest E24 value, 39 kΩ.)
$Z_{in} = 2$ MΩ

4 **a)** $A = -R_F/R_A = -(1 \times 10^6)/330 = -3030$
$Z_{in} = R_A = 330\,\Omega$
b) $A = -R_F/R_A = -(100 \times 10^3)/(10 \times 10^3) = -10$
$Z_{in} = R_A = 10$ kΩ
c) $A = -R_F/R_A = -(2.2 \times 10^6)/(470 \times 10^3) = -4.68$
$Z_{in} = R_A = 470$ kΩ

5 See pp 84–85.

6 **a)** $A = (R_A + R_F)/R_A$
$= (270 \times 10^3 + 1 \times 10^6)/(270 \times 10^3) = 4.70$
b) $A = (R_A + R_F)/R_A$
$= (10 \times 10^3 + 100 \times 10^3)/(10 \times 10^3) = 11.0$
c) $A = (R_A + R_F)/R_A$
$= (820 \times 10^3 + 390 \times 10^3)/(820 \times 10^3) = 1.48$

7 Current through R_A is $v_A/10\,000$ A. Current through R_B is $v_B/20\,000$ A. Total current flowing towards the inverting input is $i = (2v_A + v_B)/10\,000$ A. This current flows on through R_F. The pd across R_F is:
$i.R_F = (2v_A + v_B)/10\,000 \times 56\,000 = 5.6(2v_A + v_B)$
$v_{out} = -5.6(2v_A + v_B)$
With the given voltages:
$v_{out} = -5.6(2 \times 0.2 + 0.15) = -3.08$ V

8 R_1/R_2 is a potential divider. Call its output v_B, which equals $12 \times R_2/(R_1 + R_2)$. IC1 is a voltage follower, used to prevent excessive current drain from the potential divider, which would result in a drop in v_B. The output of IC1 (equal to v_B) is mixed with the input v_A by IC2. Current flowing through R_3 is v_A/R_3. Current through R_4 is v_B/R_4. The combined current is $v_A/R_3 + v_B/R_4$, and this passes through R_5. The voltage drop across R_5 is $(v_A/R_3 + v_B/R_4) \times R_5$. Substituting the value of v_B:

$$v_{out} = -(v_A/R_3 + 12 \times R_2/R_4\,[R_1 + R_2]) \times R_5$$

As the light level rises, the resistance of R_1 decreases; v_B rises. v_A provides a variable offset to adjust the level at which the output of IC2 becomes saturated.

9 This requires an inverting amplifier, as in Fig. 6.4 (p. 85). Select a suitable value for R_A, for example $R_A = 10$ kΩ. Then R_F is 24 times greater: $R_F = 240$ kΩ. To equalise the current flowing to the two inputs, make R_B equal to R_A and R_F in parallel. Working in kilohms,
$R_B = (24 \times 10)/(24 + 10) = 9.60$ kΩ. The nearest E24 value is 10 kΩ. The input impedance is R_A, which is 10 kΩ. For higher Z_{in}, use resistors of higher values, in the same ratio, such as $R_A = 100$ kΩ and $R_F = 2.4$ MΩ. Alternatively, feed the signal to a voltage follower before the amplifying circuit.

10 Refer to Fig. 6.5, p. 85. Working in kilohms,
gain = $(33 + 470)/33 = 15.2$.
$R_B = (33 \times 470)/(33 + 470) = 30.8\,k\Omega$. The nearest E24
value is $30\,k\Omega$.
Z_{in} is typically $2\,M\Omega$ for BJT inputs, up to $1\,T\Omega$ for JFET
inputs.

11 See Fig. A6.1. For the inverting amplifier in Fig. 6.20a,
p. 91, the output at B is such that point A is at $0\,V$ and
$v_{out} = v_{in} \times (-R_2/R_1)$. The equation indicates that the
output is a positive pulse during *negative* half-cycles of
the input, and $0\,V$ during positive half-cycles. B is
approximately $0.7\,V$ higher than v_{out}, which compensates
for the forward voltage drop across D1. In a simple half-
wave rectifier, output pulses occur only during the
positive half-cycles. There is no compensation for the
drop across the diode, and the output of the rectifier is
thus $0.7\,V$ lower than v_{in}. This introduces a
proportionately serious error when the amplitude of v_{in}
is only a few volts.

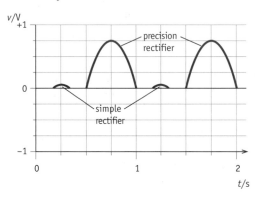

Figure A6.1

12 See Fig. 6.8, p. 87. $f_c = 1/(2\pi RC) = 40.2\,Hz$. The
frequency response is as in Fig. 6.13, with $f_c = 40.2\,Hz$.

13 See Fig. 6.9, p. 87. Let $R_A = 10\,k\Omega$. To obtain a passband
gain of 2.4, $R_F = 10\,k\Omega \times 2.4 = 24\,k\Omega$.
$C = 1/(2\pi f_c R_A) = 114\,nF$. Use $100\,nF$ or $120\,nF$.
The frequency response is as in Fig. 6.14, with $f_c = 140\,Hz$.
The roll-off of a first-order filter is $+6\,dB/octave$.

14 See Fig. 6.8, p. 87. Let $R_A = 10\,k\Omega$. To obtain a passband
gain of 1.5, $R_F = 10\,k\Omega \times 1.5 = 15\,k\Omega$.
$C = 1/(2\pi f_c R_A) = 159\,nF$. Use $150\,nF$.
Passband is from dc to $100\,Hz$, so bandwidth is $100\,Hz$.

15 See Fig. 6.10, p. 87. Let $R_A = 10\,k\Omega$. Then, working in
kilohms, $(10 + R_F)/10 = 2$, so $R_F = 10\,k\Omega$.
Let $C = 10\,nF$. Then:
$R = 1/(2\pi \times 10 \times 10^{-9} \times 2000) = 7958\,\Omega$. Use the nearest
E24, $8.2\,k\Omega$.

16 See Fig. A6.2. This is a bandpass filter consisting of a
highpass filter:
$f_c = 1/2\pi RC = 1/(2 \times \pi \times 800 \times 100 \times 10^{-9})$
$\qquad = 1989\,Hz \approx 2\,kHz$
and a lowpass filter:
$f_c = 1/2\pi RC = 1/(2 \times \pi \times 200 \times 100 \times 10^{-9})$
$\qquad = 7958\,Hz \approx 8\,kHz$
The bandwidth is $8\,kHz - 2\,kHz = 6\,kHz$.

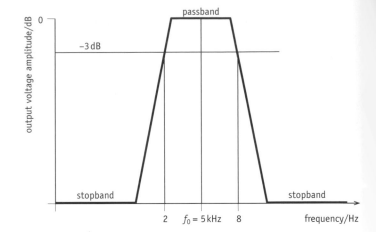

Figure A6.2

17 Use a $500\,Hz$ highpass filter, followed by a $2\,kHz$ lowpass
filter (Fig. A6.3).
Upper cut-off point $= 500 + 2000 = 2500\,Hz$. Centre
frequency is the mean of the lower and upper cut-off
points, which is $(500 + 2500)/2 = 3000/2 = 1.5\,kHz$.

For the highpass filter, if $C_1 = 10\,nF$, then:
$R_1 = 1/(2\pi \times 500 \times 10 \times 10^{-9}) = 31.8\,k\Omega$
Use $33\,k\Omega$.

For the lowpass filter, if $C_2 = 10\,nF$, then:
$R_2 = 1/(2\pi \times 2000 \times 10 \times 10^{-9}) = 7958\,\Omega$
Use $8.2\,k\Omega$.

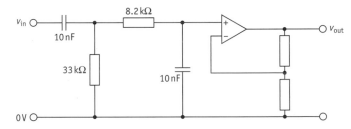

Figure A6.3

18 See Fig. 6.12 (p. 87) and p. 88.
The amplitude of the output falls off at high frequencies
because the open-loop gain of the op amp falls, reaching 1
at its transition frequency.

19 See Fig. A6.4. The photodiode D1 is reverse biased and a
small leakage current flows through R_1. The current, and
hence the voltage at A, is proportional to the light
intensity. R_1 should have a high value to produce a useful
voltage; $330\,k\Omega$ is suggested, but any value in this region
is acceptable. The voltage is fed to a voltage follower
(IC1), which draws minimum current from the D1/R_1
network. The output of IC1 goes to a lowpass filter based
on IC2. A suitable value for the cut-off point is $1\,Hz$, to
allow the circuit to ignore flashes of light lasting less than
approximately 1 second. If $C_1 = 10\,\mu F$, then:
$R_F = 1/2\pi f_c C_1 = 15\,915\,\Omega$. Use $16\,k\Omega$.
To give a passband gain of 10, with $R_F = 16\,k\Omega$, make
$R_A = R_F/10 = 1.6\,k\Omega$.

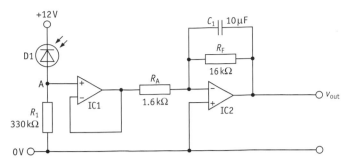

Figure A6.4

20 See Fig. A6.5.

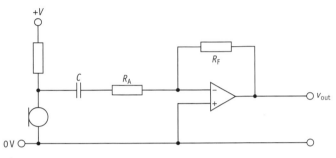

Figure A6.5

In the absence of sound there is a small quiescent voltage at the junction between the microphone and its series resistor. With a piezo-electric (crystal) microphone, or with an electret microphone, sound causes the microphone to generate an oscillating voltage at that junction. With a resistive (carbon granule) microphone, the microphone and resistor act as a potential divider, and a similar oscillating voltage is produced. The oscillating signal passes across the capacitor and is amplified (and inverted) by the op amp, wired as an inverting amplifier. The signal is amplified because R_F is several times greater than R_A.

The signal is filtered because C and R_A form a highpass RC filter, one end of R_A being in effect connected to 0 V (virtual earth), By using a low-value capacitor the cut-off frequency is made high, so that the circuit becomes particularly sensitive to high-frequency sounds.

21 See p. 89.

22 a) *Working:* $V_{ref} = V_S R_2/(R_1 + R_2)$
$= 15 \times 3300/6600 = 7.5$ V
Let $R = R_4/(R_3 + R_4) = 470\,000/940\,000 = 0.5$
UTV $= V_{ref} + R(V_S - V_{ref}) = 7.5 + 0.5(15 - 7.5)$
$= 7.5 + 0.5 \times 7.5 = 11.25$ V
LTV $= V_{ref}(1 - R) = 7.5(1 - 0.5) = 3.75$ V
Solutions: UTV $= 11.25$ V, LTV $= 3.75$ V.

b) *Working:* $V_{ref} = V_S R_2/(R_1 + R_2)$
$= 15 \times 2700/5400 = 7.5$ V
Let $R = R_4/(R_3 + R_4) = 220\,000/550\,000 = 0.4$
UTV $= V_{ref} + R(V_S - V_{ref}) = 7.5 + 0.4(15 - 7.5)$
$= 7.5 + 0.4 \times 7.5 = 10.5$ V
LTV $= V_{ref}(1 - R) = 7.5(1 - 0.4) = 7.5 \times 0.6 = 4.5$ V
Solutions: UTV $= 10.5$ V, LTV $= 4.5$ V.

c) *Working:* $V_{ref} = V_S R_2/(R_1 + R_2)$
$= 12 \times 1000/3000 = 4$ V
Let $R = R_4/(R_3 + R_4) = 470\,000/800\,000 = 0.5875$
UTV $= V_{ref} + R(V_S - V_{ref}) = 4 + 0.5875(12 - 4)$
$= 4 + 0.5875 \times 8 = 8.7$ V
LTV $= V_{ref}(1 - R) = 4(1 - 0.5875) = 4 \times 0.4125$
$= 1.65$ V
Solutions: UTV $= 8.7$ V, LTV $= 1.65$ V.

d) *Working:* $V_{ref} = V_S R_2/(R_1 + R_2) = 9 \times 1800/2800$
$= 5.786$ V
Let $R = R_4/(R_3 + R_4) = 220\,000/320\,000 = 0.6875$
UTV $= V_{ref} + R(V_S - V_{ref})$
$= 5.786 + 0.6875(9 - 5.786)$
$= 5.786 + 0.6875 \times 3.214 = 8.00$ V
LTV $= V_{ref}(1 - R) = 5.786(1 - 0.6875)$
$= 5.786 \times 0.3125 = 1.81$ V
Solutions: UTV $= 8.00$ V, LTV $= 1.81$ V.

23 a) *Working:* $H =$ UTV $-$ LTV $= 12 - 10 = 2$ V
Lct $V = H/(H + V_S) = 2/(2 - 18) = 2/20 = 0.1$
$V_{ref} =$ UTV$/(1 - V) = 12(1 - 0.1) = 12 \times 0.9 = 10.8$ V
Let $R_2 = 100$ kΩ. $R_1 = R_2(V_S - V_{ref})/V_{ref}$
$= 100\,000(18 - 10.8)/10.8 = 100\,000 \times 7.2/10.8$
$= 66.7$ kΩ
Let $R_4 = 100$ kΩ. $R_3 = R_4(1 - V)/V$
$= 100\,000(1 - 0.1)/0.1 = 90\,000 \times 0.1 = 900$ kΩ
Solutions: $R_1 = 66.7$ kΩ, $R_2 = 100$ kΩ, $R_3 = 900$ kΩ,
$R_4 = 100$ kΩ.

b) *Working:* $H =$ UTV $-$ LTV $= 8 - 7 = 1$ V
Let $V = H/(H + V_S) = 1/(1 + 15) = 1/16 = 0.0625$
$V_{ref} =$ UTV$/(1 - V) = 8(1 - 0.0625) = 8 \times 0.9375 = 7.5$ V
Let $R_2 = 100$ kΩ. $R_1 = R_2(V_S - V_{ref})/V_{ref}$
$= 100\,000(15 - 7.5)/7.5 = 100\,000 \times 7.5/7.5 = 100$ kΩ
Let $R_4 = 100$ kΩ. $R_3 = R_4(1 - V)/V$
$= 100\,000(1 - 0.0625)/0.0625$
$= 100\,000 \times 0.9375/0.0625 = 1.5$ MΩ
Solutions: $R_1 = R_2 = 100$ kΩ, $R_3 = 1.5$ MΩ,
$R_4 = 100$ kΩ.

c) *Working:* $H =$ UTV $-$ LTV $= 3 - 2 = 1$ V
Let $V = H/(H + V_S) = 1/(1 + 15) = 1/16 = 0.0625$
$V_{ref} =$ UTV$/(1 - V) = 3(1 - 0.0625) = 3 \times 0.9375$
$= 2.8125$ V
Let $R_2 = 100$ kΩ. $R_1 = R_2(V_S - V_{ref})/V_{ref}$
$= 100\,000(15 - 2.8125)/2.8125$
$= 100\,000 \times 12.1875/2.8125 = 433.3$ kΩ
Let $R_4 = 100$ kΩ. $R_3 = R_4(1 - V)/V$
$= 100\,000(1 - 0.0625)/0.0625$
$= 100\,000 \times 0.9375/0.0625 = 1.5$ MΩ
Solutions: $R_1 = 433.3$ kΩ, $R_2 = 100$ kΩ, $R_3 = 1.5$ MΩ,
$R_4 = 100$ kΩ.

d) *Working:* $H =$ UTV $-$ LTV $= 4.5 - 4.0 = 0.5$ V
Let $V = H/(H + V_S) = 0.5/(0.5 + 6) = 0.5/6.5 = 0.0769$
$V_{ref} =$ UTV$/(1 - V) = 4.5(1 - 0.769) = 4.5 \times 0.9321 =$
4.1945 V
Let $R_2 = 100$ kΩ. $R_1 = R_2(V_S - V_{ref})/V_{ref}$
$= 100\,000(6 - 4.1945)/4.1945$
$= 100\,000 \times 1.8055/4.1945 = 43.0$ kΩ
Let $R_4 = 100$ kΩ. $R_3 = R_4(1 - V)/V$
$= 100\,000(1 - 0.0769)/0.0769$
$= 100\,000 \times 0.9321/0.0769 = 12.12$ MΩ
Solutions: $R_1 = 43.0$ kΩ, $R_2 = 100$ kΩ, $R_3 = 12.12$ MΩ,
$R_4 = 100$ kΩ.

■ Section 7

Ten quick questions
1 Differential amplifier (or difference amplifier).
2 The contacts open and close several times in quick succession before finally becoming open or closed.
3 Clamping.
4 Flash ADC.
5 24 kΩ.
6 Removes peaks and troughs.
7 15
8 12 cycles.
9 Greater precision.
10 Noise.

Questions on signal processing
1 a) See p. 30.
   b) See Fig. 7.1 (either a or b), p. 93.

2 See Fig. 7.2, p. 94.

3 The comparator has no external components; its gain is the open-loop gain of the op amp. A differential amplifier has feedback and input resistors, so its gain is much less and is set by the values of the resistors. The output of a comparator swings to saturation in either direction, depending on which input voltage is the greater. The output of a differential amplifier swings within the permitted range and is proportional to the difference between the inputs.

4 a) $v_{out} = (v_2 - v_1) \times R_2/R_1 = 0.21 \times 3.03 = 0.636$ V
   b) Rearranging the equation:
   $v_2 = v_{out} \times R_1/R_2 + v_1 = -0.24 \times 0.18 + 3.42 = 3.38$ V

5 See p. 94.

6 CMRR = 130/0.2 = 650. In decibels, this is $20 \times \log_{10}(130/0.2) = 56.3$ dB.

7 See p. 95.

8 See p. 96 and Fig. 7.5. Applications include converting analogue audio signals into digital form, radar circuits, speech recognition, satellite control systems.

9 a) $V_n = V_5 = 10 \times (2 \times 5 + 1)/16 = 6.875$ V
   $V_{n+1} = 10 \times (2 \times 6 + 1)/16 = 8.175$ V
   v_{in} is between 6.875 V and 8.125 V. That is, $v_{in} = 7.5$ V ± 0.625 V.
   b) $V_n = V_2 = 12 \times (2 \times 2 + 1)/16 = 3.75$ V
   $V_{n+1} = 12 \times (2 \times 3 + 1)/16 = 5.25$ V
   v_{in} is between 3.75 V and 5.25 V. That is, $v_{in} = 4.5$ V ± 0.75 V.

10 Given $2^m = 2^6 = 64$, the ADC needs $(2^6 - 1) = 63$ comparators.
   $V_n = V_{20} = 5 \times (2 \times 20 + 1)/128 = 1.602$ V
   $V_{n+1} = 5 \times (2 \times 21 + 1)/128 = 1.680$ V
   v_{in} is between 1.602 V and 1.680 V. That is, $v_{in} = 1.641$ V ± 0.039 V.

11 See p. 98.

12, 13 See pp 96–99.

14 12 clock cycles = $12 \times 1/500\,000 = 24$ μs

15 See Fig. A7.1. Note this is Fig. 6.7 (p. 86), slightly modified.

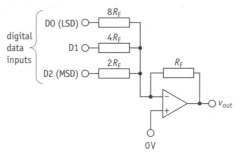

Figure A7.1

16 The input resistors of an op amp adder have different values, so that some inputs are more significant (have more weight) than others. In the DAC, the input resistors are weighted according to a binary plan, each resistor having double the resistance of the next one in the series.

17 $R_C = 24$ kΩ, $R_B = 48$ kΩ, $R_A = 96$ kΩ. R_A is the least significant digit.
   Currents are $i_C = 5/24\,000 = 208$ μA,
   $i_B = 5/48\,000 = 104$ μA, $i_A = 5/96\,000 = 52$ μA.
   With input 101, $i_{total} = -(208 + 52) = -260$ μA.
   $v_{out} = -206 \times 12$ [μA × kΩ] = -3.12 V.

18 Scaling factor is $-8/v_H = -8/5 = -1.6$.
   $v_{out} \times$ scaling factor = $-3.12 \times -1.6 = 5$ V, which is the equivalent, in volts, of the binary input 101.

19 $R_D = 20$ kΩ, $R_C = 40$ kΩ, $R_B = 80$ kΩ, $R_A = 160$ kΩ. R_A is the least significant digit.
   Currents are $i_D = 8/20\,000 = 400$ μA,
   $i_C = 8/40\,000 = 200$ μA, $i_B = 8/80\,000 = 100$ μA,
   $i_A = 8/160\,000 = 50$ μA.
   With input 1011, $i_{total} = 400 + 100 + 50 = 550$ μA.
   $v_{out} = -550 \times 10$ [μA × kΩ] = -5.5 V

20 Scaling factor is $-16/v_H = -16/8 = -2$.
   $v_{out} \times$ scaling factor = $-5.5 \times -2 = 11$ V, which is the equivalent, in volts, of the binary input 1011.

■ Section 8

Ten quick questions
1 Pulsed dc.
2 100 Hz.
3 Amplitude increases.
4 40
5 Current-limiting, thermal shut-down.
6 Increase the smoothing capacitance.
7 To isolate the circuit from the mains.
8 $12.5 - 2(0.7) = 11.1$ V
9 Reservoir capacitor.
10 Load regulation.

Questions on power supplies

In answers to design problems, the specified values of components used are those that are actually manufactured and readily available, so they may not give the exact output intended.

1 See Fig. A8.1 (This is a combination of Figs 8.2, 8.3, 4.22a and 8.4.)

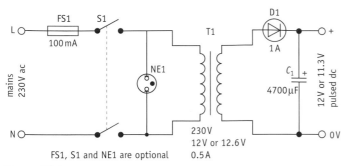

Figure A8.1

The transformer is rated for 230 V with 12 V (or 12.6 V) output at 0.5 A. A 12.6 V transformer is a standard type that compensates for the single diode drop; if a 12 V transformer is used, the actual peak voltage is 11.3 V. If a fuse is used, it must be rated to supply the maximum primary current corresponding to 0.5 A secondary current. This is $0.5 \times 12/230 = 26$ mA. The closest available fuse value is likely to be 100 mA. The rectifier diode is rated at 1 A.

Assuming an average smoothed voltage that is 1 V below the peak at full load:
$C = I/2f(V_s - V_p) = 0.5/(2 \times 50 \times 1) = 0.005$ F $= 5000$ μF
The closest standard value is 4700 μF, but 6800 μF could be used to give improved ripple reduction.

Instead of the neon lamp, an LED and series resistor (about 470 Ω) could be connected on the output side.

2 See Fig. A8.2. (This is a combination of Figs 8.2, 8.3, 4.23a, 8.4 and 8.8.)
See the comments about the fuse and the neon lamp in the answer to question 1.

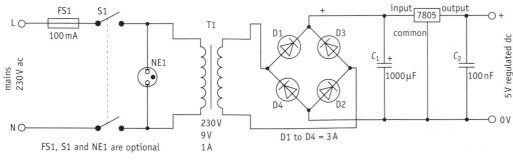

Figure A8.2

The transformer is rated for 230 V with 9 V output (to be more than 2.5 V greater than final output) at 1 A. The rectifier diodes are rated at 3 A. The capacitor can be 1000 μF (the regulator eliminates most of the ripple). The regulator is a 7805.

3 See Fig. A8.3. (This is a combination of Figs 8.3, 4.23a, 8.4 and 4.3. Items in Fig. 8.2 are probably not essential.)

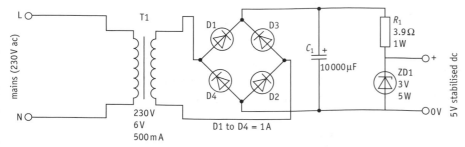

Figure A8.3

The transformer is rated for 230 V with 6 V output at 500 mA. The rectifier diodes are rated at 1 A. Assuming an average smoothed voltage that is 0.2 V below the peak, $C = 0.4/(4 \times 50 \times 0.2) = 10\,000$ μF.

The Zener is rated at 3 V. Voltage across capacitor is $6 - 1.4 = 4.6$ V. Voltage drop across resistor is $4.6 - 3 = 1.6$ V. Maximum power dissipated in Zener is 3×405 [V × mA] = 1.215 W. Use a 5 W Zener.

Current through resistor is 405 mA, so resistance = 1.6/405 [V/mA] = 3.95 Ω. Use next lowest E24 value: 3.9 Ω.

Power dissipated in resistor = 405×1.6 [mA × V] = 648 mW. Use a 1 W resistor.

4   a)   Change in output = $9 - 7.9 = 1.1$ V.
          Load regulation is $1.1/9 \times 100 = 12.2\%$.
     b)   Change in output = $24 - 23.4 = 0.6$ V.
          Load regulation is $0.6/24 \times 100 = 2.5\%$.

5   Higher precision, better load regulation, better line regulation, current-limiting, thermal shut-down.

6   a)   The useful output range is when V_S is 11–15 V, because the output is much reduced when $V_S < 11$ V. A change in V_S of 4 V produces a change of 0.07 V in V_{out}. The line regulation is $0.07/4 \times 100 = 1.75\%$.
     b)   The useful output range is when V_S is 15–28 V, because the output is much reduced when $V_S < 15$ V. A change in V_S of 13 V produces a change of 0.004 V in V_{out}. The line regulation is $0.004/13 \times 100 = 0.03\%$.

Section 9

Ten quick questions

1   Firing angle.
2   At the end of the half-cycle.
3   1 : 1
4   90°
5   105°
6   Isolating a low-voltage control circuit from the high-voltage thyristor or triac circuit.
7   Diac.
8   Main terminal 1, main terminal 2, gate (see Fig. 3.10, p. 33).
9   1 V
10 The firing angle can be between 90° and 180°.

Questions on power switching systems

1   See p. 107 and Fig. 9.2.

2   See Fig. 9.3, p. 108.

3   See pp 107 and 109.

4   See Fig. A9.1. The output of the microphone is first amplified by an internal amplifier (not shown in the diagram). Peaks of the amplified signal trigger the thyristor into conduction. The motor runs until the press-to-break button is pressed, interrupting the current through the thyristor.

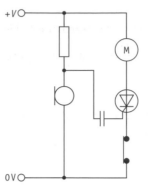

Figure A9.1

5   See p. 110.

6   See pp 107–109.

7   $X_C = 1/(2\pi \times 50 \times 15 \times 10^{-9}) = 212$ kΩ.
    $\phi = \tan^{-1}(R/X_C) = \tan^{-1}(220/212) = \tan^{-1} 1.038 = 46.1°$

8   $X_C = 1/(2\pi \times 60 \times 47 \times 10^{-9}) = 56.4$ kΩ.
    $\tan 60° = R/X_C$
    From a calculator, $\tan 60° = 1.732$.
    $R = 1.732 \times 56.4$ [kΩ] = 97.7 kΩ

Section 10

Ten quick questions

1   Error signal.
2   Bang-bang control.
3   The output range reasonably close to the set point, in which the controlled device is switched off.
4   Servo system.
5   The rate of change of output is proportional to the difference between the output and the set point.
6   Closed-loop.
7   It is negative feedback.
8   Open-loop.
9   Reference voltage.
10 An open-loop system has no feedback.

Questions on analogue control systems

1   See p. 112. The advantage is that it is cheap to install.

2   With negative feedback, the level of the output is sensed and compared with the set point, and their difference is used to generate an error signal. The polarity of the error signal, or the way in which it is processed, is such that it alters the output so as to decrease the error signal.

3   See p. 114.

4   Overshoot causes hunting; avoid this by incorporating a dead band into the system.
    Lack of hysteresis or insufficient hysteresis may lead to rapid oscillations; avoid this by increasing the hysteresis.

5   a)   See p. 115.
     b)   See p. 115.

Section 11

Ten quick questions

1   Opcode.
2   A bit in the status register that indicates whether a certain event has or has not occurred.

3 Random access memory.

4 When the power is switched off, the data stored in RAM is lost but that stored in ROM is not lost.

5 Three of: floppy disk, hard disk, CD-ROM disc, CD-R/RW disc, DVD.

6 Data bus.

7 10

8 Difficult and expensive to modify once it has been built.

9 Logic 0, logic 1, high-impedance.

10 An interrupt service routine, stored in ROM, to which the CPU jumps when it is interrupted.

Questions on digital control systems

1 See p. 123.

2 See pp 123–124.

3 See p. 120.

4 See p. 123 and the answers to questions 12 and 16.

5 See Fig. 11.1 and pp 118–120.

6 See p. 120.

7 See p. 119.

8 See p. 122.

9 See Fig. 11.2, p. 121.

10 See pp 122–123. Use the coding technique specified by your examining board. About 5 lines of program is sufficient, and it should be explained by comments or remarks incorporated into the program. Try to use at least three different logical operations.

11 See Fig. A11.1. The alarm is connected to a pin labelled *alarm*. The siren is switched on when *alarm* = 1. The program begins by making *alarm* equal to 0, so that there is no chance of the siren sounding when the system is first switched on. The three IR sensors are connected to three pins in Port A, so that, when any or more of them is triggered, one or more of the bits goes high and the value downloaded from Port A is greater than zero. If *alarm* = 1 the program runs through a 5 minute delay. In the flowchart, this is implemented as two nested loops, with loop counters *loop 1* and *loop 2*. The pair of loops requires $n \times m$ iterations, before the program loops back to the beginning and turns the siren off. With a fast clock, this will probably not take 5 minutes, but the time may be lengthened by adding a third or fourth loop, or (in BASIC) by including a time-consuming operation in *loop 2*, such as a FOR … NEXT loop with a large number of iterations.

    The system may have a built-in real-time clock or a timer. These can be used to create lengthy delays, but the programming would be specific to the system and details cannot be given here.

12 See Fig. A11.2, p. 176. The lamp to illuminate the 'Full' sign is driven by an output pin labelled *full*. The lamp comes on when *full* = 1. There is a seven-segment display that is driven from seven outputs of a port. There is light-beam sensor at the gate, which gives a high output when a car breaks the beam. The number of cars in the park is registered by a variable *cars*. The program starts by turning the 'Full' sign off, to prevent it coming on by

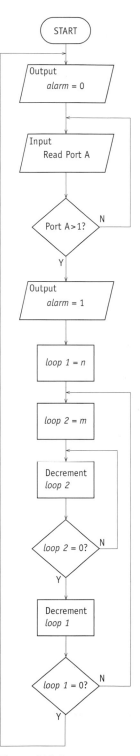

Figure A11.1

chance when the power is switched on. The *cars* variable is set to 0. The sensor must be read twice, waiting for the appropriate input each time. It first has to detect the arrival of a car, then to detect that the car has moved on into the park. If the second check were not done, the program would count up to 8 while the first car was still breaking the beam. Each time *cars* is incremented, the processor looks in a look-up table for the appropriate code and outputs this to the seven-segment display.

Additional revision: extend the program to monitor cars leaving the park by a different gateway, and to display the reduced number.

13 See Fig. A11.3. A light-beam sensor detects when a block of cheese reaches the weighing platform. Then the weighing mechanism is read to find its weight. This is compared with the limits already set (this demonstrates how to program an OR operation). If the block is within the range, the block continues to be packed and the program loops round to wait for the next block. If the block is outside the range, the reject mechanism is actuated. The 'beep' device is also triggered. A 1-second beep is specified but the program does not have time to wait for this to end. One solution is to trigger a 555 monostable. If a timer is available in the system, the 'beep' generator is switched on and the timer is set to cause an interrupt 1 s later. The ISR switches the 'beep' generator off.

This program is over-simplified and readers may have devised additional steps. For example, the weighing platform must be allowed to settle before the weight is read.

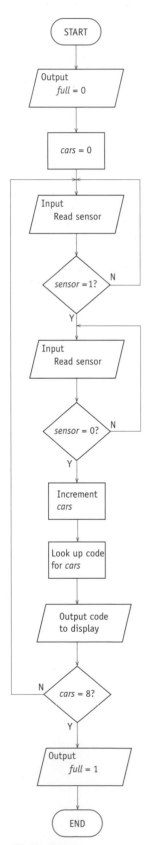

Figure A11.2

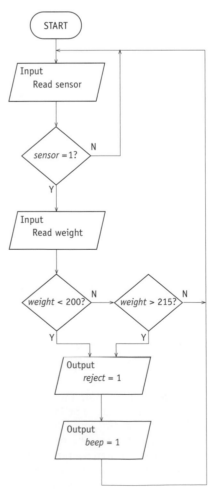

Figure A11.3

14 See Fig. A11.4. The outputs are to a pin labelled *beep*, which controls a beeper, and to a port that switches a seven-segment display. There is a 3-bit input from the encoder, and the fourth bit is wired to 0 V. The variable *encoder* is obtained by reading all four bits. The program uses two variables: *point 1* is the previous wind direction and *point 2* is the present wind direction. The program begins by switching off the beeper, so that it does not accidentally sound when the system is switched on. Variables *point 1* and *point 2* start with an offscale value, so that the first reading of the encoder is bound to differ from these. The encoder is read and *point 2* takes this

value. If it has not changed since the previous value, the program loops back. Otherwise the program continues by displaying the new wind direction and sounding the beeper. The delay routine could be nested loops, as in question 11.

15 See Fig. A11.5 below. There are two 1-bit outputs labelled *heater* and *lamp*. The devices are on when these are '1'. The temperature of the greenhouse is *temp*, and there is a constant, *settemp*, which is the set point with its value written into the program. Hysteresis is provided because the heater is not switched on until the temperature is 2° below the set point, and is not switched off until it is 2° above.

16 See Fig. A11.6, p. 178. A *button* input reads '0' when the button is not pressed, and '1' when it is pressed. *Score* is the variable that indicates the current face of the dice. There is a look-up table containing the codes for the traditional dice face, which needs seven LEDs. The controller uses *score* to obtain the correct code from the table. The first input routine waits for the key to be pressed, then waits for the button to be released before going on to the next stage. The next input routine does

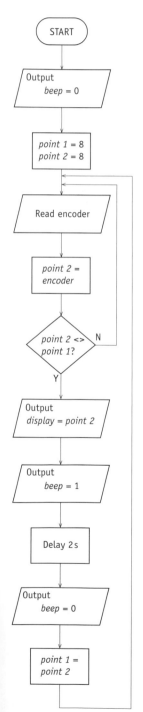

Figure A11.4

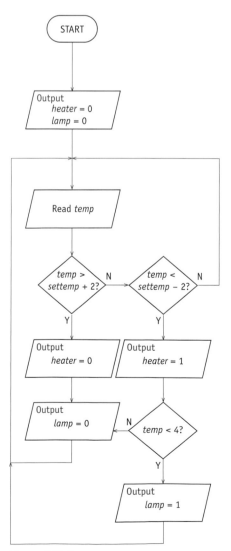

Figure A11.5

not wait; the 'rolling' loop continues if the button is not pressed, but stops if it is pressed. If it continues, *score* is incremented for the next loop. However, if *score* has been incremented to 7, it is reduced to 1, to keep it within the

range of possible scores. If the button is pressed, the display is frozen, giving an opportunity to read it. Note that the program cannot continue until the button is released. It then loops back to the top of the flowchart, waiting in a loop for the button to be pressed. The button needs to be debounced, either by a circuit as in Fig. 7.2 (p. 94), or by debouncing software (not included in the flowchart).

Additional revision: extend the program to simulate the roll of two independent dice. Arrange for a beep to sound if both dice show the same score, or if the total score is seven.

17 The program waits for the button to be pressed. If the button is pressed briefly, the lamps are flashed for 0.5 s, in order and repeating indefinitely in a loop. The flashing continues until the button is pressed again. Then the lamps are put out and the program ends. If the button is pressed and held, the flashing sequence is executed only once. The delay is a subroutine (p. 123) and button-reading could also be written as a subroutine.

There are other ways of programming the lamps, such as using a 'rotate' command on the contents of the accumulator, or multiplying by 2, or using a look-up table, but the technique used here is more straightforward and easily altered to produce different sequences.

A possible application is to have each output drive a set of lamps, arranged so that every third lamp belongs to the same set. This gives a 'travelling lights' effect for a decorative display.

18 The label *volts* is given to a variable or an 8-bit register. The first loop increments *volts* from 0 to 255 in 255 steps. Then the program drops through to the second loop, where it is decremented in 255 steps to 0. The cycles repeats indefinitely. At each step the 8-bit value is output to the DAC. If this is an 8-bit DAC, the output voltage rises linearly from 0 V to the reference voltage and back, repeating. The program is a triangular wave generator. Taking only the delay subroutines into account, each step takes 2 μs so each cycle takes $2 \times 10^{-6} \times 510 = 1.02$ ms; frequency = 977 Hz.

Additional revision: Modify the program to produce **a)** a sawtooth wave, frequency 400 Hz; **b)** a square wave, frequency 750 Hz.

19 The number of flashes still to be made is held in the variable *count*. This is initially set to 10. The program waits for the button to be pressed, then turns the LED on for a period set by a 1-second delay subroutine. The LED is turned off, there is a further delay of 2 seconds and then *count* is decremented. The loop repeats if *count* has not been reduced to zero. If the program is being written in assembler or machine code it is simple to test for *count* becoming zero: test the zero flag with a conditional command such as 'Jump if zero'. This is why we count down from 10 to zero, rather than count up from 0 to 10. In a BASIC program we could just as easily count up.

Additional revision: Add a routine to the beginning of the program to allow the user to key in the number of flashes required, which must be between 3 and 24.

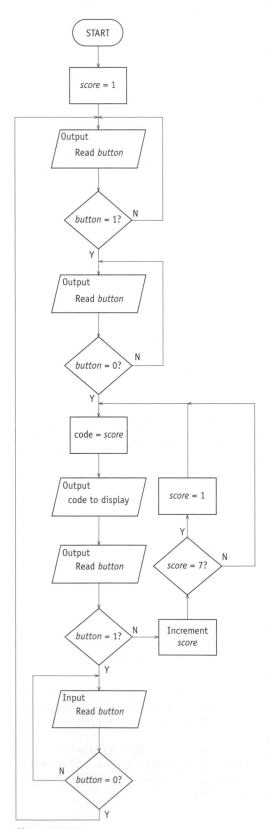

Figure A11.6

■ Section 12

Ten quick questions

1 Pre-amplifier.
2 Routes different frequency bands to the correct speaker.
3 Source output impedance must be lower than input impedance of the next stage.
4 Speaker with greatest response in bass frequencies.
5 Mount the speaker on a baffle or in an enclosure.
6 Corrects for unevenness in a frequency response.
7 Common-collector (emitter follower).
8 Source output impedance must be equal to the input impedance of the next stage.
9 Wider bandwidth.
10 To avoid generation of noise.

Questions on audio systems

1 **a)** Only a monophonic (single channel) system is required. Most of the input is from microphones: for the person announcing the events (for example, the steward), for one or more commentators, for one or more judges, and there could be another microphone for the police or crowd control officials. All these microphones provide input to the main system, with a single power amplifier feeding speakers placed at several points in the stadium. The main audio system also has input from a CD player for providing music.

   Additional microphones, with additional lower-power channels, might be provided for communication between the steward and changing rooms, marshalling areas and similar facilities.

   b) Only a monophonic system is required. Usually the main function of the audio system in a supermarket is to provide music, so a CD player is required (perhaps a tape player instead in older systems). There will also be a CD or tape player, for making announcements to customers (for example, warning about handbag examinations at the checkouts) and a microphone for issuing emergency instructions to staff members on duty in the store.

2 See text and figures of section 12.

3 See p. 130.

4 See text of section 12.

5 See pp 53–54 and pp 130–131.

6 **a)** See p. 86.
   b) Voice of singer (microphone) over melody played on an electronic keyboard; voice of karaoke singer over CD track; voice of compere over cross-fading CDs; two microphones, one for soloist, one for band back-up.

7 $P_{max} = 12^2/(4 \times 4) = 9\,\text{W}$; the same in the amplifier, 9 W.

8 $V_S^2 = P_{max} \times 4 \times 8 = 640$
   $V_S = \sqrt{640} = 25.3\,\text{V}$
   This supply voltage has a maximum power output of 20 W, so is the minimum voltage able to provide the output specified.

■ Section 13

Ten quick questions

1 Crosstalk.
2 Frequency shift keying.
3 Single sideband transmission: suppressing the carrier and one sideband, and transmitting only the other sideband.
4 $50\,\Omega$
5 Optical fibre.
6 Full duplex.
7 Digital signals are 'squared up' and re-transmitted.
8 Optical fibre in which the refractive index increases smoothly from the centre to the outside.
9 The intrinsic layer separates the n-type and p-type layers, so decreasing capacitance and allowing rapid response.
10 The frequency (often 455 kHz) onto which the signal is modulated for amplification and filtering. (It is the beat frequency of the carrier and local oscillator frequencies combined.)

Questions on communications systems

1, 2, 3 See p. 137.

4 See pp 138 and 147.

5 See p. 138.

6 See pp 138–139.

7 **a)** See Fig. 13.2, p. 139, and p. 147.
   b) At 800 MHz, the wavelength is
   $\lambda = 3 \times 10^8/(800 \times 10^6) = 0.375\,\text{m}$.
   The length of the dipole is $0.375 \times 0.46 = 0.1725\,\text{m}$. (The factor 0.46 instead of 0.5 accounts for the lower velocity of the electromagnetic wave in the material of the conductor.)

8 The antenna consists of a dipole, a reflector element (possibly three, arranged centrally and to the left and right of the axis) and a number or director elements. The optimum wavelength is $0.150/0.46 = 0.326\,\text{m}$; frequency $= 3 \times 10^8/0.326 = 920\,\text{MHz}$.

9 **a)** See p. 140.
   b) $\text{SNR} = 10 \log_{10} (V_S^2/V_N^2) = 20 \log_{10} (V_S/V_N) = 20 \log_{10} (0.3/25 \times 10^{-9}) = 142\,\text{dB}$
   c) The rms signal voltage is $1.5/\sqrt{2} = 1.061\,\text{V}$.
   $\text{SNR} = 20 \log_{10} (1.061/7 \times 10^{-9}) = 164\,\text{dB}$

10 See p. 141.

11 **a)** See p. 141; **b)** see pp 141–142.

12 See pp 142–143.

13 **a)** See p. 141 and pp 143–144.
   b) Bandwidth is twice the highest audio frequency: 24 kHz.

14 Less wasteful of power; reduces bandwidth of transmission; 12 kHz.

15 **a)** See p. 144 and Fig. A13.1 (overleaf), which shows four signals modulated onto four different frequencies spaced within the bandwidth of the transmitter–receiver system.
   b) Bandwidth of system $= 108 - 64 = 44\,\text{kHz}$.
   Number of channels available $= 44/3.4 = 12.9$. This allows bandwidth for 12 channels, with a small gap between adjacent channels.

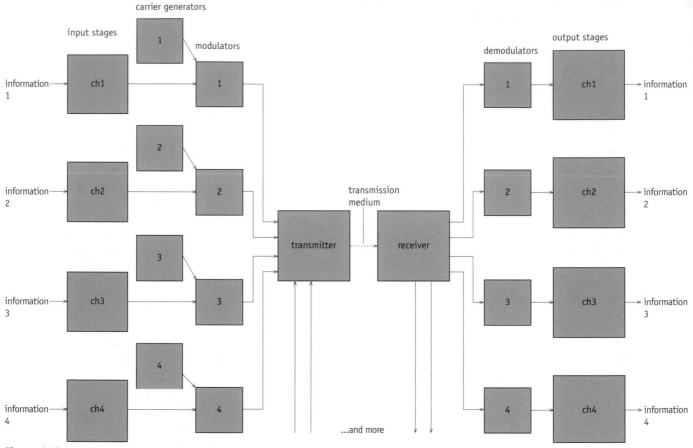

Figure A13.1

16 See pp 144–145.

17 See p. 145.

18 See pp 149–150.

19 See pp 138, 141, 143 and 147, and Fig. A13.2 below.

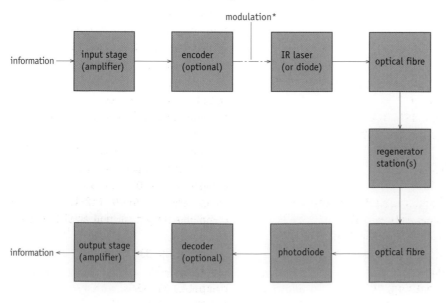

*amplitude modulation for IR diode;
amplitude, frequency, phase or polarisation modulation for IR laser

Figure A13.2

Index

ac power control, 33, 109
accumulator, 122
active components, 30–33
active filters, 86–8
actuators, 35–8
   audible warning device (AWD), 38
   filament lamp, 35
   light-emitting diode (LED), 35–6, 62
   loudspeaker, 38, 131
   low voltage dc motor, 37
   neon lamp, 35
   relay, 36–7
   servomotor (servo), 38, 115
   solenoid, 36
   stepper motor, 37–8
ADC (analogue-to-digital converter), 96–9
adder, 86, 99
address bus, 120, 122
ALU (arithmetic/logic unit), 122
AM (amplitude modulation), 141
AM receiver, 148–9
amplifier
   BJT and MOSFET compared, 53
   differential, 94–5
   operational, 83–9
   power, 130–31
   see also class A (etc.) amplifier and
      common-collector (etc.)
      amplifier
amplitude modulation (AM), 141
analogue-to-digital converter (ADC), 96–9
analogue circuits, 42–56
analogue communication, 137
analogue control systems, 112–16
AND function, 18
anode, 29, 32
antenna, 138, 139
arbitrary truth table, 65
arithmetic/logic unit (ALU), 122
arithmetical operation, 118
ASCII, 146
assembler, 124
astable, 47, 48–9, 62, 69
asynchronous counter, 70–73

asynchronous transmission, 137
attenuation, communication, 140
audible warning device (AWD), 38
audio systems, 129–34
AWD, 38

baffle, of loudspeaker, 38, 131
bandpass filter, 87
bandwidth
   communication, 143–4
   full power, 84, 130
bang-bang control, 115
base speaker, 131
BASIC, 125
battery, 102
BCD (binary-coded decimal), 66
BCD counter, 73
BCD-to-7-segment decoder, 66–7
beats, 149
binary-coded decimal (BCD), 66
binary-to-decimal converter/decoder, 64–5
binary counter, 70–73
bipolar junction transistor (BJT), 30–31
bistable, 67–8
BJT (bipolar junction transistor), 30–31
Boolean algebra, 19–20
bridge rectifier, 56
broadcast, radio, 138, 139
bus
   address, 120, 122
   control, 120
   data, 120, 122
bus contention, 120

cathode, 29, 32
capacitor
   charging, see RC networks
   commutating, 109
   discharging, see RC networks
   microphone, 34
   reactance, 7
   smoothing, 103
carrier wave, 141
CD, 129, 134
CD-ROM, 119

central processing unit (CPU), 118, 122, 123
changeover contacts, 37
channel, communication, 144
characteristic impedance, cable, 145
clamping diode, 42–3
class A amplifier, 50–53
class AB amplifier, 53–4, 130–31
class B amplifier, 53–4, 130–31
   crossover distortion, 54
clipping, 93
clock, sequential logic, 69, 70, 71, 74, 75, 76
clocked interrupt, 123
closed-loop control
   on–off, 112–13
   proportional, 113–14
closed-loop gain, operational amplifier, 86
CMRR (common mode rejection ratio), 94
coaxial cable, 137–8, 145
combinational logic, 62–7
common-collector amplifier, 52, 53
   uses, 52, 130
common-drain amplifier, 52, 53
   uses, 130
common-emitter amplifier, 50–51, 53
   uses, 51, 54, 104, 130, 148
common-source amplifier, 52, 53
   uses, 52, 130
common mode gain, 94
common mode rejection ratio (CMRR), 94
communication systems, 136–50
commutating capacitor, 109
compact disc (CD), 129, 134
comparator, 84, 96–9, 112-13
complementary push-pull amplifier, 53
components
   active, 30–33
   passive, 28–30
computer, 61, 134
conditional jump, 123
conduction angle, 108
contact bounce, 93–4

control bus, 120
controlled rectifier, 107–9
    uses, 108
conversion time, 99
counter ADC, 97
counters
    BCD, 73
    ripple, 70–73
    modulo-n, 72
    modulo-n synchronous, 75, 78–80
    synchronous, 73–4
    walking ring, 75–8
coupling, 51
CPU (central processing unit), 118, 122, 123
crossover distortion, 54
crossover network, 131
crosstalk, 140
current division rule, 2
current gain, BJT, 30
current limiting resistor, 45
current source, 62
cut-off frequency, 49

D-type flip-flop, 69–70
DAC (digital-to-analogue converter), 99–100
Darlington pair, 45–6
data bit, 147
data bus, 120, 122
data decoder, 66
data distributor, 66
data flip-flop, 69–70
data selector, 65–6
data storage, 119
dc level restoration, 42–3
de Morgan's theorem, 21
dead band, 115
decibel, 6
decimal-to-binary converter/decoder, 64
demodulator, 148–9
demultiplexer, 66
    in PCM system, 142
detector, 148–9
diac, 109
differential amplifier, 94–5
differential mode gain, 94
digital-to-analogue converter (DAC), 99–100
    adder, 99
    scaling factor, 100

digital communication, 137
digital control systems, 117–25
digital interfaces, 61–2
digital versatile disc (DVD), 129, 134
diode, 28–30
    anode, 28
    avalanche photodiode, 147
    cathode, 28
    forward bias, 28, 29
    light-emitting diode (LED), 29, 35–6
    photodiode, 33–4, 147
    PIN photodiode, 147
    power diode, 29
    reverse bias, 28, 29
    small signal diode, 29
    Zener diode, 30, 93
diode applications
    clamping, 42–3, 93
    clipping, 93
    protection, 42, 45
    voltage stabiliser, 43–4, 103, 104
diode clamp, 42–3, 93
dipole, 139
direct addressing, 123
directional transmission, 139
display, seven-segment, 67
distortion, communication, 140
divide-by-two circuit, 70
divider, 70
domestic audio system, 129–31
duplex communication, 137
DVD, 129, 134

effective resistance, 2
electret microphone, 34
electromagnetic interference (EMI), 94, 137–8, 140
emitter follower amplifier, 52
emulator software, 121
enclosure, of loudspeaker, 131
encoder, shaft, 126
equaliser, 130
error signal, 115
exclusive-OR (EX-OR) function, 18, 19

FDM (frequency division multiplexing), 144
feedback, 32, 51, 112–15
FET (field effect transistor), 31–2
fetch–execute cycle, 122
field effect transistor (FET), 31–2

filters
    bandpass, 87
    highpass, 50, 87, 131
    lowpass, 10, 12, 49–50, 87, 131
    passband, 11, 49, 50
    RLC, 11–12
    stopband, 49, 50
    transition region, 50, 87
firing angle, 108
flash ADC, 96–7
flip-flop
    data (D-type), 69–70
    set-reset (S-R), 67–8
    toggle (T-type), 70
floppy disk, 119
flowchart, 125
FM, 140, 141
forward bias, diode, 28, 29
forward transfer characteristic
    BJT, 30–31
    MOSFET, 31–2
forward voltage drop
    diode, 29
    BJT, 31
frequency division multiplexing (FDM), 144
frequency modulation (FM), 140, 141
frequency response, *RC* network, 10
frequency shift keying (FSK), 143
frequency spectrum, 143
FSK (frequency shift keying), 143
full-wave controlled rectifier, 108–9
full-wave rectifier, 56, 103
full adder, 63
full duplex communication, 137
full power bandwidth, 84, 130

gain
    common mode, 94
    current, 30
    differential mode, 94
    op amp configurations, 85
gain–bandwidth product, 84
gate, logic, 18–19
general-purpose register, 122
graded index fibre, 138
Gray code, 79–80, 126

half-wave controlled rectifier, 107–8
half-wave rectifier, 55–6, 103
half adder, 62–3
half duplex communication, 137

half power level, 49
hard disk, 119
hardwired systems, 117–18
heat sink, 44, 54
h_{fe} (BJT small signal current gain), 30
h_{FE} (BJT large signal current gain), 30
high-level language, 125
highpass filter, 50, 87
holding current, thyristor, 32
hunting, 115
hysteresis, 116

I/O peripherals, 120
I/O ports, 120
identities, 21
IF (intermediate frequency), 149
IF amplifier, 149
impedance, 7
impedance matching, 86
indirect addressing, 123
inductor, 7
    see also passive components
input/output (I/O) peripherals, 120
input/output (I/O) ports, 120
input impedance, 45, 53, 85
instruction register, 122
interference, 140, 141, 142
intermediate frequency (IF), 149
intermediate frequency amplifier, 149
interrupt, 123–4
    see also polling
interrupt flag, 124
interrupt service routine (ISR), 123
invert function, 18
inverting amplifier, 51
inverting input, 83
inverting operational amplifier, 85
isolation, 110
ISR (interrupt service routine), 123

JFET (junction field effect transistor), 31
jump, program, 123

Karnaugh maps, 23
Kirchhoff's laws, 2, 3

ladder logic, 125
languages, programming, 124–5
lamps, filament, 35
LC networks, 10–13
    quality factor, 11–13

resonance, 10–11
LDR, 33
leakage current, diode, 29, 33
LED, 35–6, 62
light-dependent resistor (LDR), 33
light-emitting diode (LED), 35–6, 62
line driver, 145–7
line receiver, 145–7
line regulation, 103
line transmitter, 145–7
load regulation, 103, 104
local oscillator, 149, 150
logic circuits, 18–24, 61
logic gates, 18–19
logic state, 18, 61
logic switch, 61
logic symbols, 18
logical equations
    Boolean algebra, 19–20
    de Morgan's theorem, 21
    identities, 21
    Karnaugh maps, 23
    NAND or NOR logic, 24
    race hazard theorem, 22
    redundancy theorem, 21
logical identities, 21
logical operations, 18–21
look-up table, 123
loudspeaker, 38, 131
low-voltage dc power supply, 102–5
lowpass filter, 10, 12, 49–50, 87, 131

machine code, 124
majority logic, 63
marking, data transmission, 146
maximum power transfer, 130, 132–3
memory, 119
memory map, 121–2
metal oxide silicon field effect
    transistor, 32
microcontroller, 61, 120–21
microphone, 34, 129, 134
microprocessor, 118–20
    address bus, 120, 122
    central processing unit (CPU), 118, 122
    control bus, 120
    data bus, 120, 122
    data storage, 119
    input/output (I/O) devices, 119
    input/output (I/O) ports, 120
    memory, 119
    system clock, 119

microswitch, 61
mid-range speaker, 131
mixer,
    op amp adder, 86, 99, 134
    PA system, 134
    RF, 150
mnemonic, assembler, 124
modem, 120, 143
modulation, 141–3
    amplitude (AM), 129, 141
    depth, 141
    frequency (FM), 129, 140, 141
    pulse amplitude (PAM), 142
    pulse code (PCM), 141–2
    pulse position (PPM), 143
    pulse width (PWM), 142
modulator, 148
modulo-*n* counter, 72
monostable
    BJT, 46–7
    IC, 47–8, 62, 68
MOSFET, 31
    amplifier, 52
    n-channel enhancement, 31
    switch, 45
    threshold voltage, 31
    voltage-controlled resistor, 32
motors, 37–8, 115
multiplexer, 65–6
    in PCM system, 142
multiple feedback bandpass active
    filter, 87, 88
multiplexing, signal, 144–5

NAND function, 18
noise, 94, 140, 141, 142
    reduction, 94
non-conditional jump, 123
non-inverting amplifier, 52
non-inverting input, 83
non-inverting operational amplifier
    gain, 85–6
    input impedance, 85
NOR function, 18, 19
NOT function, 18

offset voltage, 84
Ohm's law, 1
on–off control, 112–13
op amp, *see* operational amplifier
opcode, 122
open-loop control, 112

open-loop voltage gain, 83
operand, assembler, 124
operational amplifier, 83–9
  full power bandwidth, 84
  ideal vs. practical, 83
  input impedance, 83
  input voltage offset, 83, 84
  inverting configuration, 85
  inverting input, 83
  non-inverting configuration, 85
  non-inverting input, 83
  open-loop voltage gain, 83
  output impedance, 83
  output voltage swing, 83
  slew rate, 83, 84
  voltage follower, 85
operational amplifier applications
  active filters, 86–8
  adder, 86, 99
  amplifier circuits, 84–6
  comparator, 84, 96–9, 112–13
  Schmitt trigger, 89
optical fibre, 138
optical receiver, 147
optical transmitter, 147
opto-isolator, 110
OR function, 18
output buffer, 62
output impedance, 53, 83

PA system, 134
PAM (pulse amplitude modulation), 142
parallel-in-parallel-out (PIPO) register, 75
parallel-in-serial-out (PISO) register, 141
parallel communication, 137
parallel resistance, 2
parasitic element, 139
parity, 147
passband, 11, 49, 50
passive components, 28–30
PCM (pulse code modulation), 141–2
peripheral, 119
peripheral interrupt, 124
phase, 9, 10, 50
photodiode, 33–4, 45, 147
phototransistor, 34, 45, 147
PIPO register (parallel-in-parallel-out register), 75
PISO register (parallel-in-serial-out register), 141

polling, 124
position control, 115
potential divider, 3, 44, 45, 49, 50, 96
potential division rule, 3
potentiometer, 35, 115
power, 5–6
power amplifier, 130–31
power supplies, 55–6, 102–5
  input stage, 102
  rectifier, 55, 56, 102, 103
  regulation, 103, 104, 105
  short-circuit protection, 105
  smoothing capacitor, 103–4
  transformer, 55, 102
  Zener stabiliser, 43, 103, 104
power switching systems, 107–10
power transfer, 132–3
PPM (pulse position modulation), 143
pre-amplifier, 130
priority encoder, 64, 96
processing error interrupt, 124
program, 122–4
  subroutine, 123
program counter, 122
programming languages, 124–5
propagation, communication
  ground waves, 138
  sky waves, 139
  space waves, 139
propagation delay, 70
proportional control, 113–4
protective diode, 42, 45
public address (PA) system, 134
pulse amplitude modulation (PAM), 142
pulse code modulation (PCM), 141–2
pulse counter, 70–3
pulse generator, 62
pulse position modulation (PPM), 143
pulse transformer, 110
pulse width modulation (PWM), 142
push–pull amplifier, 53–4
PWM (pulse width modulation), 142

quality factor (Q), 11–13
quantisation noise, 142

race hazard theorem, 22
radio, 138–9
radio frequency (RF) amplifier, 148, 149, 150
radio tuner, 129

RAM (random access memory), 119, 122, 123
ramp generator, in ADC, 99
random access memory (RAM), 119, 122, 123
RC filter
  cut-off frequency, 49
  frequency response, 10, 49
  half-power level, 49
  highpass, 50, 51
  lowpass, 10, 49
  passband, 49, 50
  phase, 9–10, 50
  stopband, 50
  transition region, 50
RC networks, 8–10
  charging, 8–9
  discharging, 8–9
  frequency response, 10
  phase, 9–10, 50
  time constant, 8
reactance, 7
read-only memory (ROM), 65, 66, 119, 122
receiver
  optical, 147
  simple AM, 148–9
  superheterodyne, 149–50
  tuned, 149
rectifier, 55–6, 103
  controlled, 107–8
redundancy theorem, 21
reference voltage, 112, 115
regenerator, 140
regulation, power supply, 103, 104, 105
regulators
  op amp series, 104
  series, 104
  three-terminal IC, 105
relay, 36–7
repeater, 140
resistance, 1
resolution, flash converter, 97
resonance, 10–11
reverse bias, diode, 28, 29, 45
RF amplifier, 148, 149, 150
ripple, 103–4
ripple counter, 70–3
rms values, 6, 7
roll off, active filter, 87
ROM (read-only memory), 65, 66, 119, 122

rotational speed control, 114–15
RS-232, 137, 146

S-R flip-flop, 67–8
Sallen and Key filter, 86–7
sample and hold, 98, 142
SAR (successive approximation register), 97, 98
Schmitt trigger
hysteresis, 89, 116
inverting, 89
non-inverting, 89
signal regeneration, 93
threshold voltages, 89
selectivity, 11, 148, 149
sensitivity, 149
sensors, 33–5, 61, 62
light-dependent resistor (LDR), 33
microphone, 34
photodiode, 33–4, 45, 147
phototransistor, 34, 45, 147
potentiometer, 35, 115
thermistor, 34–5
sequential logic, 67–80
serial-in-parallel-out (SIPO) register, 75, 142
serial-in-serial-out (SISO) register, 75
serial communication, 137
series resistance, 2
servo system, 115
servomotor (servo), 38, 115
set-reset flip-flop, 67–8
set point, 112, 115
seven-segment display, 67
shift register, 74–5
short-circuit protection, power supply, 105
side frequencies, 143
sideband, 143
signal-to-noise power ratio (SNR), 140
signal conditioning, 93–4
clamping, 42–3, 93
clipping, 93
contact bounce, 93–4
noise reduction, 94
signal regeneration, 93, 137, 138, 140
signal processing, 94–5
signal sources, 129, 134
signal transfer, 132–4
single sideband (SSB), 144
single slope ADC, 99

SIPO (serial-in-parallel-out) register, 75, 142
SISO (serial-in-serial-out) register, 75
slew rate, 84
smoothing capacitor, 103–4
SNR (signal-to-noise power ratio), 140
solenoid, 36
source follower amplifier, 52
source select, audio system, 130
speaker, 38, 131
spikes, removing, 93
SSB (single sideband), 144
stack, 123
stack pointer, 122
start bit, 137, 146
status register, 122
step-down transformer, 102
stepper motor, 37–8
stop bit, 137, 147
stopband, 49, 50
sub-woofer, 131
subroutine, 123
subtractor, 94–5
successive approximation ADC, 97–9
successive approximation register (SAR), 97, 98
summer, 86, 99
superhet (superheterodyne receiver), 149–50
superposition theorem, 4
synchronous counter, 73–4
synchronous transmission, 137
synthesiser 134
system clock, 119

T-type flip-flop, 70
tape deck, 129
TDM (time division multiplexing), 144–5
temperature coefficient, 34
thermal resistance, 55
thermistor, 34–5
thermostat control, 113, 114
Thévenin's theorem, 4
−3 dB level, 49
three-state output, 120
thresholds, of Schmitt triggers, 89
thyristor, 32–3, 107–9
advantages, 107
holding current, 32
switching, 107
time constant, 8

time division multiplexing (TDM), 144–5
timer IC, 47–9
toggle flip-flop, 70
tone control, 130
transconductance, 31
transducer, 35
transformer, 55, 102
pulse, 110
transistor
BJT, 30–31
comparison, 45
Darlington pair, 45–6
FET, 31–2
transistor switch, 44–6, 62
transition frequency, 84
transition region, 50, 87
transmission media, 137–9
cable, 137–8
optical fibre, 138
radio, 138–9
transmitter
optical, 147
radio, 147–8
triac, 33, 109
truth table, 19
arbitrary, 65
tuned RF receiver, 149
tweeter, 131
twisted pair cable, 137, 145

variable resistor, as sensor, 35, 115
V_{BE}, of BJT, 31
virtual earth, 84
voice coil, 38
voltage amplifier, 51
voltage divider, 3
voltage follower op amp, 85, 86
voltage transfer, 132
volume control, 130

walking ring counter, 75
disallowed states, 76
watt, 5–6
Wheatstone bridge, 95
wired logic, 21
woofer, 131
word, 120

Zener diode, 30, 93
Zener stabiliser, 43, 103, 104
Zener voltage, 30, 43